Teacher's Edition

Houghton Mifflin
Math
North Carolina

Grade
1

Volume 1

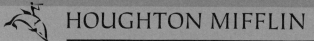 **HOUGHTON MIFFLIN**   BOSTON

An Introduction to
Houghton Mifflin
Math
North Carolina

Your Teacher's Edition is a key component for effective and easy teaching of mathematics. This section will give you an overview of *Houghton Mifflin Math.* You will learn about how the exciting features of the program can help you meet the needs of all your students, prepare students for high-stakes testing, and make lessons fun and engaging for your students and you.

Program Authors & Consultants

Authors

Dr. Carole Greenes

Professor of Mathematics Education

Boston University
Boston, Massachusetts

Dr. Matt Larson

Curriculum Specialist for Mathematics

Lincoln Public Schools
Lincoln, Nebraska

Dr. Miriam A. Leiva

Distinguished Professor of Mathematics Emerita

University of North Carolina
Charlotte, North Carolina

Dr. Jean M. Shaw

Professor Emerita of Curriculum and Instruction

University of Mississippi
Oxford, Mississippi

Dr. Lee Stiff

Professor of Mathematics Education

North Carolina State University
Raleigh, North Carolina

Dr. Bruce R. Vogeli

Clifford Brewster Upton Professor of Mathematics

Teachers College, Columbia University
New York, New York

Dr. Karol Yeatts

Associate Professor

Barry University
Miami, Florida

Consultants

Strategic Consultant

Dr. Liping Ma

Senior Scholar

Carnegie Foundation for the Advancement of Technology
Palo Alto, California

Language and Vocabulary Consultant

Dr. David Chard

Professor of Reading

University of Oregon
Eugene, Oregon

North Carolina Teacher Advisory Panel Members

Stephanie McDaniel
Grade 1
B. Everett Jordan Elementary School
Graham, NC

Yvette Smith
Grade 1
Northeast Elementary School
Pikeville, NC

Caroline Annas
Grade 2
Shepherd Elementary School
Moorsville, NC

Del Daniels
Grade 2
Meadow Lane Elementary School
Goldsboro, NC

Tracy McKeel
Grade 3
Rosewood Elementary School
Goldsboro, NC

Fran Coleman
Grade 3
Rosenwald Elementary School
Fairmont, NC

Janet Lee Blue
Grade 4
Rosenwald Elementary School
Fairmont, NC

Lynnetta Burton
Grade 4
Pleasant Grove Elementary School
Burlington, NC

Amy Janning
Grade 5
Spring Creek Elementary School
Goldsboro, NC

Brenda Sharts
Elementary Director
Cleveland County Schools
Shelby, NC

Teacher Reviewers

KINDERGARTEN

Karen Sue Hinton
Washington Elementary School
Ponca City, OK

Hilda Kendrick
W. E. Wilson Elementary School
Jefferson, IN

Debby Nagel
Assumption Elementary School
Cincinnati, OH

GRADE 1

Stephanie McDaniel
B. Everett Jordan Elementary School
Graham, NC

Juan Melgar
Lowrie Elementary School
Elgin, IL

Sharon O'Brien
Echo Mountain School
Phoenix, AZ

GRADE 2

Sally Bales
Akron Elementary School
Akron, IN

Rose Marie Bruno
Mawbey Street Elementary School
Woodbridge, NJ

Megan Burton
Valley Elementary School
Pelham, AL

GRADE 3

Jenny Chang
North Elementary School
Waukegan, IL

Patricia Heintz
PS 92
Harry T. Stewart Elementary School
Corona, NY

Allison White
Kingsley Elementary School
Naperville, IL

GRADE 4

Kathy Curtis
Hoxsie School
Warwick, RI

Lynn Fox
Kendall-Whittier Elementary School
Tulsa, OK

Barbara O'Hanlon
Maurice & Everett Haines
Elementary School
Medford, NJ

Connie Rapp
Oakland Elementary School
Bloomington, IL

Pam Rettig
Solheim Elementary School
Bismarck, ND

Tracy Smith
Carstens Elementary School
Detroit, MI

GRADE 5

Jim Archer
Maplewood Elementary School
Indianapolis, IN

Linda Carlson
Van Buren Elementary School
Oklahoma City, OK

Maggie Dunning
Horizon Elementary School
Hanover Park, IL

Mike Intoccia
McNichols Plaza
Scranton, PA

Jennifer LaBelle
Washington Elementary School
Waukegan, IL

Peg McCann
Warwick Neck School
Warwick, RI

GRADE 6

Robin Akers
Sonoran Sky Elementary School
Scottsdale, AZ

Ellen Greenman
Daniel Webster Middle School
Waukegan, IL

Angela McCray
Abbott Middle School
West Bloomfield, MI

Houghton Mifflin Math

Reaching All Learners, All Of The Time.

Houghton Mifflin Math A+

Time-Tested Approaches Ensure Proven Results

Houghton Mifflin Math really works! Here's why:

★ It's proven with scientifically based research.

★ It's based on more than 30 years of studies on how students learn best.

★ It incorporates models and strategies from high-performing classrooms.

★ It meets the needs of all learners.

A Complete System of Intervention and Challenge Means Success for All Learners

With a variety of specialized, focused teaching support, you can effectively manage instruction to meet the diverse needs of all students in your classroom.

Reaching All Learners

Practical point-of-use support is built into each lesson so that your English learners, gifted and talented students, early finishers, and struggling students can all reach their goals.

 MathTracks MP3 Audio CD

Our unique audio tutor on audio CD reteaches lessons just as you would to students who have missed instruction or who need a little extra support in mastering content and building confidence.

Ways to Success Intervention CD-ROM

Built into every lesson, this special safety net of support ensures that students stay on track with diagnostic reteaching and plenty of practice.

Chapter Challenges

Encourage advanced students to put their skills to the test and expand their thinking with challenging activities and projects linked to each chapter.

Lesson Planner

Customize daily instruction with this powerful CD-ROM to meet your state standards and school calendar, then personalize the lessons to match your teaching style, the needs of your students, and the materials you have on hand.

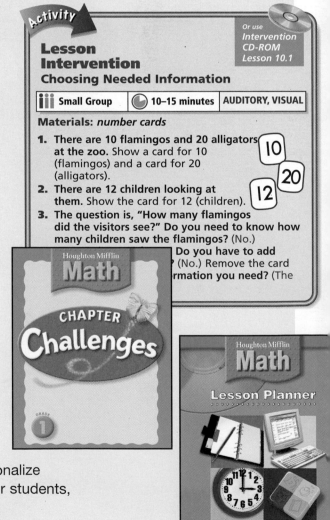

Activity

Or use Intervention CD-ROM Lesson 10.1

Lesson Intervention
Choosing Needed Information

| Small Group | 10–15 minutes | AUDITORY, VISUAL |

Materials: *number cards*

1. **There are 10 flamingos and 20 alligators at the zoo.** Show a card for 10 (flamingos) and a card for 20 (alligators).
2. **There are 12 children looking at them.** Show the card for 12 (children).
3. **The question is, "How many flamingos did the visitors see?"** Do you need to know how many children saw the flamingos? (No.) Do you have to add ? (No.) Remove the card rmation you need? (The

PLUS, a wide selection of leveled resources for Practice, Reteach, Enrichment, Problem Solving, Homework, and English learners links to each lesson for your convenience!

Compelling Literature and Real-World Connections Give Immediate Meaning to Math

With engaging literature plus strong connections, our program reinforces math concepts and demonstrates the value of mathematics in everyday life, for every student.

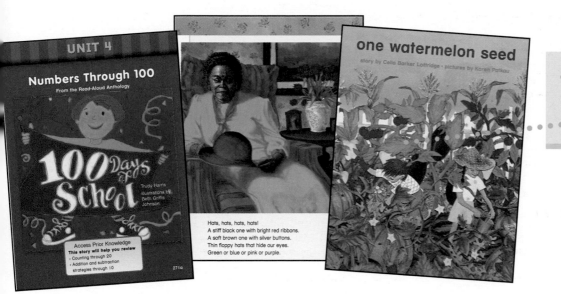

- Authentic literature selections enable young learners to connect mathematics to their own world.

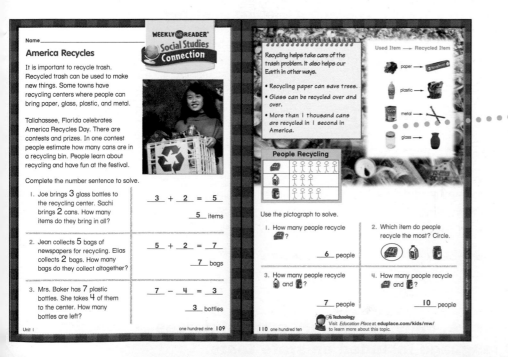

- A special partnership with *Weekly Reader®* makes our real-world and curriculum connections dynamic, relevant, and just right for your students.

A Plan for Test-Taking Success Builds Skills and Confidence

With a four-tiered plan that systematically builds critical skills, your students are sure to perform well on standardized tests, every time.

1 Using a series of guided questions, students effectively build the reasoning and thinking skills necessary for test-taking achievement.

2 With daily exposure to typical test content and questions, plus instruction on critical test-taking strategies, students feel more comfortable and focused on test days.

3 Powerful practice in listening, reading, and problem-solving strategies prepares students for the challenges of test taking.

4 With authentic practice that replicates the typical content, question format, materials, and administrative conditions of test day, you can build students' confidence and test-taking skills, all while ensuring success.

And, our comprehensive, daily vocabulary plan reinforces the mathematical language included on state tests.

Technology Solutions Help You Manage the Big Jobs of Your Classroom

A wealth of technology on CD-ROM and the Web provides everything you need to make your job easier and builds motivation and skill in your students.

Just for Students

eMathBook
With content identical to the student books, an eGlossary, and printable homework masters, our eMathBook—available on CD-ROM and via the Web—makes math readily accessible to students on the go.

Especially for Teachers

Ways to Success Intervention CD-ROM
Developed to engage students and offer self-help and extra support, our easy-to-use CD-ROM features diagnostic and prescriptive reteaching, focused practice, plus background-building opportunities for customized intervention that links to each lesson.

Ways to Assess CD-ROM (Test and Spiral Review Generator)
Create, print, and administer customized assessments in print or online form for all lessons in *Houghton Mifflin Math*. With ready-made Chapter and Unit tests, plus multiple-choice, fill-in-the-blank, and free-response question formats, you can easily choose which tests best fit your classroom. And you can instantly generate spiral reviews based on specific lesson objectives, student needs, and your own teaching sequence.

For Students, Teachers, Parents, and Caregivers

Education Place®
Packed with an array of FREE materials and support for the lessons in *Houghton Mifflin Math*, including a Math Vocabulary Glossary, Games, Brain Teasers, Extra Practice, Homework Help, Teaching Models, Manipulatives, Family Letters, and so much more, our award-winning Web site has it all!
Visit **www.eduplace.com/math/mw/** today.

Technology that gets you and your students ready for success!

Components

	K	1	2	3	4	5	6
Student Book	●	●	●	●	●	●	●
Student Book, Multi-Volume Set	●	●	●				
Big Book	●						
Teacher's Edition	●	●	●	●	●	●	●
Read-Aloud Anthologies, Volumes 1–4	●	●	●				
Trade Book Literature Library	●	●	●	●	●	●	●
Unit Resource Folders	●	●	●	●	●	●	●
Reteach/Practice/ Enrichment	●	●	●	●	●	●	●
Problem Solving/Homework/English Learners	●	●	●	●	●	●	●
Assessments/Learning Tools	●	●	●	●	●	●	●
Practice Workbook	●	●	●	●	●	●	●
Homework Workbook		●	●	●	●	●	●
English Learners Handbook	●	●	●	●	●	●	●
Building Vocabulary Kit	●	●	●	●	●	●	●
Test Prep Blackline Masters		●	●	●	●	●	●
Chapter Challenges	●	●	●	●	●	●	●
Combination Classroom Guide	●	●	●	●	●	●	●
Kindergarten Kit	●						
Busy Bear Puppet	●						
Math Songs for Young Learners	●						
Student Manipulatives Kit	●	●	●	●	●	●	●
Custom Manipulatives Kits	●	●	●	●	●	●	●
Overhead Manipulatives Kit	●	●	●	●	●	●	●
Math Center	●	●	●	●	●	●	●
Lesson Transparencies	●	●	●	●	●	●	●
Daily Routines Flip Chart	●	●	●	●	●	●	●
Teaching Transparencies	●	●	●	●	●	●	●
Test Prep Transparencies		●	●	●	●	●	●
Lesson Planner CD-ROM	●	●	●	●	●	●	●
Ways to Success Intervention CD-ROM		●	●	●	●	●	●
Chapter Intervention Blackline Masters		●	●	●	●	●	●
eMathBook (Student Book on CD-ROM)	●	●	●	●	●	●	●
Ways to Assess CD-ROM (test and spiral review generator)		●	●	●	●	●	●
MathTracks MP3 Audio CD		●	●	●	●	●	●
Learner Profile		●	●	●	●	●	●
Education Place Web site	●	●	●	●	●	●	●

Manipulatives

Program Manipulatives	Suggested Alternatives	K	1	2	3	4	5	6
Algebra Tiles	Bars and squares made from grid paper or construction paper						•	•
Attribute Blocks	Seashells, pasta, buttons	•	•	•				
Balance Scales	Ruler, paper cups, and string	•	•	•	•	•	•	•
Bill Set	Bills made from construction paper and markers	•	•	•	•	•	•	•
Blank Number Cubes with Labels	Number cards, spinners	•	•	•	•	•	•	•
Coin Set	Real coins, buttons	•	•	•	•	•	•	•
Connecting Cubes	Paper clips, string and beads or pasta	•	•	•	•	•	•	•
Counting Chips	Buttons, coins, beans	•						
Demonstration Clock	Clockface with two lengths of string fastened to the center for the hands	•	•	•	•	•	•	•
Fraction Tiles	Bars and squares made from grid paper or construction paper				•	•	•	•
Geometric Solids	Cans, boxes, balls, cones, modeling clay shapes	•	•	•	•	•	•	•
Geotool Compass							•	•
Pattern Blocks	Shapes cut out of different-colored construction paper or cardboard	•	•	•	•	•	•	•
Place-Value Blocks/ Base-Ten Blocks	Grid paper cutouts	•	•	•	•	•	•	•
Protractor							•	•
Ruler, inch and centimeter	One-inch or one-centimeter grid paper strips				•	•	•	•
Transparent Spinner	Construction paper, paper clip, and pencil	•	•	•	•	•	•	•
Two-Color Counters	Coins, washers, or beans with one side painted	•	•	•	•	•	•	•

Scope and Sequence

In the Program...

Number and Operations

Addition

	K	1	2	3	4	5	6
Adding decimals				●	●	▲	▲
Adding fractions				●	●	▲	▲
Adding integers and rational numbers					●	●	▲
Adding measurements						●	▲
Adding mixed numbers					●	●	▲
Adding money	●	●	●	●	▲	▲	▲
Adding multi-digit numbers	●	●	●	▲	▲	▲	▲
Adding whole numbers	●	●	▲	▲	▲	▲	▲
Basic facts	●	●	▲				
Equations						●	▲
Estimating sums		●	●	▲	▲	▲	▲
Expressions						●	●
Inverse operations						●	▲
Mental math		●	●	●	▲	▲	▲
Missing addends	●	●	●	▲	▲		
Number sentences	●	●	●	▲	▲	▲	▲
Problem-solving applications	●	●	●	▲	▲	▲	▲
Properties of addition		●	●	●	▲	▲	▲
Regrouping to add			●	●	▲	▲	▲
Strategies for adding	●	●	●	▲	▲		
Three or more addends		●	▲				

Comparing and Ordering Numbers

	K	1	2	3	4	5	6
Decimals				●	●	▲	▲
Decimals and fractions				●	●	●	▲
Decimals, fractions, and percents						●	▲
Fractions			●	●	●	▲	▲
Integers						●	▲
Money amounts	●	●	●	▲			
Percents						●	▲
Rational numbers						●	●
Using <, >, and = symbols		●	●	●	▲	▲	▲
Whole numbers	●	●	●	▲	▲	▲	▲

Counting, Reading, Writing Numbers

	K	1	2	3	4	5	6
Decimals				●	●	●	▲
Fractions		●	●	●	▲	▲	▲
Integers						●	●
Mixed numbers				●	●	▲	▲
Money	●	●	▲	▲			
Ordinal Numbers	●	●	●	▲			
Percent						●	●
Powers and exponents						●	●
Rational numbers						●	●
Roman and other numerals			●	●	●	▲	▲
Scientific notation						●	●
Square numbers				●	●	●	
Square roots							●
Whole numbers	●	●	●	●	●	▲	▲

KEY Teach and Apply ● Practice and Apply ▲ Teacher's Edition Lesson ★

In Level 1...

Number and Operations

Addition

adding money 609, 622
adding whole numbers
　basic facts 35–54, 125–137, 429–446, 557–570
　fact families 155–156, 429–446, 465–470, 591–594
　one-digit numbers without regrouping
　　models 605–606
　　place value chart 605–606
　related facts 153–154, 465–470, 591–592
　three addends 443–444, 569–570
　two-digit numbers without regrouping
　　models 607–608
　　number form 607–614
　　place-value chart 608, 610–612
estimating sums 615–616
horizontal addition 35–48
hundred chart 324, 326, 328
meaning of sum 39–40
mental math 45–46, 603–604
missing addends 48, 130, 156, 432, 445–446
number sentences 39–40, 42, 51–53, 135–137, 154, 470, 571–572, 592
problem-solving applications 51–53, 135–137, 571–573, 615–617
properties of addition
　Associative Property 443–444
　Commutative Property 45–46, 435–436, 569–570
　Zero Property 41–42
relating addition and subtraction 153–154, 465–470, 591–592, 637–638
strategies for adding
　counting on 125–128, 133–134, 429–430, 439–440
　drawing a picture 133–134
　making ten 431–434, 439–440, 559–562
　using double facts 129–131, 133–134, 439–440, 557–558
　using models 35–50, 125–126, 133–134, 429–435, 557–568
　using number lines 127–128, 133–134, 429–430
　using properties 41–42, 45–46, 435–436, 569–570
using symbols 39–40
vertical form 49–50

Comparing and Ordering Numbers

money amounts 402, 407
whole numbers
　before, after, between 17–18, 303–304
　greater than, less than 23–24
　is equal to 21–22, 313–314
　is greater than, is less than 21–24, 311, 313–314
　more, fewer, same 7–8
　more than, less than 327–328
　two-digit numbers 303–304, 311–314
　using models 311–314
　using a number line 23–24, 303–304
　using place value 311–314
　writing <, >, or = 313–314, 566
Ordering
　whole numbers
　　before, after, between 17–18, 303–304
　　two-digit numbers 303–304

Number and Operations

Number and Operations

Decimals

	K	1	2	3	4	5	6
Adding decimals				●	●	▲	▲
Comparing decimals				●	●	▲	▲
Decimal notation			●	●	▲	▲	▲
Decimals and fractions				●	●	▲	▲
Decimals and mixed numbers				●	●	▲	▲
Decimals and percents						●	▲
Dividing decimals						●	▲
Estimating decimals					●	●	▲
Modeling decimals				●	▲		
Multiplying decimals						●	▲
Ordering decimals				●	●	▲	▲
Place value of decimals				●	●	▲	▲
Reading decimals			●	●	●	▲	▲
Repeating and terminating						●	●
Rounding decimals					●	▲	▲
Subtracting decimals				●	●	▲	▲
Writing decimals			●	●	▲	▲	▲

Division

	K	1	2	3	4	5	6
Basic facts			●	●	▲		
Checking division with multiplication				●	▲	▲	▲
Dividing decimals						●	▲
Dividing fractions						●	▲
Dividing integers and rational numbers							●
Dividing mixed numbers						●	▲
Dividing money				●	●	▲	▲
Dividing whole numbers			●	●	●	▲	▲
Division as equal groups			●	▲	▲		
Equations						●	▲
Estimating the quotient				●	●	▲	▲
Expressions					●	▲	▲
Fact families				●	▲		
Missing factors				●	▲	▲	▲
Number sentences				●	▲		
Problem-solving applications			●	●	▲	▲	▲
Relating multiplication and division				●	▲	▲	▲
Relating subtraction and division				●	▲		
Remainders				●	●	▲	
Strategies for dividing			●	●	▲		

Counting, Reading, Writing Numbers

fractions 239–246
money
  amounts
    dime 389–390, 393–404
    half-dollar 402
    nickel 389–392, 395–404
    penny 389–404
    quarter 399–404
on a counting board 634
ordinal numbers 305–306
skip-counting
  by 2's 322–324
  by 5's 325–326, 389–390
  by 10's 277–278, 389–390
whole numbers
  0 through 9 9–12
  10 through 20 13–16
  forward and backward 19, 304
  one hundred 291–292
  through 100 277–295
  word form 9–16, 277–278, 280–284, 291–292

KEY   Teach and Apply ●   Practice and Apply ▲   Teacher's Edition Lesson ★

Scope and Sequence

In the Program...

Number and Operations

	K	1	2	3	4	5	6
Estimating							
Benchmarks		●	●	●	▲	▲	▲
Estimated or Exact Answer?				●	●	●	●
Estimating decimals				●	●	●	▲
Estimating differences				●	●	▲	▲
Estimating fractions					●	▲	▲
Estimating measures	●	●	●	▲	▲	▲	▲
Estimating money			●	●			
Estimating products				●	●	▲	▲
Estimating quotients				●	●	▲	▲
Estimating sums		●	●	▲	▲	▲	▲
For reasonableness of answer			●	●	▲	▲	▲
Quantities	●	▲					
Using a referent	●	●	▲	▲			
Using strategies		●	●	●	●	▲	▲
Fractions							
Adding fractions				●	●	▲	▲
Comparing fractions			●	●	●	▲	▲
Decimals and fractions				●	●	▲	▲
Decimals and percents						●	▲
Dividing fractions						●	▲
Equivalent fractions				●	●	▲	▲
Improper fractions			●	●	●	▲	▲
Meaning of fractions	●	●	●	●	●	▲	▲
Measurement and fractions				●	▲	▲	▲
Mixed numbers				●	▲	▲	▲
Modeling fractions	●	●	●	▲	▲	▲	▲
Multiplying fractions						●	▲
Ordering fractions			●		▲	▲	▲
Ratios and fractions						●	▲
Reciprocals						●	●
Simplifying fractions					●	●	▲
Subtracting fractions				●	●	●	▲
Integers and Rational Numbers							
Absolute value						●	▲
Adding and subtracting integers					●	●	▲
Comparing and ordering						●	▲
Graphing on the number line					●	●	▲
Meaning					●	●	▲
Multiplicative inverse							●
Multiplying and dividing integers							●
Negative numbers on a thermometer				●	●	▲	▲
Operations with rational numbers							●
Opposites					●	●	●
Scientific notation						●	●

KEY   Teach and Apply ●   Practice and Apply ▲   Teacher's Edition Lesson ★

In Level 1...

Number and Operations

Estimating
benchmarks (measures) 511, 513
measures 503–506, 511–514
quantities 307–308
sums 615–616
using a referent 115, 307–308, 315–316
using strategies
  rounding to the nearest ten 653
whole numbers 307–308

Fractions
equal parts 237–238
fractional parts
  of a set 245–246
  of a whole 237–243
meaning of fractions 237–238
modeling fractions
  less than one whole 237–246
reading fractions 237–246
unit fractions
  one half 239–240
  one third, one fourth 241–243

In the Program...

Number and Operations

	K	1	2	3	4	5	6
Mental Math							
Addition		●	●	●	●	▲	▲
Division				●	▲	▲	▲
Multiples and powers of 10		●	●	●	▲	▲	▲
Multiplication				●	▲	▲	▲
Patterns	●	●	▲	▲	▲	▲	▲
Problem-solving applications			●	▲	▲	▲	▲
Subtraction		●	●	▲	▲	▲	▲
Use properties		●	●	●	●	▲	▲
Mixed Numbers							
Adding mixed numbers					●	▲	▲
Decimals and mixed numbers				●	●	▲	▲
Dividing mixed numbers						●	▲
Meaning of mixed numbers				●	▲	▲	▲
Multiplying mixed numbers						●	▲
Subtracting mixed numbers					●	▲	▲
Using a number line with mixed numbers				●	▲	▲	▲
Writing mixed numbers				●	▲	▲	▲
Multiplication							
Arrays			●	▲			
Basic facts		●	●	●	▲		
Concrete/pictorial representations	●	●	●	▲			
Drawing a picture to multiply		●	●	▲			
Equations						●	▲
Estimating products				●	●	▲	▲
Expressions					●	▲	▲
Horizontal and vertical forms				●	▲		
Mental math				●	▲	▲	▲
Missing factors					●	▲	▲
Multiplication as equal groups	●	●	●	▲			
Multiplying decimals						●	▲
Multiplying fractions						●	▲
Multiplying integers and rational numbers							●
Multiplying mixed numbers						●	▲
Multiplying money				●	●	▲	▲
Multiplying three factors				●	▲	▲	▲
Multiplying whole numbers		●	●	▲	▲	▲	▲
Number sentences			●	▲	▲		
Problem-solving applications		●	●	▲	▲	▲	▲
Properties of multiplication			●	▲	▲	▲	▲
Related facts				●	▲		
Related to other operations			●	●	▲	▲	▲
Skip-counting to multiply	●	●	●	●	▲		
Square numbers				●	▲	▲	▲
Strategies			●	●	▲		

In Level 1...

Number and Operations

Mental Math

addition 603–604, 615–616
counting on, counting back 627
multiples of 10 293–296, 569–570, 603–604, 611, 625–636. 631–632
patterns 333–334
subtraction 625–626
use properties
  make a ten, use a double 569–570, 613
  to add in any order 443–444, 569–570

Multiplication Readiness

concrete/pictorial representations 322–326
drawing a picture to multiply 324
equal groups 323–324
multiplying with 2
  skip-counting 322–324
  using a hundred chart 324
multiplying with 5
  skip-counting 325–326
  using a hundred chart 326
multiplying with 10
  skip-counting 277–278
problem-solving applications 324, 326
skip-counting 322–326
strategies
  using patterns 333–334

KEY Teach and Apply ● Practice and Apply ▲ Teacher's Edition Lesson ★

Scope and Sequence

In the Program...

Number and Operations

	K	1	2	3	4	5	6
Number Theory							
Even and odd numbers	●	●	●	▲	▲	▲	▲
Factor trees				●		▲	▲
Factors			●	●	▲	▲	▲
Figurate numbers				●		▲	▲
Greatest common factor						●	▲
Least common denominator						●	▲
Least common multiple						●	▲
Multiples			●	●		●	▲
Prime factorization						●	▲
Prime and composite numbers					●	●	▲
Reciprocals						●	▲
Rules for divisibility						●	▲
Place Value							
Decimals				●	●	▲	▲
Expanded form			●	▲	▲	▲	▲
Millions and billions					●	●	▲
Money				●	●	▲	▲
Standard form	●	●	●	▲	▲	▲	▲
Using a place-value chart		●	●	●	▲	▲	▲
Whole numbers	●	●	●	▲	▲	▲	▲
Ratio, Proportion, and Percent							
Estimation with percents						●	●
Finding a percent of a number						●	●
Meaning of percents				●	●	●	●
Percents related to circle graphs						●	●
Percents related to fractions and/or decimals					●	●	●
Rates					●	●	▲
Reading and writing ratios						●	●
Writing and solving proportions						●	●
Subtraction							
Basic facts	●	●	●	▲			
Checking subtraction		●	●	●	▲	▲	▲
Equations						●	▲
Estimating differences			●	●	▲	▲	▲
Expressions						●	▲
Mental math		●	●	▲	▲	▲	▲
Number sentences	●	●	●	▲	▲	▲	▲
Problem-solving applications	●	●	▲	▲	▲	▲	▲
Properties of subtraction				●	●	▲	▲
Regrouping to subtract				●	▲	▲	▲
Strategies for subtracting	●	●	●	▲	▲		
Subtracting decimals					●	●	▲
Subtracting fractions					●	●	●
Subtracting integers						●	▲
Subtracting mixed numbers						●	▲
Subtracting measurements							●
Subtracting money	●	●	●	●	▲	▲	▲
Subtracting whole numbers	●	●	▲	▲	▲	▲	▲
Subtracting with zeros				●	●	▲	▲

In Level 1...

Number and Operations

Number Theory

Even numbers 331–332
Odd numbers 331–332

Place Value

addition 607–614
expanded form 289–290
standard form 9–24, 277–295
subtraction 629–638
whole numbers
  through 20 9–24
  through 100 277–297, 311–314
  using models 9–18, 21–27, 277–294
word form 9–16, 277–278, 280–284, 291–292
Place-value chart
  in addition 605–612
  in subtraction 629–638
  through 99 279–284, 287–288, 311–314

Subtraction

basic facts
  to 10 63–75
  to 12 457–478, 459–475
  to 20 581–594
checking subtraction with addition 637–638
comparing 149–150
difference 67–68
fact families
  through 10 155–156, 465–470
  through 12 465–470
  through 20 591–594
horizontal form 65–68
inverse relationship to addition 153–154, 465–470, 591–592, 637–638
mental math 625–626
missing numbers 48, 304, 432, 445–446, 590
number sentences 73–74, 154, 434, 470
problem-solving applications 146, 148, 150, 159–161, 473–475, 584, 592, 595–596
related facts 153–154, 465–470, 591–592
strategies
  counting back 145–146, 157–158
  drawing a picture 157–158
  using a number line 147–148, 157–158, 457–458
  using addition 157–158
  using double facts 581–582
  using models 61–75, 625–630
  using part-part-whole 459–462, 467–470, 583–586, 589–590
subtracting money 633
subtracting whole numbers
  modeling with base-ten blocks 629–630
  one-digit numbers without regrouping
    models 627–628
    number form 627–628
    place-value chart 627–628
  two-digit numbers without regrouping
    models 629–630
    number form 629–638
    place-value chart 629–632
using a number line 147–148, 157–158, 457–458
  using symbols 65–66
  vertical form 75–76
  zero in subtraction 71–72

In the Program...

Algebra

	K	1	2	3	4	5	6
Readiness and Applications							
Addition and subtraction number sentences	●	●	●	▲	▲		▲
Analyze change	●	●	●	▲	▲	▲	▲
Fact families		●	●	●	▲		
Inverse operations		●	●	●	●	▲	▲
Meaning of equality				●	●	▲	▲
Missing addends	●	●	●	▲	▲		
Missing digits			▲	▲	▲		▲
Missing factors				●	●	▲	▲
Missing measurements and units				●	●	●	▲
Missing operations	●	●	●	▲	▲		
Multiplication and division number sentences				●	●		▲
Proportional reasoning	●	●	●	▲	▲		▲
Symbols showing relations	●	●	●	▲	▲	▲	▲
Variables				●	●	▲	▲
Venn diagrams		●	●	●	●	▲	▲
Writing and solving number sentences or equations	●	●	●	●	●	●	●
Coordinate Graphs							
Graphing ordered pairs			●	●	▲	▲	▲
Ordered pairs			●	●	▲	▲	▲
Equations and Inequalities							
Equations with more than one variable						●	●
Graphing an equation						●	▲
Linear equations						●	▲
Modeling equations		●	●	●	▲	▲	▲
Formulas					●	▲	▲
Solving addition and subtraction equations						●	▲
Solving equations by using inverse operations						●	▲
Solving multiplication and division equations						●	▲
Writing an equation or number sentence					●	●	▲	▲
Writing and solving proportions						●	▲
Writing and solving percent equations						●	▲

KEY   Teach and Apply ●   Practice and Apply ▲   Teacher's Edition Lesson ★

In Level 1...

Algebra

Readiness and Applications

addition and subtraction number sentences 39–40, 42, 51–53, 73–74, 135–137, 154, 434, 470, 571–572, 592
analyze change 215–218
classifying and sorting 183–185, 187–188, 189, 191–192, 193–194
fact families—addition and subtraction
  through 10 155–156, 465–470
  through 12 465–470
  through 20 591–594
inverse operations 153–154, 465–466
meaning of equality 39–40, 65–66
missing addends 48, 130, 156, 432, 445–446
missing operation symbols 135–137
proportional reasoning
  equivalences in measures and money 365, 375, 377, 389–390, 393–394, 403–404, 525–526
  fraction of a set 245–246
  trading coins 390, 397
symbols showing relations 313–314
writing and solving number sentences
  addition 39–40, 42, 51–53, 135–137, 154, 434, 470, 571–572, 592
  subtraction 73–74, 154, 470
Venn diagrams 194

Equations and Inequalities

using <, >, and = symbols 23–24, 313–314, 566

Scope and Sequence

In the Program...

Algebra

	K	1	2	3	4	5	6
Expressions							
Evaluate by substitution					●	●	▲
Evaluate by using order of operations					●	●	▲
Exploring expressions		●	●	●	▲		
Expressions with exponents						●	▲
Inverse relationship of addition and subtraction		●	●	▲	▲	▲	▲
Inverse relationship of multiplication and division					●	▲	▲
Order of operations				●	▲	▲	▲
Pi as a ratio						●	▲
Writing expressions					●	●	▲
Patterns and Functions							
Continuing patterns	●	●	●	●	●	▲	▲
Describing patterns	●	●	●	●	●	▲	▲
Function tables						●	●
Input/output tables	●	●	●	▲	●	▲	▲
Measurement patterns			●	●	▲	▲	▲
Numerical patterns	●	●	●	▲	▲	▲	▲
Patterns in the coordinate plane						●	▲
Special patterns and sequences	●	●	●	▲	▲	▲	▲
Tessellations			●	●	▲	▲	▲
Using patterns to solve problems	●	●	▲	▲	▲	▲	▲
Visual patterns	●	●	●	▲	▲	▲	▲
Properties							
Associative Property		●	●	●	▲	▲	▲
Commutative Property		●	●	▲	▲	▲	▲
Distributive Property					●	●	▲
Equality Property							●
Identity Property				●	▲	▲	▲
Inverse Property							●
Zero Property		●	●	●	▲	▲	▲

In Level 1...

Algebra

Expressions
exploring Expressions 567–568
fact families
   through 10 155–156, 465–470
   through 12 465–470
   through 20 591–594

Patterns and Functions
functions 132, 462
completing and/or continuing patterns
   numerical patterns 50, 322–336, 389–390, 472, 603–604
   visual patterns 219–222, 227–228
describing patterns 50, 219–222, 227–228, 323–335, 472
in a hundred chart 324, 326–328, 330
skip-counting
   by 2's 322–324
   by 5's 325–326
   by 10's 277–278, 389–390
special patterns and sequences
   even and odd numbers 331–332
   one more one less, ten more ten less 327–328
time patterns 367, 378
using patterns
   in addition 50, 322–326, 603–604
   in multiplication 322–326, 389–390
   in subtraction 71–72, 625–626
   to solve problems 219–220, 333–335

Properties
Associative Property
   of addition 443–444
Commutative Property
   of addition 45–46, 435–436, 569–570
Zero Property
   of addition 41–42

KEY Teach and Apply ● Practice and Apply ▲ Teacher's Edition Lesson ★

Geometry

Geometry

Basic Figures

	K	1	2	3	4	5	6
Attributes of plane figures		●	●	●	▲	▲	▲
Basic figures: square, rectangle, triangle, and circle	●	●	●	▲	▲	▲	▲
Classifying and sorting figures and shapes	●	●	●	●	▲	▲	▲
Geometric patterns	●	●	●	▲	▲	▲	▲
Pattern blocks: triangle, square, rhombus, trapezoid, hexagon	●	●	●		▲		▲
Real-life objects	●	●	▲	▲			
Sides, corners, square corners		●	●	▲			

Plane Figures and Spatial Sense

	K	1	2	3	4	5	6
Angles			●	●	▲		▲
Circles	●	●	●	●	▲	▲	▲
Circumference						●	▲
Comparing angles				●	●	▲	▲
Complex figures		●		▲	▲	▲	▲
Constructing angles						●	▲
Constructing circles, using a compass						●	▲
Classifying polygons				●	●		▲
Congruent figures		●	●	●	▲	▲	▲
Intersecting lines				●	●		▲
Line of symmetry	●	●	●	▲	▲	▲	▲
Line segments				●	▲	▲	▲
Lines				●	▲	▲	▲
Making and drawing polygons		●	●	▲	▲	▲	▲
Making and drawing quadrilaterals		●	●	▲	▲	▲	▲
Measuring angles, using a protractor					●		
Orientations						●	▲
Parallel lines				●	▲	▲	▲
Perpendicular lines				●	▲	▲	▲
Polygons				●	▲	▲	▲
Points				●	▲	▲	▲
Pythagorean Theorem							●
Quadrilaterals				●	▲	▲	▲
Radius, diameter, chord					●	●	▲
Rays				●	▲	▲	▲
Relating solid and plane figures	●	●	▲	▲	▲	▲	▲
Right angles				●	▲	▲	▲
Sides, angles, and diagonals of polygons				●	●	●	▲
Similar figures				●	▲	▲	▲
Symmetry	●	●	●	▲	▲	▲	▲
Subdividing and combining		●	●	▲	▲	▲	▲
Tesselations and tangrams			●	●	▲	▲	▲
Vertex			●	▲	▲	▲	▲
Visual Thinking	●	●	●	▲	▲	▲	▲

Basic Figures

combining shapes 186
corners 185–186, 191–192
geometric patterns 219–221
plane figures
  circle 185–189
  identifying, classifying, and describing 185–189
  rectangle 185–186
  square 185–186
  triangle 185–186
pattern blocks 197–198, 215–218
sides 185–186

Plane Figures and Spatial Sense

drawing geometric figures 184–186
circle 185–189
congruent figures 226
identifying, classifying, and describing 185–189
rectangle 185–186
square 185–186
triangle 185–186
relating solids and plane figures 195–196
symmetry 223–224
Using visual thinking, spatial reasoning, and geometric modeling to solve problems 225–226

KEY Teach and Apply ●   Practice and Apply ▲   Teacher's Edition Lesson ★

Scope and Sequence

Geometry

Solid Figures (3-dimensional objects)

	K	1	2	3	4	5	6
Complex figures				●		●	▲
Cone	●	●	●	▲	▲	▲	▲
Cube	●	●	●	▲	▲	▲	▲
Cylinder	●	●	●	▲	▲	▲	▲
Face, edge, vertex		●	●	▲	▲	▲	▲
Identifying, classifying, and describing solid figures		●	●	▲	▲	▲	▲
Nets			●	●	●	▲	▲
Prisms	●	●	●	▲	▲	▲	▲
Pyramids		●	●	▲	▲	▲	▲
Sphere	●	●	●	▲			

Transformations

	K	1	2	3	4	5	6
Constructions, using a compass to draw arcs						●	▲
Degrees turned						●	▲
Flips (Reflections)	●	●	●	●	●	▲	▲
Slides (Translations)	●	●	●	●	●	▲	▲
Transformations in the coordinate plane						●	●
Turns (Rotations)	●	●	●	●	●	▲	▲

Measurement

Area and Perimeter

	K	1	2	3	4	5	6
Complex figures					●	●	▲
Estimating area, using square units			●	▲			▲
Finding area, using a formula					●	●	▲
Finding area, using square units			●	▲			
Finding circumference						●	●
Finding perimeter			●	●	▲	▲	▲
Finding perimeter, using a formula					●	●	▲
Meaning of area			●	▲	▲	▲	▲
Meaning of perimeter			●	▲	▲	▲	▲
Problem-solving applications			●	●	▲	▲	▲
Pythagorean theorem						●	●
Relating area and perimeter				●	●	▲	▲
Surface area						●	▲
Surface area, using a formula					●	●	▲

Capacity

	K	1	2	3	4	5	6
Conversion table		●	●	●	▲	▲	▲
Customary system		●	●	●	▲	▲	▲
Equivalent units		●	●	●	▲	▲	▲
Estimating capacity	●	●	●	▲	▲	▲	▲
Measuring capacity	●	●	●	▲	▲	▲	▲
Metric system		●	●	●	▲	▲	▲
Problem-solving applications	●	●	●	▲	▲	▲	▲

KEY Teach and Apply ●   Practice and Apply ▲   Teacher's Edition Lesson ★

Geometry

Solid Figures (3-dimensional objects)

cone 191–192
cube 191–192
cylinder 191–192
face 191–192
identifying, classifying, and describing 191–192, 193–194, 195–196
pyramid 191–192
real-life objects 191–192
rectangular prism 191–192
sphere 191–192

Transformations

readiness
 flip 215–218
 slide 215–218
 turn 215–218

Measurement

Capacity

comparing 523–524
estimating 523–524, 527–528
customary system
 comparing 525–526
 conversion table 525
 cup, pint, quart 525–526
 measuring 525
metric system
 comparing 527–529
 estimating 527–529
 liter 527–529
problem solving 498–514, 523–534

Measurement

Length

	K	1	2	3	4	5	6
Centimeter		●	●	▲	▲	▲	▲
Choosing appropriate unit		●	●	●	▲	▲	▲
Conversion table			●	●	▲	▲	▲
Customary measurement		●	●	▲	▲	▲	▲
Distance formula							●
Equivalent units			●	●	▲	▲	▲
Estimating length	●	●	●	▲	▲	▲	▲
Fractions and measurement			●	●	▲	▲	▲
Foot, yard			●	▲	▲	▲	▲
Inch	●	●	▲	▲	▲	▲	▲
Indirect measurement					●	●	▲
Kilometer				●	▲	▲	▲
Measuring instruments		●	●	▲	▲	▲	▲
Measuring length	●	●	●	▲	▲	▲	▲
Meter		●	●	●	▲	▲	▲
Metric measurement		●	●	●	▲	▲	▲
Mile				●	▲	▲	▲
Problem-solving applications	●	●	●	●	▲	▲	▲

Money

	K	1	2	3	4	5	6
Adding and subtracting money		●	●	●	▲	▲	▲
Comparing amounts			●	●	▲	▲	▲
Consumer applications	●	●	●	▲	▲	▲	▲
Counting coins and bills	●	●	▲	▲	▲	▲	▲
Counting on with money	●	●	▲	▲	▲		
Decimals, fractions, and money				●	▲	▲	▲
Equivalent amounts	●	●	●	▲	▲		
Estimating money			●	●	▲		
Identifying coins and bills	●	●	▲	▲			
Making change			●	●	▲	▲	▲
Multiplying and dividing money				●	●	▲	▲
Place value					●	▲	▲
Problem-solving applications	●	●	●	●	▲	▲	▲
Rounding money				●	▲		
Symbolic notation	●	●	●	▲	▲	▲	▲

Temperature

	K	1	2	3	4	5	6
Celsius scale			●	▲	▲	▲	▲
Estimating temperature				●	▲		
Fahrenheit scale		●	●	▲	▲	▲	▲
Interpreting a thermometer		●	●	▲	▲	▲	▲
Negative numbers					●	▲	▲
Relating Celsius scale to Fahrenheit scale						●	●
Writing temperature			●	●	▲	▲	▲

KEY Teach and Apply ● Practice and Apply ▲ Teacher's Edition Lesson ★

Measurement

Length

centimeter
    measuring 505–506
choosing appropriate unit 533–534
comparing length 499–500
estimating length 503–506
inch
    measuring 503–504
non-standard units 501–502
problem solving 498–514, 523–534

Money

adding money 609, 622
coins
    dime 389–390, 393–404
    half-dollar 402
    nickel 389–392, 395–404
    penny 389–404
    quarter 399–404
comparing amounts 402, 407
consumer applications
    making purchases 405–407
counting coins 389–404
counting on 389–404
equivalent amounts 399–401, 403–404
modeling and writing amounts 389–404
problem-solving applications 390, 392, 394, 396, 404–407
subtracting money 633
symbolic notation
    cent symbol (¢) 389–404, 633
value of money 389–404

Temperature

Fahrenheit 531–532
interpreting a thermometer 531–532

In the Program...

Measurement

	K	1	2	3	4	5	6

Time

	K	1	2	3	4	5	6
A.M. and P.M.			•	•	▲		
Analog clock	•	•	•	▲			
Calendar concepts	•	•	▲	▲			
Digital clock	•	•	•	▲			
Elapsed time		•	•	▲	▲	▲	▲
Equivalent units			•	▲			
Estimating time	•	•	▲	▲			
Ordinal numbers	•	•	▲	▲			
Problem-solving applications	•	•	•	•	▲	▲	▲
Schedules		•	•	▲			
Sequencing events	•	•	▲	▲			
Telling time	•	•	•	▲			
Time line				•	•	▲	▲
Time zones					•	•	▲

Volume

	K	1	2	3	4	5	6
Estimating volume				•	▲	▲	▲
Finding volume, counting cubic units				•	▲	▲	▲
Finding volume, using a formula					•	•	▲
Meaning of volume				•	•	▲	▲
Problem-solving applications				•	•	•	▲

Weight and Mass

	K	1	2	3	4	5	6
Conversion table				•	•	▲	▲
Equivalent units				•	•	▲	▲
Estimating weight and mass	•	•	•	•	▲	▲	▲
Finding weight and mass			•	•	▲	▲	▲
Gram and kilogram		•	•	•	▲	▲	▲
Ounce				•	•	▲	▲
Pound		•	•	▲	▲	▲	▲
Problem-solving applications	•	•	•	•	▲	▲	▲
Ton					•	•	▲

In Level 1...

Measurement

Time

calendar concepts
  days in a week 375–376
  making a calendar 19, 376
  months before and after 377–378
  months of the year 377–378
  ordinal numbers 375–376
  reading a calendar 375–376
clocks
  analog clock 363–374
  digital clock 363–374
comparing 369–371
elapsed time
  how long an activity will be 369–371
  when an activity will end 369–371
estimating time 361–362
hour 363–364
minute 365–367
schedules 379–380
sequencing events 359–360
telling time
  nearest five minutes 368
  nearest half hour 365–367, 373–374
  nearest hour 363–364, 373–374
  solving problems involving time 364, 371, 374
  writing time two ways 363–374

Weight and Mass

comparing 513–514
estimating 513–514
kilogram 513–514
comparing weight 511–512
estimating weight 511–512
non-standard units 509–510
pound 511–512
problem solving 498–514, 523–534

KEY   Teach and Apply ●   Practice and Apply ▲   Teacher's Edition Lesson ★

Data Analysis and Probability

In the Program...

Data Analysis and Probability

Data Analysis

	K	1	2	3	4	5	6
Analyzing and interpreting data	●	●	●	●	▲	▲	▲
Average				●	▲	▲	▲
Bar graphs	●	●	●	▲	▲	▲	▲
Box-and-whisker plots							●
Choosing an appropriate display				●	●	▲	▲
Circle graph				●	●	●	▲
Cluster						●	▲
Collecting, organizing, and displaying data	●	●	●	●	▲	▲	▲
Double bar graphs					●		▲
Double line graphs						●	▲
Frequency tables/tally charts	●	●	●	●	●	▲	▲
Gap						●	▲
Histogram					●	●	▲
Line graphs		●		●	●	▲	▲
Line plots		●	●	●	▲	▲	▲
Making tables and charts	●		●	▲	▲	▲	▲
Mean				●	▲	▲	▲
Measures of central tendency				●	●	●	▲
Median				●	●	▲	▲
Misleading data or graphs						●	▲
Mode				●	●	▲	▲
Organized lists				●	●	●	▲
Outliers					●	●	▲
Pictographs	●	●	●	▲	▲	▲	▲
Problem-solving applications	●	●	●	▲	▲	▲	▲
Quartiles							●
Range			●	●	▲	▲	▲
Reading tables and charts	●	●	●	▲	▲	▲	▲
Sampling techniques						●	●
Scatter plot							●
Stem-and-leaf plots						●	▲
Surveys	●	●	●	●	▲	▲	▲

Probability

	K	1	2	3	4	5	6
Calculating probability of simple event				●	●	▲	▲
Compound events					●	▲	▲
Developing and analyzing predictions and inferences	●	●	●	●	▲		▲
Fair or unfair			●	▲			
Fundamental Counting Principle							●
Likelihood of an event	●	●	●	▲	▲	▲	▲
Permutations and combinations							●
Possible outcomes				●	●	▲	▲
Probability experiments	●	●	●	●	▲	▲	▲
Problem-solving applications	●	●	●	▲	▲	▲	▲
Recording outcomes	●	●	●	●	▲	▲	▲
Representing likelihood as a number from 0 to 1					●	●	●
Theoretical probability						●	▲
Using a tree diagram or grid					●	●	▲
Using coins, cubes, or spinners	●	●	●	▲	▲	▲	▲

KEY — Teach and Apply ● Practice and Apply ▲ Teacher's Edition Lesson ★

In Level 1...

Data Analysis and Probability

Data Analysis

collecting and organizing 87–88
reading and interpreting data
  bar graphs 95–96, 101–103
  pictographs 89–92
  pictures 405–407
tables or charts 379–380
formulate questions 458, 638
graphs
  bar graph
    making 97–99
    reading and interpreting 95–96, 101–103
  line plots 478
  pictograph
    making 91–92
    reading and interpreting 89–90
making a table 334–335, 447–448
sorting 87–88, 91–93, 97–98
survey 93
tally charts 87–88, 96, 99, 248, 253, 285, 478

Probability

develop and analyze predictions and inferences 99, 247–248, 251–252
likelihood of an event 247–249
making predictions 247–249
probability experiments 247–248
recording outcomes 247–248
tally 247–248
using cubes 249, 251
using spinners 247–248

Scope and Sequence

In the Program...
Problem Solving

	K	1	2	3	4	5	6
Applications / Decisions							
Addition applications	●	●	●	▲	▲	▲	▲
Building new knowledge	●	●	●	●	●	●	●
Choosing a computation method		●	●	●	●	▲	▲
Choosing an operation		●	●	▲	▲	▲	●
Curriculum connections	●	●	●	●	●	●	●
Data applications	●	●	●	▲	▲	▲	▲
Decimal applications				●	●	▲	▲
Division applications			●	●	●	▲	▲
Estimated or exact answers				●	●	▲	▲
Fraction applications	●	●	●	●	●	▲	▲
Geometry applications	●	●	●	●	●	▲	▲
Integer applications						●	▲
Interpreting remainders				●	●		▲
Measurement applications		●	●	●	▲	▲	▲
Money applications		●	●	●	▲	▲	▲
Multiplication applications			●	▲	▲	▲	▲
Number and operations		●	●	●	▲	●	●
Percent applications							●
Place-value applications			●	●	●	▲	▲
Probability applications	●	●	●	▲	▲	▲	▲
Ratio applications						●	▲
Solving multi-step problems		●	●	●	●	●	▲
Subtraction applications	●	●	▲	▲	▲	▲	▲
Time applications		●	●	●	●	▲	▲
Too much information or too little information		●	●	▲	▲	▲	▲
Using a bar graph		●	●	▲	▲	▲	▲
Using a diagram					●	▲	▲
Using a formula						●	▲
Using a number sentence		●	●	▲	▲	▲	▲
Using a pattern	●	●	●	▲	▲	▲	▲
Using a pictograph	●	●	●	▲	▲	▲	▲
Using a picture, graph, or map	●	●	●	▲	▲	▲	▲
Using a table or chart	●	●	●	▲	▲	▲	▲
Using an equation						●	▲
Using estimation				●	●	●	▲
Using functions and graphs					●	●	●
Strategies							
Act it out with models	●	●	●	●	▲	▲	▲
Choose a method		●	●	●	▲	▲	▲
Draw a picture or diagram	●	●	●	●	●	▲	▲
Find a pattern	●	●	●	▲	▲	▲	▲
Guess and check	●	●	●	●	▲	▲	▲
Make a model	●	●	●	●	●	▲	▲
Make a table or chart	●	●	●	●	▲	▲	▲
Make an organized list			●	●	▲	▲	▲
Monitor and reflect on the process	●	●	●	●	▲	▲	▲
Solve a simpler problem				●	●	▲	▲
Use logical reasoning	●	●	●	●	▲	▲	▲
Work backward				●	●	▲	▲
Write a number sentence or equation	●	●	●	●	●	▲	▲

KEY Teach and Apply ● Practice and Apply ▲ Teacher's Edition Lesson ★

In Level 1...
Problem Solving

Applications

addition applications 51–53, 135–137, 571–573, 615–617
building new knowledge 39–40, 65–66, 75–76, 243, 313–314, 367, 401, 443–444, 605–614, 627–638
choosing a strategy 27, 53, 79, 103, 133–134, 137, 161, 199, 229, 253, 335, 381, 449, 475, 573, 617, 641
choosing an operation 159–161, 473–475, 639–640
curriculum connections 30, 82, 106, 140, 164, 202, 232, 256, 298, 310, 318, 338, 384, 452, 464, 518, 536, 598, 610, 620, 634, 644
data applications 89–92, 95–96, 101–103, 379–380, 458
fraction applications 238, 240, 242, 246
geometry applications 188, 194, 196–199, 208–210, 227–230
measurement applications 498–514, 523–534
money applications 390, 392, 394, 396, 404–407
number and operations applications 8, 25–27
place-value applications 282, 292–295, 315–316
probability applications 249–250, 252–253
solving multi-step problems 632, found in every Problem Solving lesson
subtraction applications 146, 148, 150, 159–161, 473–475, 584, 592, 595–596
time applications 360, 364, 367, 371, 374, 376, 378–381
too much information 595–596
using a bar graph 95–96, 101–103
using a number sentence 39–40, 42, 51–53, 73–74, 135–137, 154, 470, 571–572, 592
using a pattern 50, 219–222, 227–228, 333–335
using a pictograph 89–92
using a picture 251–253, 405–407
using a table or chart 379–380

Strategies

act it out 77–79
choose an operation 159–161
draw a picture or diagram 25–27, 199
find a pattern 50, 219–222, 227–228, 333–335
guess and check 615–617
make a table 334–335, 400, 447–448
monitor and reflect on the process 315–316, 533–534
use logical reasoning 92, 99, 134, 515–516
write a number sentence 39–40, 42, 51–53, 73–74, 135–137, 154, 434, 470, 571–572, 592

In the Program...
Reasoning and Proof

Analyzing

	K	1	2	3	4	5	6
Algebraic Thinking				▲	▲	▲	▲
Analyzing	●	●	●	●	▲	▲	▲
Checking reasonableness of answers		●	●	●	▲	▲	▲
Classifying	●	●	●	●	●	▲	▲
Creating and solving problems	●	●	●	●	●	●	●
Developing arguments and proof	●	●	●	●	▲	▲	▲
Drawing conclusions	●	●	●	●	▲	▲	▲
Explaining reasoning	●	●	●	●	●	▲	▲
Generalizing	●	●	●	●	●	▲	▲
Identifying relationships					●	▲	▲
Identifying relevant information		●	●	●	▲	▲	▲
Logical thinking	●	●	●	●	▲	▲	▲
Making and investigating conjectures			●	●	●	▲	▲
Making decisions	●	●	●	●	●	▲	▲
Making predictions	●	●	●	●	●	▲	▲
Number relationships	●		●	●	●	●	▲
Reading mathematics	●	●	●	●	▲	▲	▲
Reasonableness of method and solution			●	●	▲	▲	▲
Using logic	●	●	●	●	▲	▲	▲
Using strategies to find solutions	●	●	●	●	▲	▲	▲
Visual thinking	●	●	●	▲	▲	▲	▲

Communication

Analyzing and Evaluating Strategies

	K	1	2	3	4	5	6
Act it out with models	●	●	●	●	▲	▲	▲
Choose a method		●	●	●	▲	▲	▲
Choose an operation	●	●	●	▲	▲	▲	▲
Draw a picture or diagram	●	●	●	●	●	▲	▲
Find a pattern	●	●	●	●	▲	▲	▲
Guess and check	●	●	●	●	▲	▲	▲
Make a table or chart	●	●	●	●	●	▲	▲
Make an organized list				●	●	▲	▲
Monitor and reflect on the process	●	●	●	●	▲	▲	▲
Solve a simpler problem				●	●	▲	▲
Use logical reasoning	●	●	●	●	▲	▲	▲
Work backward				●	●	▲	▲
Write a number sentence or equation	●	●	●	●	●	▲	▲

KEY Teach and Apply ●   Practice and Apply ▲   Teacher's Edition Lesson ★

In Level 1...
Reasoning and Proof

Analyzing

analyzing 215–218, 309, 531–532
checking reasonableness of answers 315–316, 533–534
classifying and sorting 183–184, 187–189, 193–194
creating and solving problems 43, 69, 93, 151, 437, 587
developing arguments and proof 183–184, 187–189, 193–194
drawing conclusions 183–184, 187–189, 193–194
explaining reasoning 315–316, 533–534
generalizing 183–184, 187–189, 193–194
identifying relevant information 595–596
justifying thinking 315–316, 533–534
logical thinking 92, 134, 515–516
making and investigating conjectures 615–617
making decisions
   choosing a method 27, 53, 79, 103, 133–134, 137, 161, 199, 229, 253, 335, 381, 449, 475, 573, 617, 641
   choosing a strategy 27, 53, 79, 103, 133–134, 137, 161, 199, 229, 253, 335, 381, 449, 475, 573, 617, 641
   choosing an operation 159–161, 473–475, 639–640
   determining reasonableness of an answer 315–316, 533–534
   too much information 595–596
making predictions 247–249
number relationships 65–66
reading mathematics 42, 96, 186, 210, 280, 312, 460, 568, 630
reasonableness of method and solution 315–316, 533–534
using logic 92, 99, 134, 515–516
using strategies to find solutions 27, 53, 79, 103, 133–134, 137, 161, 199, 229, 253, 335, 381, 449, 475, 573, 617, 641
visual thinking 225–226

Communication

Analyzing and Evaluating Strategies

act it out with models 77–79
choose a method 27, 53, 79, 103, 133–134, 137, 161, 199, 229, 253, 335, 381, 449, 475, 573, 617, 641
choose an operation 159–161
draw a picture or diagram 25–27, 199
find a pattern 50, 219–222, 227–228, 333–335
guess and check 615–617
make a table or chart 334–335, 400, 447–448
monitor and reflect on the process 315–316, 533–534
use logical reasoning 92, 99, 134, 515–516
write a number sentence 39–40, 42, 51–53, 73–74, 135–137, 154, 434, 470, 571–572, 592

Scope and Sequence

In the Program...

Communication

	K	1	2	3	4	5	6

Analyzing and Evaluating Thinking

	K	1	2	3	4	5	6
Determining reasonableness of an answer		●	●	●	▲	▲	▲
Estimating or exact answer			●	●	▲	▲	▲
Explaining reasoning	●	●	●	●	▲	▲	▲
Identifying relevant information		●	●	▲	▲	▲	▲
Justifying thinking	●	●	●	●	▲	▲	▲
Making predictions	●	●	●	▲	▲	▲	▲
Too much or too little information		●	●	▲	▲	▲	▲

Communicating Mathematical Thinking

	K	1	2	3	4	5	6
Clarifying understanding	●	●	●	●	▲	▲	▲
Drawing a picture or diagram	●	●	●	●	●	▲	▲
Using manipulatives	●	●	●	●	▲	▲	▲
Talk About It/Write About It		▲	▲	▲	▲	▲	▲

Organizing and Consolidating Thinking

	K	1	2	3	4	5	6
Classifying	●	●	●	●	●	▲	▲
Drawing conclusions		●	●	●	▲	▲	▲
Generalizing	●	●	●	●	●	▲	▲

Using Mathematical Language

	K	1	2	3	4	5	6
Creating and solving problems	●	●	●	●	●	●	●
Describing problems and solutions	●	●	●	●	▲	▲	▲
Vocabulary		▲	▲	▲	▲	▲	▲

Connections

Building Upon Prior Knowledge

	K	1	2	3	4	5	6
Adding	●	●	●	▲	▲	▲	▲
Dividing			●	●	▲	▲	▲
Multiplying		●	●	●	▲	▲	▲
Subtracting	●	●	●	▲	▲	▲	▲
Using money	●	●	●	●	▲	▲	▲

Recognizing and Applying Mathematics in Context

	K	1	2	3	4	5	6
Curriculum connections	●	●	●	●	●	●	●
Real-life applications	●	●	●	●	●	●	●

Recognizing and Using Connections

	K	1	2	3	4	5	6
Decimals, fractions, and mixed numbers					●	●	▲	▲
Drawing conclusions		●	●	●	▲	▲	▲
Generalizing	●	●	●	●	●	▲	▲
Measurement and time	●	●	●	●	●	▲	▲
Money	●	●	●	●	▲	●	▲
Patterns	●	●	●	▲	▲	▲	▲
Related facts	●	●	●	●	▲		

KEY Teach and Apply ● Practice and Apply ▲ Teacher's Edition Lesson ★

In Level 1...

Communication

Analyzing and Evaluating Thinking

determining reasonableness of an answer 315–316, 533–534
estimating or exact answer 315–316
explaining reasoning 315–316, 533–534
identifying relevant information 595–596
justifying thinking 315–316, 533–534
making predictions 247–249
too much information 595–596

Communicating Mathematical Thinking

clarifying understanding (See Explain Your Thinking in lessons.)
drawing a picture 25–27, 199
Talk About It 14, 19, 35, 61, 64, 74, 87, 88, 92, 99, 189, 191, 192, 240, 242,
   247, 288, 290, 309, 332, 378, 396, 404, 407, 462, 499, 504, 509, 511,
   513, 523, 524, 525, 526, 527, 570, 582, 608, 628
using manipulatives 9–18, 21–27, 35–50, 61–75, 125–126, 133–134,
   277–294, 311–314, 429–435, 557–568, 625–630

Organizing and Consolidating Thinking

classifying 183–184, 187–189, 193–194
drawing conclusions 183–184, 187–189, 193–194
generalizing 183–184, 187–189, 193–194

Using Mathematical Language

creating and solving problems 43, 69, 93, 151, 437, 587
describing problems and solutions 7–8, 23–24, 185–189, 193–196,
   207–210, 215–216, 247–249, 305–306, 311–312, 329–330, 503–504,
   505–506, 511–512, 513–514, 525–526, 527–528, 531–532
Math At Home—Vocabulary 3, 121, 179, 273, 355, 425, 495, 553
Reading Math—Vocabulary 42, 72, 210, 280, 306, 312, 460, 506, 586, 630

Connections

Building Upon Prior Knowledge

adding 39–40, 443–444, 569–570, 605–614
fractions 243
numbers 313–314
subtracting 65–66, 75–76, 633, 627–638
time 365–367
using money 401, 633

Recognizing and Applying Mathematics in Context

curriculum connections 30, 82, 106, 140, 164, 202, 232, 256, 298, 310,
   318, 338, 384, 452, 464, 518, 536, 598, 610, 620, 634, 644
real-life applications 87–88, 91–92, 97–98, 207–212, 363–378, 384,
   389–404, 503–506, 511–514, 525–528, 531–532

Recognizing and Using Connections

drawing conclusions 183–184, 187–189, 193–194
generalizing 183–184, 187–189, 193–194
measurement 525–526, 531–532
money 399–401, 403–404
patterns 50, 219–222, 227–228, 333–335
related facts 153–154, 465–470, 591–592
time 363–376

Representation

Organizing, Recording, and Communicating Ideas	K	1	2	3	4	5	6
Making a list			●	●	●	▲	▲
Using a bar graph	●	●	●	▲	▲	▲	▲
Using a circle graph			●	●	●	▲	▲
Using a double bar graph				●	●	▲	▲
Using a double line graph						●	▲
Using a line graph					●	▲	
Using a line plot		●	●	●	▲	▲	
Using a pictograph	●	●	●	▲	▲		
Using a picture or diagram			●		●	▲	▲
Using a stem-and-leaf plot					●	●	
Using a table or chart	●	●	●	▲	▲	▲	▲
Using measurement	●	●	●	●	▲	▲	▲
Using probability	●	●	●	▲	▲	▲	▲
Using symbols	●	●	●	▲	▲	▲	▲

Selecting, Applying, and Translating Among Representations	K	1	2	3	4	5	6
In decimals, fractions, and money				●	▲		
In geometry	●	●	●	●	▲	▲	▲
In measurement	●	●	●	●	▲	▲	▲
In percent						●	▲
In time		●	●	▲	▲		

Using Representations to Model and Interpret Mathematics	K	1	2	3	4	5	6
Algebraic equations	●	●		●	●	●	▲
Arrays			●	●	●	▲	▲
Counters, connecting cubes	●	●	●	●	▲	▲	▲
Data	●	●	●	●	▲	▲	▲
Decimal models				●	●	●	▲
Fraction models		●	●	●	▲	▲	▲
Geoboard/dot or grid paper		▲	●	●	●	▲	
Geometric tools (compass, protractor, straightedge)					●	●	●
Hundreds chart	●	●	●	▲	▲		
Integer models				●	●	●	●
Make a model (act it out)	●	●	●	●	●	●	▲
Manipulatives or models	●	●	●	●	▲	▲	▲
Modeling solids	●	●	●	●	●	▲	▲
Money and coins	●	●	▲	▲	▲	▲	▲
Multiplication table				●	▲		
Number lines	●	●	●	●	●	●	▲
Part/part whole models	●	●	●	▲	▲	▲	
Pattern blocks	●	●	▲	▲	▲	▲	▲
Percent models				●	●	●	●
Pictures/diagrams	●	●	●	●	▲	▲	▲
Place-value models		●	●	▲	▲		
Symbols	●	●	●	●	▲	▲	▲
Technology	▲	▲	▲	▲	▲	▲	▲

KEY Teach and Apply ● Practice and Apply ▲ Teacher's Edition Lesson ★

Representation

Organizing, Recording, and Communicating Ideas

using a bar graph 95–96, 101–103
using a line plot 478
using a pictograph 89–92
using a picture 251–253, 405–407
using a table or chart 379–380
using mathematical language 7–8, 23–24, 185–189, 193–196, 207–210, 215–216, 247–249, 305–306, 311–312, 329–330, 503–504, 505–506, 511–512, 513–514, 525–526, 527–528, 531–532
using measurement 499–514, 523–532
using probability 247–250, 252–253
using symbols 39–40, 65–66, 313–314, 389–404, 633

Selecting, Applying, and Translating Among Representations

in geometry 188–189, 193–194, 215–225
in measurement 501–502, 525–526
in time 363–374

Using Representations to Model and Interpret Mathematics

algebraic expressions, equations, and number sentences 39–40, 42, 51–53, 73–74, 135–137, 154, 434, 470, 571–572, 592
connecting/snap cubes 45–48, 73–74, 129, 153–155, 249–250, 251, 277–278, 331–332, 445–446
counters 9, 11, 13, 15, 35–38, 63–65, 131, 431–434, 557–562, 565, 567, 580
data 89–92, 95–96, 101–103, 379–380, 458
fraction models 236, 239–243, 245–246
geoboard/dot or grid paper 226
hundreds chart 324, 326, 327, 329
make a model (act it out) 77–80, 293–296
modeling solid shapes 191–192, 195–196
money and coins 388, 389–396, 397, 399–404, 419, 609, 633
number cards 100
number cubes 131
number lines
  adding and subtracting 127–128, 147–148, 429–430, 457–458
  counting and ordering 18
  line plots 478
  to compare and order 23–24, 303–304
  to estimate to the nearest ten 653
part/part whole workmats 37–38, 63–65, 135, 153–156, 459–462, 565, 567–568, 580, 583–584, 585, 589
pattern blocks 197–198, 215–218
pictures/diagrams 25–27, 199, 251–253, 267, 405–407
place -value (base ten) blocks 274, 281–282, 285, 287–292, 293–294, 311, 313, 315, 603–608, 625–630
place -value tables 274, 281–282, 311, 313, 605–608, 627–630
real objects 49–50, 182
spinners 247–248, 329, 636
symbols 39–40, 65–66, 313–314, 389–404, 633
technology 116, 174, 268, 350, 420, 490, 548, 654
ten frames 13–16, 431–434, 559–562, 565
thermometers 531–532, 534
Venn diagrams 158, 594

Student Handbook

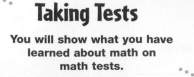

Houghton Mifflin Math

Welcome To Grade 1 Math

Your book will help you learn about numbers, shapes, graphs, and patterns.

You will start with things you already know—counting, sorting, and ordering. You will learn about adding, subtracting, and solving problems.

You will work with your teacher and classmates to understand math.

xxii Student Handbook

Taking Tests

You will show what you have learned about math on math tests.

When you take a test, you need to know how to think about the math and how to take a test.

As you work on the lessons, you will see this special sign near **Explain Your Thinking.**

TEST TIPS This sign points out questions that help you think about math.

Some hints for reading problems

★ Always read the problem twice. First, to understand the question. Then, to find information.

★ Make a picture of the problem on paper or in your mind to help you think about the question.

Student Handbook xxiii

Some pages in your book have special signs that help you practice taking tests.

You will find where you will practice listening to test questions.

You can use a **Practice Test** to see what taking a test is like.

These pages will help you get ready for real tests.

Some hints for taking tests

★ Listen carefully while your teacher reads the question.

★ If you are not sure how to answer a question, go on to the next one.

★ Reread the problem to make sure you have answered the question.

★ Be careful to fill in the space for the answer you want.

xxiv Student Handbook

Notes:

Pacing Guide

Grade One

Houghton Mifflin Math encourages you to customize instruction to meet the needs of your students. As a guide, we have identified lessons as review, core, or extend for typical first grade level content. As these categories may vary based on your local curriculum, consider this chart as a guide to help you plan your teaching year.

Unit	Chapter	Review Lessons	Number of Days	Core Lessons	Number of Days	Extend Lessons	Number of Days	Days to Assess
1	1	1–3	3	5–7	3	4	1	1
	2			1–8	8			1
	3	2	1	1, 3–8	7			1
	4	2	1	1, 3–6	5			2
2	5	3	1	1, 2, 4, 5	4			1
	6			1–7	7			2
3	7	1, 2, 4	3	5–7	3	3	1	1
	8	1, 5	2	2–4, 6–7	5	8	1	1
	9	1	1	2, 4, 6	3	3, 5	2	2
4	10			1–8	8			1
	11			1–6	6			1
	12			1–5	5			2
5	13	1	1	2, 3, 5–9	7	4	1	1
	14	1	1	2–4, 6–7	5	5	1	2
6	15			1–8	8			1
	16			1–8	8			2
7	17	1, 5	2	2–4, 6–8	6			1
	18	1	1	2–5	4			2
8	19			1–7	7			1
	20			1–7	7			1
	21			1, 2, 4–6	5	3	1	1
	22			1–3, 5–7	6	4	1	2
Totals		Review	17	Core	127	Extend	9	30

Table of Contents

As you read through the Table of Contents (it begins on the next page), you will see that *Houghton Mifflin Math* is organized into 8 units. Each unit consists of 2–4 chapters related to the big mathematical idea of the unit. Chapters have from 5 through 9 lessons, two Quick Checks, and a Chapter Review/Test. At the end of each unit is a Unit Test.

This unit/chapter organization promotes the kind of effective teaching and assessment that will help you reach all the learners in your class. Daily Lesson Quizzes make you aware of which students may be in need of help and which have mastered the material. Quick Checks and Chapter and Unit Tests are all linked to immediate and focused remediation and intervention tools—*Reteach* resources and the *Ways to Success* Intervention CD-ROM. *Enrichment* resources and *Chapter Challenge*s are available for those students who are ready for some extra challenge. If algebra is an important element in your mathematics curriculum, you will find special support for this teaching in those lessons with an Algebra label.

Be sure to look for the *Weekly Reader Connection* icons—these indicate activities for which students can find additional information by visiting the Weekly Reader link at Houghton Mifflin's Education Place Web site (**www.eduplace.com/kids/mw/**).

Number Concepts, Operations, and Graphing
STARTING THE UNIT

Number Concepts Through 20

Addition Concepts

Algebra Indicates lessons that include algebra instruction.

3 Subtraction Concepts

4 Data and Graphing

FINISHING THE UNIT

Technology

Ways to Assess Customized
   Spiral Review and Test Generator CD
Lesson Planner CD-ROM
Ways to Success Intervention CD-ROM
MathTracks CD-ROM
Education Place:
www.eduplace.com/math/mw
Houghton Mifflin Math eBook CD-ROM
eManipulatives
eGames

 Indicates WEEKLY WR READER® Connection

Addition and Subtraction Facts Through 10
STARTING THE UNIT

5 Addition Strategies Through 10

Algebra Indicates lessons that include algebra instruction.

6 Subtraction Strategies Through 10

FINISHING THE UNIT

Technology
Ways to Assess Customized
   Spiral Review and Test Generator CD
Lesson Planner CD-ROM
Ways to Success Intervention CD-ROM
MathTracks CD-ROM
Education Place:
www.eduplace.com/math/mw
Houghton Mifflin Math eBook CD-ROM
eManipulatives
eGames

 Indicates **WEEKLY WR READER° Connection**

Geometry and Fractions
STARTING THE UNIT

7 Plane and Solid Shapes

8 Spatial Sense and Patterns

Algebra Indicates lessons that include algebra instruction.

Technology

Ways to Assess Customized
    Spiral Review and Test Generator CD

Lesson Planner CD-ROM

Ways to Success Intervention CD-ROM

MathTracks CD-ROM

Education Place:
www.eduplace.com/math/mw

Houghton Mifflin Math eBook CD-ROM

eManipulatives

eGames

 Indicates WEEKLY WR READER® Connection

Numbers Through 100
STARTING THE UNIT

10 Place Value to 100

11 Order and Compare Numbers

Algebra Indicates lessons that include algebra instruction.

12 Number Patterns

FINISHING THE UNIT

Technology

Ways to Assess Customized
   Spiral Review and Test Generator CD
Lesson Planner CD-ROM
Ways to Success Intervention CD-ROM
MathTracks CD-ROM
Education Place:
www.eduplace.com/math/mw
Houghton Mifflin Math eBook CD-ROM
eManipulatives
eGames

Ⓦ Indicates **WEEKLY WR READER® Connection**

Time and Money
STARTING THE UNIT

13 Time and Calendar

Algebra Indicates lessons that include algebra instruction.

14 Using Money

FINISHING THE UNIT

Technology

Ways to Assess Customized
   Spiral Review and Test Generator CD
Lesson Planner CD-ROM
Ways to Success Intervention CD-ROM
MathTracks CD-ROM
Education Place:
www.eduplace.com/math/mw
Houghton Mifflin Math eBook CD-ROM
eManipulatives
eGames

 Indicates **WEEKLY WR READER® Connection**

Addition and Subtraction Facts Through 12

STARTING THE UNIT

15 Addition Facts Through 12

Algebra Indicates lessons that include algebra instruction.

16 Subtraction Facts Through 12

FINISHING THE UNIT

Technology

Ways to Assess Customized
    Spiral Review and Test Generator CD
Lesson Planner CD-ROM
Ways to Success Intervention CD-ROM
MathTracks CD-ROM
Education Place:
www.eduplace.com/math/mw
Houghton Mifflin Math eBook CD-ROM
eManipulatives
eGames

 Indicates **WEEKLY WR READER® Connection**

Measurement
STARTING THE UNIT

17 Length and Weight

18 Capacity and Temperature

Algebra Indicates lessons that include algebra instruction.

Technology

Ways to Assess Customized
    Spiral Review and Test Generator CD
Lesson Planner CD-ROM
Ways to Success Intervention CD-ROM
MathTracks CD-ROM
Education Place:
www.eduplace.com/math/mw
Houghton Mifflin Math eBook CD-ROM
eManipulatives
eGames

FINISHING THE UNIT

Two-Digit Addition and Subtraction
STARTING THE UNIT

19 Addition Facts Through 20

 Indicates **WEEKLY WR READER® Connection**

Subtraction Facts Through 20

Adding Two-Digit Numbers

Algebra Indicates lessons that include algebra instruction.

22 Subtracting Two-Digit Numbers

FINISHING THE UNIT

END OF BOOK RESOURCES

Technology
Ways to Assess Customized
   Spiral Review and Test Generator CD
Lesson Planner CD-ROM
Ways to Success Intervention CD-ROM
MathTracks CD-ROM
Education Place:
www.eduplace.com/math/mw
Houghton Mifflin Math eBook CD-ROM
eManipulatives
eGames

(WR) Indicates **WEEKLY WR READER® Connection**

Number Concepts, Operations, and Graphing

Unit at a Glance

Assessment System

Assessing Prior Knowledge

Check whether children understand the prerequisite concepts and skills.

- **CHAPTER PRETEST** (Unit Resource Folder or *Ways to Success* Intervention CD-ROM)
- **WARM-UP ACTIVITY:** Every TE Lesson
- **UNIT LITERATURE ACTIVITY:** PE p. 2

Ongoing Assessment

Monitor whether children are acquiring new concepts and skills.

- **PROBLEM OF THE DAY:** First page of every TE lesson
- **QUICK REVIEW:** First page of every TE lesson
- **LESSON QUIZ:** First page of every TE lesson
- **COMMON ERROR:** Every TE Lesson
- **QUICK CHECK:** PE pp. 20, 29, 44, 55, 70, 81, 94, 105
- **KEY TOPIC REVIEW:** PE pp. 30, 56, 82, 106

 ## Test Prep and Practice

Help children prepare for state and standardized tests.

- **DAILY TEST PREP:** Every TE Lesson
- **CUMULATIVE TEST PREP:** PE pp. 117–118
- **PROBLEM SOLVING FOR TESTS:** pp. 28, 54, 80, 104
- **TEST PREP ON THE NET:** eduplace.com/kids/mw
- **TEST-TAKING STRATEGIES:** eduplace.com/math/mw

Summary Assessment

Assess children's mastery of new concepts and skills.

- **CHAPTER TEST:**
  - ✔ PE pp. 31–32, 57–58, 83–84, 107–108
  - ✔ Unit Resource Folder
- **UNIT TEST:**
  - ✔ PE pp. 111–112
  - ✔ Test A, Unit Resource Folder
  - ✔ Test B, Unit Resource Folder

TEST TIPS Student Self-Assessment

Allow children to evaluate their own understanding.

- **EXPLAIN YOUR THINKING:** PE pp. 7, 17, 21, 23, 37, 39, 41, 45, 47, 49, 63, 65, 67, 71, 73, 75, 89, 91, 95

Performance Assessment

Evaluate children's ability to use mathematics in real-world situations.

PERFORMANCE ASSESSMENT: PE pp. 113–114
WRITE ABOUT IT OR TALK ABOUT IT: in Hands-On lessons
WRITING MATH: CREATE AND SOLVE: PE pp. 43, 69, 93

Technology Options

Use computer-based assessment to make testing and reporting easier.

- **WAYS TO ASSESS** (CD-ROM, LAN, or Web spiral review and test creation, administration, scoring, and report generation)
- **LEARNER PROFILE** (observations, evaluations, and reports from your handheld or desktop computer)

Reaching All Learners

Resources	On Level Students	Extra Support Students	English Learners	Inclusion/ Special Needs	Advanced Learners	Mathematically Promising
Student Editions						
Building Vocabulary	●	●	●	●	●	●
Guided Practice ✱	●	●	●	●	●	●
MathTracks MP3 Audio CD 💿	●	●	○	○		
Teacher's Editions						
Building Vocabulary Strategies	●	●	○	○	●	○
Teacher Support	●	○	●		○	○
Intervention Activities	○	●	●	●		
Other Resources						
Chapter Challenges	○				●	●
Combination Classroom Guide	●	●	●	●	●	●
English Learners Handbook	○	○	●	○		
Ways to Success CD-ROM 💿	○	●	●	●		

KEY   ● **Highly Appropriate**   ○ **Appropriate**   ✱ **Scaffolded Instruction**

Documenting Adequate Yearly Progress

National Test Correlations

UNIT 1 Objectives		ITBS	Terra Nova (CTBS)	CAT	SAT	MAT
1A	Recognize, count, order and compare numbers and sets through 20.	●	●	●	●	●
1B	Read and write numbers through 20.	●	●	●	●	●
1C	Model addition concepts and use addition properties to solve problems and find sums through 8.	●	● ●	●	●	●
1D	Model subtraction concepts and use subtraction properties to solve problems and subtract from 8 or less.	●	● ●	●	●	●
1E	Read, make, and use graphs to compare information.		●	●	●	●
1F	Apply skills and strategies to solve problems.	●	●	●	●	●

Activities for Reaching All Learners

Home-School Activity

Number Line Race

Materials: number cards 0–10, blank number line

For each player prepare number cards 0–10 and a blank number line with 11 tick marks. Place cards facedown. At the count of three, players turn over their top card. The first player to identify their number as greater than, less than, or equal to their opponent's gets to write the number on their number line. Completed number line wins.

Unit Vocabulary Activity

Number Match

Materials: number cards 10–20, number word cards ten to twenty

Children work in small groups. Prepare a set of number cards 10–20 and a set of number word cards ten to twenty. Shuffle cards and place in an array. Children take turns turning over 2 cards to find a match. Children collect each match or turn facedown again. Most matches wins the game.

Remediation

MathTracks Lessons: 1.1, 1.2, 1.4, 1.6, 2.2, 2.3, 2.7, 3.2, 3.3, 3.7, 4.2, 4.3, 4.4, 4.6

Use the MathTracks CD-ROM to help children who need a quick review or extra support for the lesson, to provide children who were absent with a complete lesson presentation, or to assist children with reading difficulties.

Intervention

Ways to Success CD-ROM

Use the Ways to Success CD-ROM to help children who need extra help with lessons. This software is designed to reteach the lesson objective, provide extra guided and independent practice, and if needed, reteach a key prerequisite skill.

Unit Project

Addition and Subtraction with Fruit and Vegetables

Math Topics

- counting sets of 1 through 9 objects
- addition sentences using + and =
- subtraction sentences using − and =
- using tally charts to make bar graphs

To Begin

- Ask children to brainstorm lists of fruits and vegetables.
- Children will make picture cards and use them to solve addition and subtraction sentences.

Ongoing

- Have children paste pictures of fruits and vegetables to make number cards showing sets from 1 to 9. Have each child make several cards.
- Have children use the picture cards to model addition and subtraction sentences.
- For Connecting the Unit Project, see page 5D for Chapter 1, page 33D for Chapter 2, page 59D for Chapter 3, and page 85D for Chapter 4.

To Finish

- Display number cards in order from 1 to 9. Write an addition and subtraction sentence. Have children use the cards to solve each sentence.
- See page 110 to Wrap Up the Unit Project.

Starting Unit 1
Accessing Prior Knowledge

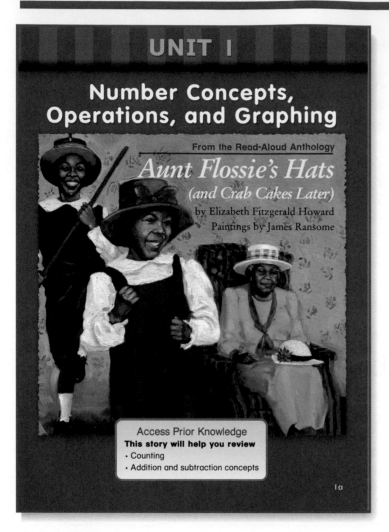

UNIT 1

Number Concepts, Operations, and Graphing

From the Read-Aloud Anthology

Aunt Flossie's Hats
(and Crab Cakes Later)
by Elizabeth Fitzgerald Howard
Paintings by James Ransome

Access Prior Knowledge
This story will help you review
• Counting
• Addition and subtraction concepts

1a

Hats, hats, hats, hats!
A stiff black one with bright red ribbons.
A soft brown one with silver buttons.
Thin floppy hats that hide our eyes.
Green or blue or pink or purple.

1b from *Aunt Flossie's Hats (and Crab Cakes Later)*

Accessing Prior Knowledge

In Kindergarten, children:
• read and write numbers to 20
• order numbers to 20
• model addition and subtraction
• complete addition and subtraction sentences
• read and interpret pictographs

This selection from the Unit Opener gives you the opportunity to review some of these prerequisite skills.

• You may wish to review numbers 1–20 by writing them on the board and asking volunteers to identify them.

• Next, review number order to 20 by writing the numbers 1, 6, 11, 15, and 18 on the board and having volunteers tell the numbers that come between.

• Then review addition by writing addition sentences for sums to 10, using 1 and 2 as addends.

Story Summary

Today you will be reading a story about hats. The title of the story is *Aunt Flossie's Hats (and Crab Cakes Later)*. The author is Elizabeth Fitzgerald Howard.

Reading the Story

You can find the entire text of the book at the end of the Teacher's Edition on page T 50.

Read the selection aloud to the children. Then read the selection again. Have the children name different types of hats listed in the selection. On the board, record the number of each different hat the children name and then discuss.

This story is available in the Read-Aloud Anthology, Volume 1

Some have fur and some have feathers.
Look! This hat is just one smooth soft rose,
but here's one with a trillion flowers!
Aunt Flossie has so many hats!

1c

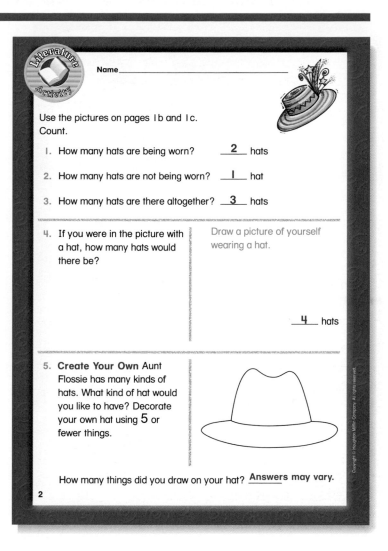

Name_____

Use the pictures on pages 1b and 1c.
Count.

1. How many hats are being worn?   **2** hats

2. How many hats are not being worn?   **1** hat

3. How many hats are there altogether?   **3** hats

4. If you were in the picture with a hat, how many hats would there be?

   Draw a picture of yourself wearing a hat.

   4 hats

5. **Create Your Own** Aunt Flossie has many kinds of hats. What kind of hat would you like to have? Decorate your own hat using 5 or fewer things.

How many things did you draw on your hat? **Answers may vary.**

2

Unit Bibliography

Aunt Flossie's Hats (and Crab Cakes Later) by Elizabeth Fitzgerald Howard

The Best Vacation Ever by Stuart J. Murphy

Can You Count Ten Toes? by Lezlie Evans

Fish Eyes by Lois Ehlert

Just Enough Carrots by Stuart J. Murphy

Just One More by Michelle Koch

Lemonade for Sale by Stuart J. Murphy

Over in the Meadow, a Rhyme Illustrated by Ezra Jack Keats

Ten Little Mice by Joyce Dunbar

See also the **Math and Literature Bibliography** in the Teacher Support Handbook at the back of this Teacher's Edition.

Literature Activity

Purpose: This activity provides an opportunity to informally assess children's understanding of counting on by ones.

Using This Page
- Observe children as they work to complete Exercises 1–3. **How can we find out how many hats in all?** (Count on from 2.)
- Discuss with children the strategy of counting on from the new sum of 3 to solve Exercise 4.
- Ask volunteers to share their work for Exercise 5.

Math At Home

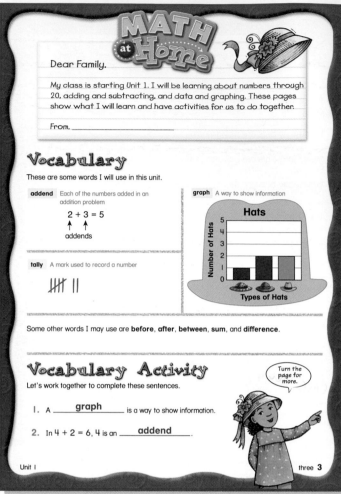

Dear Family,

My class is starting Unit 1. I will be learning about numbers through 20, adding and subtracting, and data and graphing. These pages show what I will learn and have activities for us to do together.

From _____

Vocabulary

These are some words I will use in this unit.

addend Each of the numbers added in an addition problem

2 + 3 = 5
↑   ↑
addends

tally A mark used to record a number

‖‖‖ ‖

graph A way to show information

Hats

(bar graph: Number of Hats vs Types of Hats)

Some other words I may use are **before**, **after**, **between**, **sum**, and **difference**.

Vocabulary Activity

Let's work together to complete these sentences.

Turn the page for more.

1. A ___graph___ is a way to show information.

2. In 4 + 2 = 6, 4 is an ___addend___ .

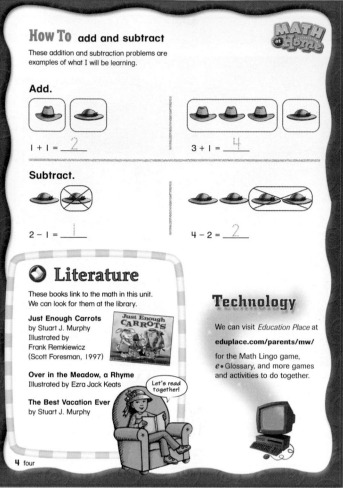

How To add and subtract

These addition and subtraction problems are examples of what I will be learning.

Add.

$1 + 1 = 2$

$3 + 1 = 4$

Subtract.

$2 - 1 = 1$

$4 - 2 = 2$

Literature

These books link to the math in this unit. We can look for them at the library.

Just Enough Carrots
by Stuart J. Murphy
Illustrated by
Frank Remkiewicz
(Scott Foresman, 1997)

Over in the Meadow, a Rhyme
Illustrated by Ezra Jack Keats

The Best Vacation Ever
by Stuart J. Murphy

Let's read together!

Technology

We can visit *Education Place* at

eduplace.com/parents/mw/

for the Math Lingo game, *e•Glossary*, and more games and activities to do together.

Math at Home

Discuss the letter to the family with children. You may want to use this letter as an introduction to the unit. Highlight for children what they will be learning in the unit. Tell children that as they go through the unit they will be able to answer the questions on these pages.

Math at Home is available in Spanish and other languages on Education Place.
www.eduplace.com/math/mw/

Literature

Encourage parents to find the suggested books and read them with their children.

Technology

Education Place is an award-winning website with engaging activities for students and helpful information for parents. Look for the eGlossary, the Math Lingo Game, and more.

Building Vocabulary

Strategies for Building Vocabulary

Using a Glossary

Have children look at the picture glossary on Student Edition pp. 657–668. Print *difference* on the board and ask children how they can find words listed in a glossary. Elicit that words are listed in alphabetical order and that children will find **difference** among words that start with the letter *d*. Have children locate *difference* and describe what it means in their own words. Then, ask them to identify words that come before and after *difference* in the glossary. Record their responses on a Before and After chart.

Repeat this exercise with the term *minus sign*.

Graphic Organizer: Chart

Before difference	After difference
between	graph
cone	nickel
cup	rectangle

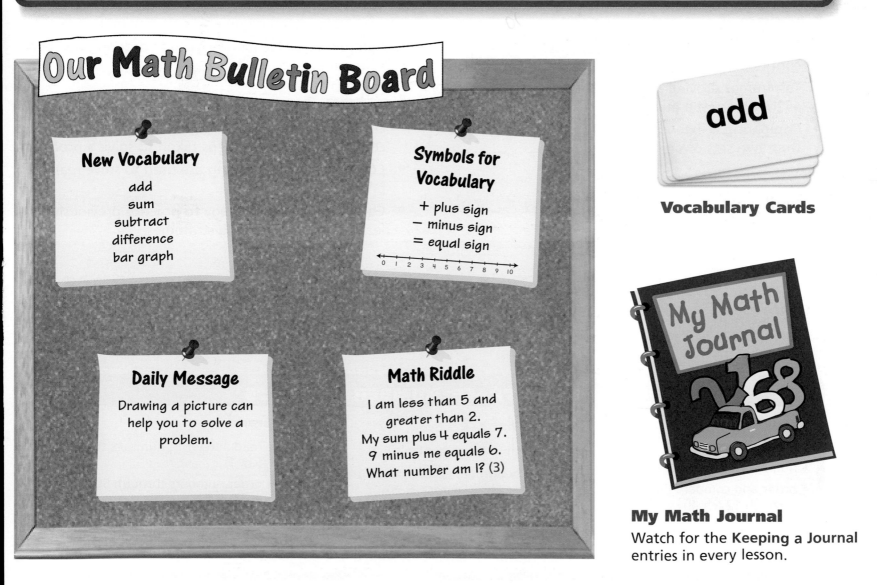

Our Math Bulletin Board

New Vocabulary
add
sum
subtract
difference
bar graph

Symbols for Vocabulary
+ plus sign
− minus sign
= equal sign

0 1 2 3 4 5 6 7 8 9 10

Daily Message
Drawing a picture can help you to solve a problem.

Math Riddle
I am less than 5 and greater than 2.
My sum plus 4 equals 7.
9 minus me equals 6.
What number am I? (3)

add

Vocabulary Cards

My Math Journal

My Math Journal
Watch for the **Keeping a Journal** entries in every lesson.

Lesson by Lesson Overview
Number Concepts

Lesson 1

- Children use one-to-one correspondence to match sets of objects to compare.
- The words *same, more,* and *fewer* are used to describe how one set compares to the other.
- Related objects in pairs of sets provide a context for comparing.

Lesson 2

- A review of numbers 0 through 9 is accomplished through hands-on activities.
- Using counters to model numbers and drawing the counters provides an opportunity for children to connect concrete representation to pictorial.
- Word names along with pictures extend counting and numeral writing to include reading.

Lesson 3

- Numbers 10 through 20 are developed as a continuation of the previous lesson.
- Ten frames provide a visual benchmark for children as they learn the numbers 11 through 19.
- Comparing is extended to include comparing more than two sets of objects.

Lesson 4

- Using number lines to order introduces children to a useful model that will be revisited in later chapters.
- The words *before, after,* and *between* are used to describe the relative position of numbers on a number line.
- A calendar page provides a real-life example of numbers in order.

Lesson 5

- Comparing progresses from sets to numbers.
- The vocabulary of comparing numbers is introduced as *less than, greater than, equal to.* Symbols will be taught in a later chapter.

Lesson 6

- This lesson combines the skills of the previous lessons as children compare numbers on a number line.
- Comparing is extended to include ordering numbers from greatest to least.

Lesson 7

- Drawing a picture as a problem-solving strategy helps children visualize the steps taken to solve a problem.
- Comparing and reasoning are used to solve real-life problems.
- Children choose a strategy to practice previously learned problem-solving strategies.

SKILLS TRACE: NUMBER CONCEPTS

Grade K	Grade 1	Grade 2
• numbers 0 through 5 (ch. 4)	• compare sets of objects	• read and write numbers through 50 (ch. 1)
• numbers 6 through 12 (ch. 7)	• recognize, count, read, and write numbers through 20	• order numbers through 50 (ch. 1)
• order and compare numbers through 12 (ch. 8)	• order numbers through 20	• compare numbers through 50 (ch. 1)
• numbers 13 through 20 (ch. 15)	• compare numbers through 20	
• numbers through 31 (ch. 16)		

Chapter Planner

Lesson	Objective	Vocabulary	Materials	✔ NCTM Standards
1.1 **More, Fewer, and Same** p. 7A	Use one-to-one correspondence to compare sets of objects using the terms more, fewer, and same.	more fewer same	cubes in two colors	Develop understanding of the relative position and magnitude of whole numbers and of ordinal and cardinal numbers and their connections.
1.2 **Numbers 0 Through 9** **(Hands-On)** p. 9A	Recognize and count sets of 0 through 9 objects; read and write the numbers 0 through 9.	number words for 0 through 9	number cards 0–9 (Learning Tool (LT) 14), counters, number dot cards 1–9 (LT 17), ten-frame transparency	Count with understanding and recognize "how many" in sets of objects.
1.3 **Numbers 10 Through 20** **(Hands-On)** p. 13A	Recognize and count sets of 10 through 20 objects; read and write the numbers 10 through 20.	number words for 10 through 20	number card 18 (LT 13), counters, ten frame transparency, grid paper (LT 29), grid paper transparency, Workmat 1 and 2, number dot card 11 (LT 17)	Count with understanding and recognize "how many" in sets of objects.
1.4 **Order** p. 17A	Order numbers using the words before, after, and between; identify the missing numbers in a sequence; count backward.	number line before after between	number cards through 20 (LT 14 and 15), hundred chart (LT 7), counters, blank transparency, calendar page (LT 35)	Develop understanding of the relative position and magnitude of whole numbers and of ordinal and cardinal numbers and their connections.
1.5 **Comparing Numbers** p. 21A	Compare numbers using the terms greater and lesser.	less than greater than equal to	dot cards 0–10 (LT 17), blank transparencies, cubes	Develop understanding of the relative position and magnitude of whole numbers and of ordinal and cardinal numbers and their connections.
1.6 **Greater Than, Less Than** p. 23A	Use a number line to compare numbers.		blank transparency, counters, number cards 0–10 (LT 14)	Develop understanding of the relative position and magnitude of whole numbers and of ordinal and cardinal numbers and their connections.
1.7 **Draw a Picture** p. 25A	Draw pictures to solve problems.		cubes, counters, blank transparency	Apply and adapt a variety of appropriate strategies to solve problems.

Resources For Reaching All Learners

LESSON RESOURCES: Reteach, Practice, Enrichment, Problem Solving, Homework, English Learners, Daily Routines, Transparencies, Math Center.

ADDITIONAL RESOURCES FROM HOUGHTON MIFFLIN: Chapter Challenges, Combination Classroom Planning Guide, Every Day Counts, Math to Learn (Student Handbook)

Every Day Counts
The Counting Tape Activities in Every Day Counts support the math in this chapter.

Assessing Prior Knowledge

Before beginning the chapter, you can assess student understandings in order to assist you in differentiating instruction.

Complete Chapter Pretest in Unit Resource Folder

Use this test to assess both prerequisite skills (**Are You Ready?** — one page) and chapter content (**Check What You Know** — two pages).

Chapter 1 Prerequisite Skills Pretest

Chapter 1 New Content Pretest

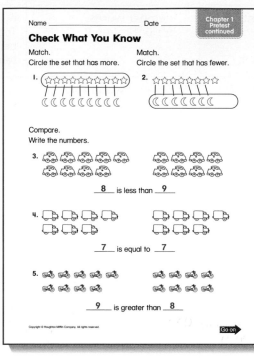

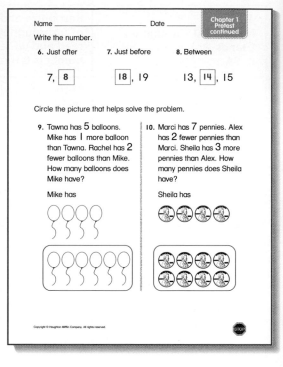

Customizing Instruction

For Students Having Difficulty

Items	Prerequisites	Ways to Success
1–4	Count and write numbers to 10.	Skillsheet 1
5–8	Understand "more" and recognize sets.	CD: 1a Skillsheet 2

Ways to Success: Intervention for every concept and skill (CD-ROM or Chapter Intervention Skillsheets).

For Students Having Success

Items	Objectives	Resources
1–2	1A Use vocabulary relating to number concepts through 20.	Enrichment 1.6
3–5	1B Read and write numbers through 20.	Enrichment 1.2, 1.3
6–8	1C Recognize, count, compare, and order sets through 20.	Enrichment 1.4, 1.5
9–10	1D Draw pictures to solve problems.	Enrichment 1.7

Use **Chapter Challenges** with any students who have success with all new chapter content.

Other Pretest Options

Informal Pretest

The pretest assesses vocabulary and prerequisite skills needed for success in this chapter.

***Ways to Success* CD-ROM**

The *Ways to Success* chapter pretest has automatic assignment of appropriate review lessons.

Chapter Resources

Activity

Assessing Prior Knowledge

Number of the Day (recognize and count sets of 1 through 9)

- For nine days, write a number from 1 to 9 on the board. Have children draw pictures to show that many objects.
- In order to help children get a feel for what the target number is, ask questions such as: Would you eat 8 eggs for breakfast? Could you hold 8 soccer balls? Do you own 8 of something?

Activity

Ongoing Skill Activity

Domino Days (one-to-one correspondence)

- Designate several days as Domino Days. Provide small groups of children with domino tiles or handmade cardboard domino cards.
- Point out that each piece has two sets of dots on it. Show children the patterns for the numbers 1 to 12 on the pieces as you count the dots aloud.
- Have one child in the group place a domino card in the center of the group. Then challenge children to work together to see how many cards or tiles they can line up by matching sets of dots.
- When they are finished, have children count the cards or tiles in their "domino train."

Activity

Connecting to the Unit Project

- Draw 6 oranges on the board.
- Have children count the oranges and write the number.
- **What number comes just before 6? What number comes just after 6?** (5, 7)

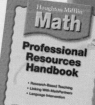

Professional Resources Handbook

Research, Mathematics Content, and Language Intervention

Research-Based Teaching

Cao (1994) found that structurally Chinese numeration clearly highlights the grouping by ten aiding Chinese children to view two-digit numbers as tens and ones. For instance, in Chinese, 2 is *er*, 10 is *shi*, 12 is *shi er*, and 22 is *er shi er*. When teaching the "teen" numbers, emphasize this basis of ten by encouraging children to think of 13 as "ten and three." See *Professional Resources Handbook, Grade 1,* Unit 1.

For more ideas relating to Unit 1, see the Teacher Support Handbook at the back of this Teacher's Edition.

Language Intervention

An important building block for learning the basic facts is understanding that a number represents the amount in a group, or set, and that a group is composed of smaller subsets. Seeing numbers as being composed of subsets of numbers will enable children to count a collection of items quickly, rather than having to count individual items on their fingers using a one-to-one correspondence. For further explanation, see "Mathematical Language and Numeration" in the *Professional Resources Handbook Grade 1.*

Technology

Time-Saving Technology Support
Ways to Assess Customized Spiral Review
   Test Generator CD
Lesson Planner CD-ROM
Ways to Success Intervention CD-ROM
MathTracks CD-ROM
Education Place: www.eduplace.com/math/mw
Houghton Mifflin Math eBook CD-ROM
eManipulatives
eGames

Starting Chapter 1
Number Concepts

CHAPTER OBJECTIVES

1A Develop and use math vocabulary relating to number concepts through 20.

1B Read and write numbers through 20.

1C Recognize, count, compare, and order sets through 20 using pictures, words, and number lines.

1D Draw pictures to solve problems.

Math Background

Number Concepts

As young children begin their formal work with numbers, they encounter number relationships and vocabulary used to compare numbers. They learn to use numbers in their cardinal sense, to tell how many. With numbers or quantities, these relationships are possible: Two sets may have the same number of items, or one set may have more or fewer items than another set. Differentiating between numbers of objects in sets is an important skill that forms a basis for number comparison.

Numbers such as 1, 2, 3, and 4 are *cardinal* or counting numbers. In preparation for skills needed in computation, children also need to be able to recognize relationships between numbers, such as 1 more and 1 less.

In counting different objects, children must learn to represent and use numbers in different contexts. As they learn to say number names by rote, children learn that they must account for each item in a collection. Once children can count orally, they are exposed to writing numerals. For practice with writing numerals see Learning Tools 10 and 11.

Number Concepts

INVESTIGATION

How many red flowers are there?

CHAPTER 1

Chapter 1   five **5**

Using The Investigation

- Hold up one hand. **How many fingers?** Review words for numbers between 1 and 20 with children by having them identify groups of items around the classroom and tell how many.

- Read the directions to children. **Look at the picture. You will see many flowers to count. Use number words to tell about what you see.**
How many red flowers are there? (12)

For more information about projects and investigations, visit Education Place. **eduplace.com/math/mw/**

Connect the Dots

Start at 1.
Finish at 10.

10 — 1   2

9   8   4   3

7   6   5

6 six

For Mathematically Promising Students

The *Chapter Challenges* resource book provides blackline masters for activities that explore, extend, and connect the mathematics in every chapter. To support this independent work, see the Teacher Notes for each activity.

Explore: Changing sets, page 1, after Lesson 1
Extend: Counting Apples, page 3, after Lesson 3
Connect: Number Stories, page 5, after Lesson 5

Using This Page

- Tell children that when they connect the dots on page 6, they will make a picture.

- **Put your pencil on dot 1. Then draw a line to dot 2. Keep connecting the dots in order until you reach dot 10.**

- Ask a volunteer to tell about the picture the connected dots make.

- Have children create their own connect-the-dot pictures using numbers 1 to 10. Have them trade papers with a partner and connect the dots.

NSF Children's Math Worlds

Houghton Mifflin has partnered with Dr. Karen C. Fuson, project director of *Children's Math Worlds,* to publish this National Science Foundation-funded, research based mathematics curriculum project.

Children's Math Worlds builds deep understanding of mathematics concepts, links concrete approaches to symbolic notation, and fosters confidence and communication skills.

More, Fewer, and Same

PLANNING THE LESSON

MATHEMATICS OBJECTIVE

Use one-to-one correspondence to compare sets of objects using the terms *more*, *fewer*, and *same*.

Use Lesson Planner CD-ROM for Lesson 1.1.

Daily Routines

Calendar

Review the days of the week. Now find if there are more, fewer, or the same number of Mondays and Tuesdays in the month by comparing the columns for the days. Repeat with other days of the week.

Vocabulary

Have children compare sets of objects in the classroom using the words **more**, **fewer**, and **same**. Example: There are more windows than doors.

Vocabulary Cards

Meeting North Carolina's Standards

1.01 Develop number sense for whole numbers through 99.

• Connect the model, number word, and number using a variety of representations.

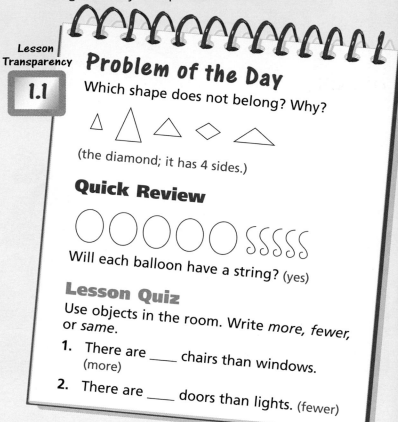

Lesson Transparency **1.1**

Problem of the Day
Which shape does not belong? Why?

(the diamond; it has 4 sides.)

Quick Review

Will each balloon have a string? (yes)

Lesson Quiz
Use objects in the room. Write *more*, *fewer*, or *same*.

1. There are ____ chairs than windows. (more)

2. There are ____ doors than lights. (fewer)

LEVELED PRACTICE

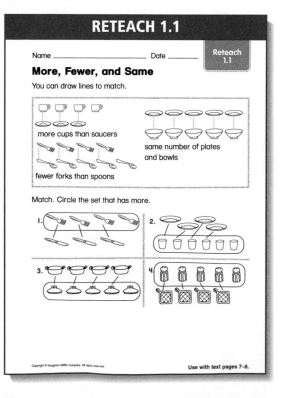

RETEACH 1.1

Name ____ Date ____   Reteach 1.1

More, Fewer, and Same

You can draw lines to match.

more cups than saucers

same number of plates and bowls

fewer forks than spoons

Match. Circle the set that has more.

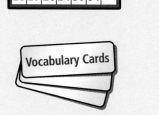

PRACTICE 1.1

Name ____ Date ____   Practice 1.1

More, Fewer, and Same

Match.
Circle the set that has fewer.

1.

Match.
Circle the set that has more.

2.

Test Prep

3. Fill in the ○ for the correct answer.
   Find the set with more.

Explain how you know which set has more in item 2.
Possible response: I drew lines to match. I had extra socks. The set of socks has more.

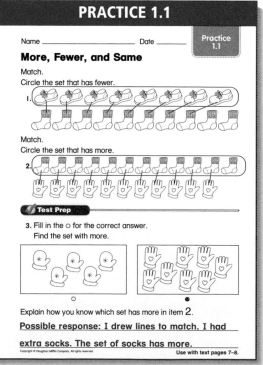

ENRICHMENT 1.1

Name ____ Date ____   Enrichment 1.1

Fewer to More

Compare each set below to the children above.
Circle the set that is the same. Use a blue crayon.
Circle the set that has more. Use a red crayon.
Circle the set that has fewer. Use a yellow crayon.

1.
red

2.
yellow

3.
blue

Write About It How could you show the same number of baseballs and children?

Possible answer: I could draw one more baseball in the set with 11 baseballs.

Use with text pages 7–8.

Practice Workbook Page 1

7A   CHAPTER 1   Lesson 1

Reaching All Learners
Differentiated Instruction

English Learners

Use Worksheet 1.1 to help children understand the comparative words *more*, *fewer*, and *same*. They will need to understand these words in order to understand the terms *greater than*, *less than*, and *equal to*.

Inclusion
VISUAL, TACTILE

Materials: *cubes*

Have child show 2 groups of cubes. Then help child make each group into a cube train. Line up the trains to compare. Explain how the lengths show whether there are more, fewer, or the same number of cubes.

Gifted and Talented
KINESTHETIC, VISUAL

Have pairs hide one hand behind their back. Together each child brings his or her hand forward with one or more fingers raised. Pairs compare the fingers raised. Have them write how many more (or fewer) fingers are raised. Write *same* if they raise the same number of fingers.

TECHNOLOGY

Spiral Review

Using the *Ways to Assess* CD-ROM, you can create **customized** spiral review worksheets covering any lessons you choose.

eBook

An electronic version of this lesson can be found in **eMathBook**.

Lesson Planner

Use the **Lesson Planner CD-ROM** to see how lesson objectives for this chapter are correlated to standards.

Social Studies Connection

Create lists of animals with the class. Decide whether they live in the city, country, or both. Then compare the groups in each category using the words more, fewer, or the same.

MATH CENTER

Vocabulary Activity

This vocabulary-building activity helps children understand and remember new words. Encourage children to use the words in math discussion.

PROBLEM SOLVING 1.1

Name _____ Date _____   Problem Solving 1.1

More, Fewer, and Same

Find the set that answers the question.

Draw or write to explain.

1. There are 6 clowns. Each needs a hat. Circle the set with the same number of hats.

2. One of the clowns gets sick. Now the clowns need 1 fewer hat. Draw a line under the set with 1 fewer hat.

3. There are 4 children who want to rent bicycles. Which set of bicycles can the children rent? Circle the set with the same number.

4. There is 1 more child who wants to rent a bicycle. Which set of bicycles should the children rent now? Draw a line under the set with 1 more bicycle.

Use with text pages 7–8.

HOMEWORK 1.1

Name _____ Date _____   Homework 1.1

More, Fewer, and Same

You can draw lines to match.

fewer cats than dogs   **same** number of cats and dogs   **more** cats than dogs

1. Match. Circle the set with more.

2. Match. Circle the set with fewer.

3. Draw a set that has the same number.

Use with text pages 7–8.

ENGLISH LEARNERS 1.1

Name _____ Date _____   English Learners 1.1

More, Fewer, and Same

More   Fewer   Same

1. Draw stars.

| | Drawing of more than 5 stars | Drawing of fewer than 5 stars | Drawing of 5 stars |

More   Fewer   Same

2. Draw hats.

| | Drawing of more than 3 hats | Drawing of fewer than 3 hats | Drawing of 3 hats |

More   Fewer   Same

To the Teacher: Use the examples at the top of the page to demonstrate the meaning of the words. Then have children draw in the boxes to show their understanding of each of the words.

Use with text pages 7–8.

Homework Workbook Page 1

TEACHING LESSON 1.1

LESSON ORGANIZER

Objective Use one-to-one correspondence to compare sets of objects using the terms *more*, *fewer*, and *same*.

Resources Reteach, Practice, Enrichment, Problem Solving, Homework, English Learners, Transparencies, Math Center

Materials Cubes in two colors

Activity

Warm-Up Activity
Modeling One-to-One Matching

| iii Small Group | ◯ 5 minutes | Auditory, Visual |

Materials: *cubes in two colors*

1. Review how to match one-to-one. Have children pick 2 equal groups of cubes. Each group is a different color. Demonstrate how to pair cubes of the second color to each cube of the first color. **Do the two groups have the same number?** (yes) **How do you know?** (They are matched one-to-one.)

2. Have children place their two groups of cubes on a piece of paper. Model how to draw a line from a cube of one color to a cube of a second color to match them one-to-one.

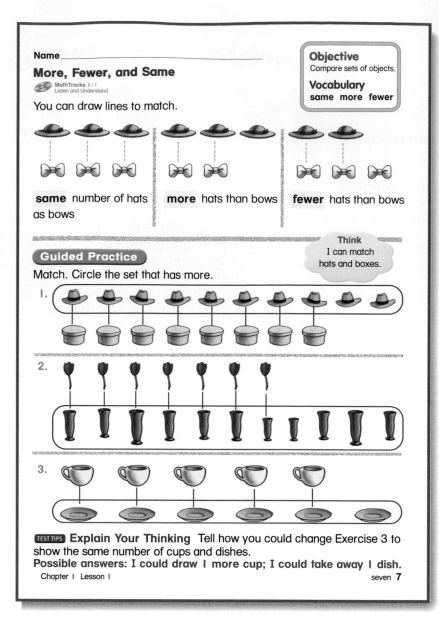

Name_____

More, Fewer, and Same

MathTracks 1/1
Listen and Understand

Objective Compare sets of objects.

Vocabulary same more fewer

You can draw lines to match.

same number of hats as bows | **more** hats than bows | **fewer** hats than bows

Think
I can match
hats and boxes.

Guided Practice

Match. Circle the set that has more.

1.

2.

3.

TEST TIPS **Explain Your Thinking** Tell how you could change Exercise 3 to show the same number of cups and dishes.
Possible answers: I could draw 1 more cup; I could take away 1 dish.

Chapter 1 Lesson 1   seven **7**

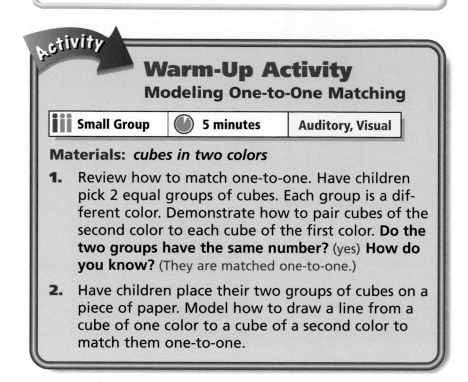

① Introduce *Activity*
Discuss More, Fewer, and Same

| iiii Whole Group | ◯ 10–15 minutes | Visual, Auditory |

Materials: *chairs*

1. Discuss things that can be matched one-to-one; for example, 1 shoe to 1 foot, 1 hand to 1 mitten, 1 snack to 1 child, 1 chair to 1 child.

2. Display 4 chairs. **This is a set of chairs. A set is a group.** Have 4 volunteers sit in the chairs. **Are there the same number of chairs as children?** (yes) **How do you know?** (They are matched one-to-one.)

3. Add a chair. **Are there more or fewer chairs than children?** (more) Take away 2 chairs. **Are there more or fewer chairs than children?** (fewer)

② Develop

Guided Learning

Teaching Example Explain the objective to the class. Guide children to see how the examples illustrate the vocabulary same, more, and fewer.

Guided Practice

Have children complete **Exercises 1–3** as you observe. Discuss children's responses to the Explain Your Thinking question.

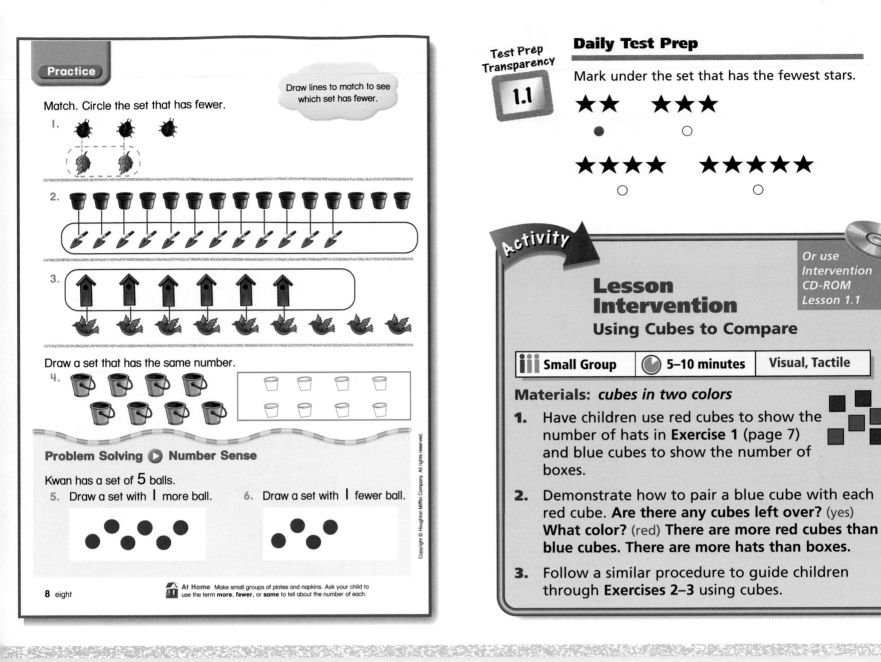

Practice

Match. Circle the set that has fewer.

Draw lines to match to see which set has fewer.

1.

2.

3.

Draw a set that has the same number.

4.

Problem Solving ▶ Number Sense

Kwan has a set of 5 balls.

5. Draw a set with 1 more ball.

6. Draw a set with 1 fewer ball.

8 eight

At Home Make small groups of plates and napkins. Ask your child to use the term **more**, **fewer**, or **same** to tell about the number of each.

Daily Test Prep

Mark under the set that has the fewest stars.

★★   ★★★
●   ○

★★★★   ★★★★★
○   ○

Activity

Or use Intervention CD-ROM Lesson 1.1

Lesson Intervention

Using Cubes to Compare

| Small Group | 5–10 minutes | Visual, Tactile |

Materials: *cubes in two colors*

1. Have children use red cubes to show the number of hats in **Exercise 1** (page 7) and blue cubes to show the number of boxes.

2. Demonstrate how to pair a blue cube with each red cube. **Are there any cubes left over?** (yes) **What color?** (red) **There are more red cubes than blue cubes. There are more hats than boxes.**

3. Follow a similar procedure to guide children through **Exercises 2–3** using cubes.

---

3 Practice

Independent Practice

Children complete **Exercises 1–4** independently.

Problem Solving

After children complete **Exercises 5–6**, call on volunteers to share their drawings and to tell how many balls are in each set.

Common Error

Confusing Fewer with More

Children may be so focused on drawing the lines to match that they confuse **fewer** with **more**. Review definitions of **fewer** and **more** using the Vocabulary Cards.

4 Assess and Close

Display 4 red cubes and 5 blue cubes.

How do you know which set has more? (You can match the red cubes and blue cubes.) **How can I make the sets show the same number?** (Add a red cube or take away a blue cube.)

Keeping a Journal

Draw a picture to show sets of things you can match one-to-one.

Hands-On: Numbers 0 Through 9

Lesson 1.2

PLANNING THE LESSON

MATHEMATICS OBJECTIVE

Recognize and count sets of 0 through 9 objects; read and write numbers 0 through 9.

Use Lesson Planner CD-ROM for Lesson 1.2.

Daily Routines

Calendar

Instruct the class to count with you by ones the number of days in each week.

Vocabulary

Review number words **zero** through nine by showing a number card. Have children hold up the matching number word Vocabulary Card.

Vocabulary Cards

Meeting North Carolina's Standards

1.01 Develop number sense for whole numbers through 99.

• Connect the model, number word, and number using a variety of representations.

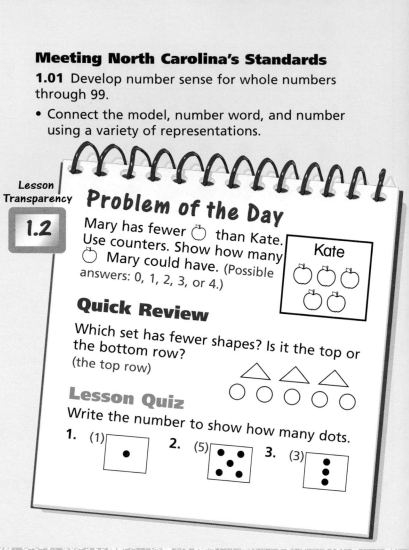

Lesson Transparency 1.2

Problem of the Day

Mary has fewer 🍎 than Kate. Use counters. Show how many 🍎 Mary could have. (Possible answers: 0, 1, 2, 3, or 4.)

Kate

Quick Review

Which set has fewer shapes? Is it the top or the bottom row? (the top row)

Lesson Quiz

Write the number to show how many dots.

1. (1) 2. (5) 3. (3)

LEVELED PRACTICE

RETEACH 1.2

Name _____ Date _____ **Reteach 1.2**

Numbers 0 Through 9

You can use dots to show how many.

| 1 • | 2 •• | 3 •• | 4 •• | 5 •• |

Use • to show the number. Arrays will differ.

1. 2 ••
2. 9 •••
3. 4 ••
4. 8 ••••
5. 0
6. 5 ••
7. 3 ••
8. 10 •••••
9. 7 ••
10. 1

Copyright © Houghton Mifflin Company. All rights reserved.
Use with text pages 9–12.

PRACTICE 1.2

Name _____ Date _____ **Practice 1.2**

Numbers 0 Through 9

Count. Write the number.

1. ▢▢ / ▢▢ **four**
2. ○○○ / ○○○ **6 six**
3. △ / △ **2 two**
4. ☆☆☆ / ☆☆☆ **9 nine**
5. ▢▢ / ▢▢ / ▢▢ **7 seven**
6. ⬠⬠⬠ / ⬠⬠⬠ **8 eight**

Test Prep

Fill in the ○ for the correct answer. NH means Not Here. How many shapes are there?

7. ♡ ♡ ♡
   five four three NH
   ○ ○ ● ○
8. △△△△△ / △△△
   0 6 10 NH
   ○ ○ ○ ●

Explain how you knew the correct answer.

__Possible response: I counted the pictures and looked for the number that matched.__

Copyright © Houghton Mifflin Company. All rights reserved.
Use with text pages 9–12.

ENRICHMENT 1.2

Name _____ Date _____ **Enrichment 1.2**

Pictures and Numbers

Count how many in each set.
Write the number next to the set.
Draw lines to match sets with the same number.

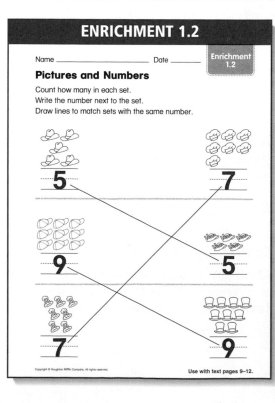

Copyright © Houghton Mifflin Company. All rights reserved.
Use with text pages 9–12.

Practice Workbook Page 2

Reaching All Learners

Differentiated Instruction

English Learners

English-language learners may not know how to read and write number words in English. Use Worksheet 1.2 to give children practice in associating number words with numbers.

Special Needs
KINESTHETIC, TACTILE

Materials: *number cards 0–9 (LT 14), counters, tray of salt*

Show a number card. Have the child move counters from one pile to another as he or she counts to that number. Then, write the number in the tray of salt with your finger. Have child trace over the number as he or she says it.

Early Finishers
VISUAL, TACTILE

Materials: *number cards 0–8 (LT 14), grid paper, crayons*

Fold sheets of paper into eighths. Have the child choose a number card and color that many squares in a row on one sheet of the grid paper. Then have the child color the same number of squares in different arrangements on another sheet of paper.

TECHNOLOGY

Spiral Review

To reinforce skills on lessons taught earlier, create **customized** spiral review worksheets using the *Ways to Assess* CD-ROM.

Education Place

Encourage students to visit **Education Place** at **eduplace.com/kids/mw/** for more student activities.

Manipulatives

Interactive Counters with several workmats are available on the *Ways to Success* CD-ROM.

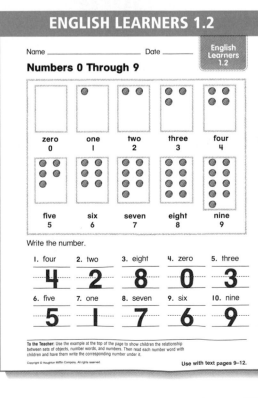

Art Connection

Have children make a nature mural on paper using seasonal cutouts or collected items. Have them use sets that show each number 0–9.

MATH CENTER

Basic Skills Activity

Motivate children to build basic skills. Use this activity to address multiple learning styles using hands-on activities related to the skills of this lesson.

PROBLEM SOLVING 1.2

Name _____ Date _____ Problem Solving 1.2

Numbers 0 Through 9

Count. Use counters if you want. Write the number.

Jon has a fish tank like the one in the picture.
How many 🐟 does Jon have?
3 🐟

Draw or write to explain.

1. How many 🦀 does Jon have?
2 🦀

2. How many 🌿 does Jon have?
5 🌿

3. How many 🐟 does Jon have?
5 🐟

4. How many 🐚 does Jon have?
0 🐚

Use with text pages 9–12.

HOMEWORK 1.2

Name _____ Date _____ Homework 1.2

Numbers 0 Through 9

You can count to show the number.
3

Count. Write the number.

1. **5**

2. **9**

3. Draw a set of 0 through 9 items you find at home. Count. Write the number.

Use with text pages 9–12.

Homework Workbook Page 2

ENGLISH LEARNERS 1.2

Name _____ Date _____ English Learners 1.2

Numbers 0 Through 9

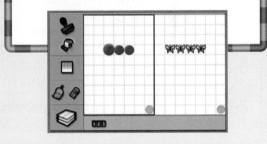

zero 0 | one 1 | two 2 | three 3 | four 4

five 5 | six 6 | seven 7 | eight 8 | nine 9

Write the number.

1. four **4**
2. two **2**
3. eight **8**
4. zero **0**
5. three **3**
6. five **5**
7. one **1**
8. seven **7**
9. six **6**
10. nine **9**

To the Teacher: Use the example at the top of the page to show children the relationship between sets of objects, number words, and numbers. Then read each number word with children and have them write the corresponding number under it.

Use with text pages 9–12.

TEACHING LESSON 1.2

LESSON ORGANIZER

Objective Recognize and count sets of 0 through 9 objects; read and write numbers 0 through 9.

Resources Reteach, Practice, Enrichment, Problem Solving, Homework, English Learners, Transparencies, Math Center

Materials Ten frame transparency, counters, number dot cards 1–9 (Learning Tool (LT) 17), number cards 0–9 (LT 14)

Activity

Warm-Up Activity
Modeling Rote Counting

| 👤👤👤👤 Whole Group | ⏱ 5 minutes | Auditory, Kinesthetic |

1. Review the counting sequence by having children march in place as they count to 9 with you.

2. Repeat with other exercises, such as jumping jacks or touching toes.

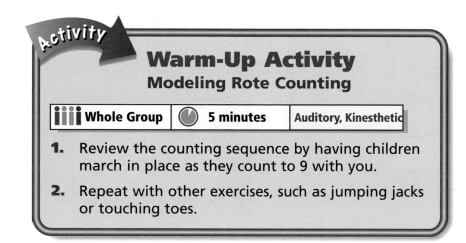

Name_____

Activity: Numbers 0 Through 9
MathTracks 1/2
Listen and Understand

0	1	2	3	4	5
zero	one	two	three	four	five

Objective
Count 0 through 9 objects; read and write the numbers.

Vocabulary
number words for 0 through 9

Work Together

Use ⬭ to show the number.
Draw to show how many.

1. 3

2. 2

3. 0

4. 5

5. 4

Chapter 1 Lesson 2   nine **9**

---

1 Introduce

Discuss Numbers 0 Through 9

| 👤👤👤👤 Whole Group | ⏱ 10–15 minutes | Visual, Auditory |

Materials: *ten frame transparency, counters, number dot cards 1–9 (LT 17)*

1. Display a ten frame on the overhead. Hold up the dot card for 1. **How many dots?** (1) Have children count with you as you place 1 counter on the ten frame. **How many counters?** (1) Model writing 1 on the board. Have children trace 1s on their desks with their fingers.

2. Repeat the steps to introduce 2, 3, 4, and 5. Then introduce 0 by taking all the counters off the ten frame.

3. Then introduce the numbers 6, 7, 8, and 9 in the same way.

2 Develop

Guided Learning

Teaching Example Introduce the objective and vocabulary to the children. Guide children to see how the dots show each number and number word for zero through five.

Work Together

Have children complete **Exercises 1–5** as you observe. Explain that children do not need to trace the counters when they draw to show how many. They can draw free hand. Have children look at the number representation for 0–5. Ask them to identify which shows the most and which shows the fewest.

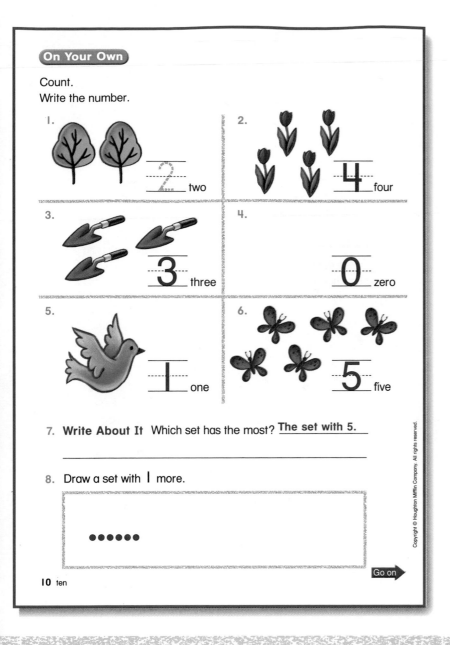

On Your Own

Count.
Write the number.

1. 2 two

2. 4 four

3. 3 three

4. 0 zero

5. 1 one

6. 5 five

7. **Write About It** Which set has the most? The set with 5.

8. Draw a set with 1 more.

● ● ● ● ● ●

Go on

10 ten

ACHIEVING Mathematical Proficiency

What Is Mathematical Proficiency?

Mathematical proficiency assumes that children understand basic concepts, perform basic computations fluently, use a variety of problem-solving strategies, reason clearly, and bring a positive attitude to mathematics learning. **Teaching for proficiency requires that lessons focus on specific learning goals.**

One specific goal focuses on building on past lessons and preparing for future lessons. By building on past lessons, children are encouraged to practice and apply what they know to new situations. In this chapter, children compare sets of objects and use math vocabulary to describe them. They learn to count objects to 20 and connect number names and numerals.

In ensuing lessons, they will build on this knowledge as they use a number line to first order, and then compare, numbers.

3 Practice

On Your Own

Children complete **Exercises 1–6** independently.

Use the **Write About It** in **Exercise 7** to review the term **most**. Children draw a picture to complete **Exercise 8**. Have volunteers share and compare their drawings with the class.

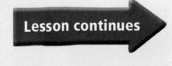

Lesson continues

Technology Connection
Counting Objects With a Calculator

In this activity, students use the constant function on their calculator to count objects.

Give each student 6 counters. Show them how to count with the constant function on their calculator.

- Explain that the constant function will continually add or subtract the same number. To program the constant to count by ones, have students key in the following sequence:

  [+] [1]

- Have students press [=] for each of their counters. Then have them count the counters by hand. Tell students to check that the number in the calculator's display matches the number they counted.

Give students various amounts of counters. Have them use the constant function on their calculators to count.

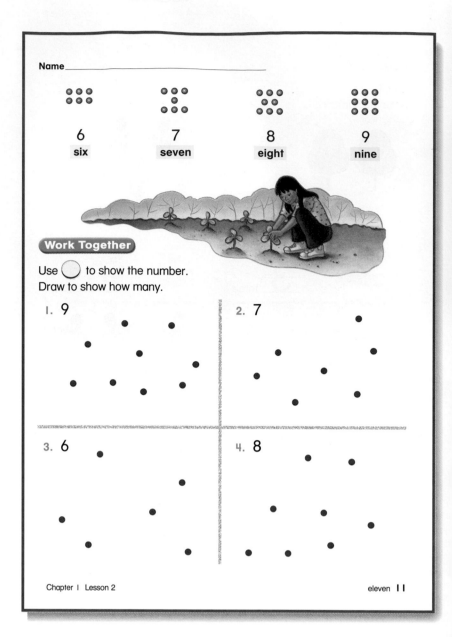

Name _____

6 six   7 seven   8 eight   9 nine

Work Together

Use ⬤ to show the number.
Draw to show how many.

1. 9

2. 7

3. 6

4. 8

Chapter 1 Lesson 2   eleven 11

---

3 Practice

Guide children to see how the dots show each number and number word for six through nine.

Work Together

Have children complete **Exercises 1–4** as you observe.

On Your Own

Have children complete **Exercises 1–4** independently. Children may be able to use 5 as a referent in exercises 2 and 3. They can start at 5 and then count on.

Use the **Talk About It** in **Exercise 5** to review the term **fewest**.

Have children complete **Exercises 6–8** independently.

Common Error

Child Does Not Count Models Accurately
Have child move each counter as he or she counts.

4 Assess and Close

Display a dot card for 8.

How many dots? (8) Have a volunteer write the number on the board.

Is 8 more or less than 5? (more)

Display a dot card for 4.

How many dots? (4) Have a volunteer write the number.

Is 4 more or less than 5? (less)

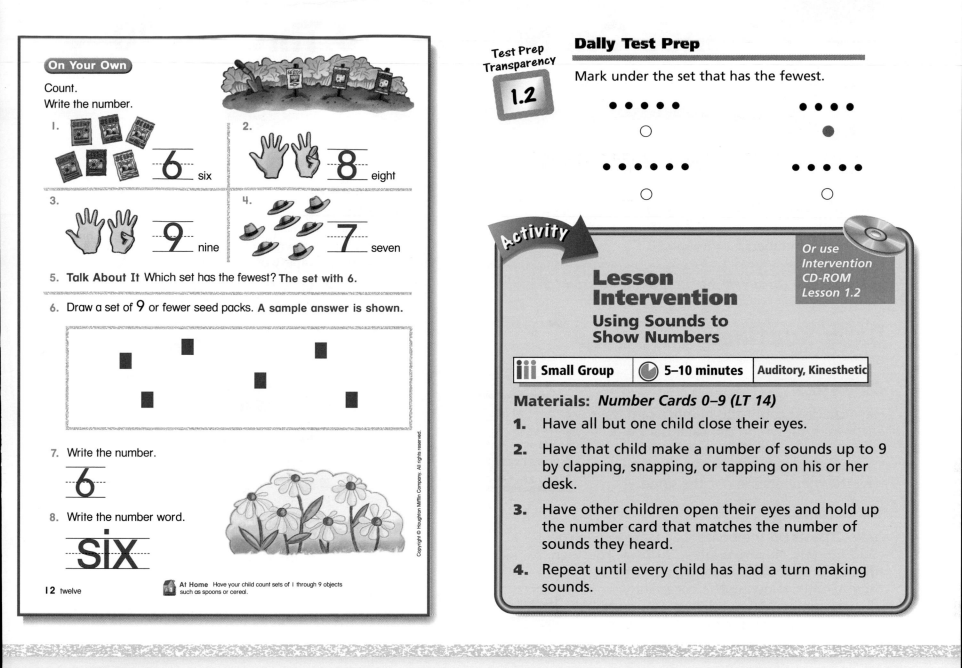

On Your Own

Count.
Write the number.

1. **6** six

2. **8** eight

3. **9** nine

4. **7** seven

5. **Talk About It** Which set has the fewest? **The set with 6.**

6. Draw a set of 9 or fewer seed packs. **A sample answer is shown.**

7. Write the number.

6

8. Write the number word.

six

At Home Have your child count sets of 1 through 9 objects such as spoons or cereal.

12 twelve

Daily Test Prep

Mark under the set that has the fewest.

• • • • •   • • • •
    ○   ●

• • • • • •   • • • • •
    ○   ○

Activity

Or use Intervention CD-ROM Lesson 1.2

Lesson Intervention

Using Sounds to Show Numbers

| Small Group | 5–10 minutes | Auditory, Kinesthetic |

Materials: Number Cards 0–9 (LT 14)

1. Have all but one child close their eyes.

2. Have that child make a number of sounds up to 9 by clapping, snapping, or tapping on his or her desk.

3. Have other children open their eyes and hold up the number card that matches the number of sounds they heard.

4. Repeat until every child has had a turn making sounds.

Keeping a Journal

Write a number from 0 through 9. Write each number word. Draw pictures to show each number.

Hands-On: Numbers 10 Through 20

PLANNING THE LESSON

MATHEMATICS OBJECTIVE

Recognize and count sets of 10 through 20 objects; read and write numbers 10 through 20.

Use Lesson Planner CD-ROM for Lesson 1.3.

Daily Routines

Calendar

Have children count the number of days in each week shown on the calendar page. Then have them count the number of Sundays, Mondays, . . . , Saturdays. Discuss why the numbers are not the same.

Sunday	Monday	Tuesday	Wednesday	Thursday	Friday	Saturday
				1	2	3	4
5	6	7	8	9	10	11
12	13	14	15	16	17	18
19	20	21	22	23	24	25
26	27	28	29	30	31	

Vocabulary

Draw 20 dots on the board. Lead children in rote counting **ten, eleven, twelve, thirteen, fourteen, fifteen, sixteen, seventeen, eighteen, nineteen, twenty** while showing the vocabulary word of each number. Then hold up a card and help volunteers say the number by counting the dots on the board.

Vocabulary Cards

Meeting North Carolina's Standards

1.01 Develop number sense for whole numbers through 99.

• Connect the model, number word, and number using a variety of representations.

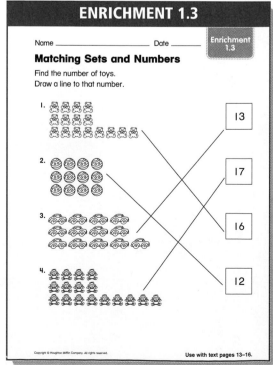

Lesson Transparency 1.3

Problem of the Day

Write the number word for each set.

▼▼▼▼▼▼▼▼ (eight)

■■■■■■ (six)

Quick Review

Write the number. Write the number word.

■■ (2, two)   ●●●●● (5, five)

Lesson Quiz

Write the number.

1. (19)

2. ten (10)

3. (15)

LEVELED PRACTICE

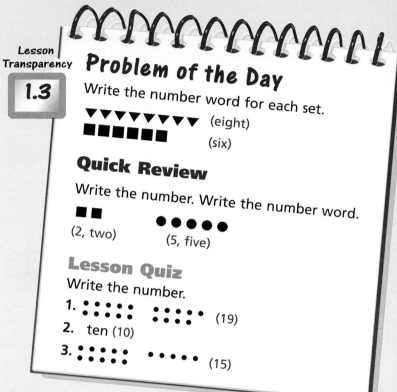

RETEACH 1.3

Name _____ Date _____   Reteach 1.3

Numbers 10 Through 20

10 ten   13 thirteen

11 eleven   14 fourteen

12 twelve   15 fifteen

Use Workmat 1 and ○ to show the number.
Draw to show how many.

1. 17   2. 12

3. 19   4. 16

Use with text pages 13–16.

PRACTICE 1.3

Name _____ Date _____   Practice 1.3

Numbers 10 Through 20

Count. Write the number.

1. fifteen

2. nineteen

3. eleven

Test Prep

Fill in the ○ for the correct answer. NH means Not Here.
How many dots are there?

4. 13 15 17 NH
    ○   ○   ●   ○

5. eighteen seventeen sixteen NH
    ●   ○   ○   ○

Use with text pages 13–16.

ENRICHMENT 1.3

Name _____ Date _____   Enrichment 1.3

Matching Sets and Numbers

Find the number of toys.
Draw a line to that number.

1. ___ 13

2. ___ 17

3. ___ 16

4. ___ 12

Use with text pages 13–16.

Practice Workbook Page 3

Reaching All Learners
Differentiated Instruction

English Learners

English-language learners may not know how to read and write number words in English. Use Worksheet 1.3 to give children practice in associating number words with numbers.

Inclusion
KINESTHETIC, TACTILE

Materials: *number cards 10–20 (LT 14 and 15), counters*

- Show a number card for 15.
- Have the child count out 15 counters.
- Have the child finger trace the numeral on the card as he or she says the number aloud.
- Repeat the activity using numbers 10–20.

Gifted and Talented
VISUAL, TACTILE

Materials: *counters, Workmat 2*

- Have the child think of items that come in sets between 10 and 20.
- Have the child draw a picture to represent the set and then write the number.
- Then direct the child to use counters to model the number on the workmat.

TECHNOLOGY

Spiral Review
Help students remember skills they learned earlier by creating **customized** spiral review worksheets using the *Ways to Assess* CD-ROM.

Lesson Planner
Use the **Lesson Planner CD-ROM** to create a report of the lessons and standards you have taught.

Education Place
You can visit **Education Place** at **eduplace.com/math/mw/** for teacher support materials.

Manipulatives
Interactive Counters with several workmats are available on the *Ways to Success* CD-ROM.

Science Connection
Children cut groups of animal photos from magazines. Have them paste groups on paper and count the number in the group. Write the number on the page and make a class book.

MATH CENTER

Real Life Activity

Help children understand the usefulness of mathematics. This activity makes math come alive by connecting the lesson skills to a real-life situation.

PROBLEM SOLVING 1.3

Name _____ Date _____ | Problem Solving 1.3

Numbers 10 Through 20

Count. Use counters if you want. Write the number.

Trina wants ♡ for her party. How many can she buy?

1. Matt wants ○ for his party. How many can he buy? | Draw or write to explain.
11 ○

2. Ming wants ○ for her party. How many can she buy?
17 ○

3. Pedro wants ○ for his party. How many can he buy?
15 ○

Use with text pages 13–16.

HOMEWORK 1.3

Name _____ Date _____ | Homework 1.3

Activity: Numbers 10 Through 20

17

11

1. Count. Write the number. 2.
12 **16**

3. Choose two numbers from 10 through 20.
Draw pictures to show each number.

Use with text pages 13–16.

ENGLISH LEARNERS 1.3

Name _____ Date _____ | English Learners 1.3

Numbers 10 Through 20

| ten 10 | eleven 11 | twelve 12 | thirteen 13 | fourteen 14 | fifteen 15 |
| sixteen 16 | seventeen 17 | eighteen 18 | nineteen 19 | twenty 20 | |

Write the number.

1. thirteen **13** 2. eighteen **18** 3. twenty **20** 4. eleven **11** 5. nineteen **19**

6. sixteen **16** 7. twelve **12** 8. fourteen **14** 9. ten **10** 10. seventeen **17**

To the Teacher: Use the example at the top of the page to show children the relationship between sets of objects, number words, and numbers. Then read each number word to children and have them write the corresponding number under it.

Use with text pages 13–16.

Homework Workbook Page 3

TEACHING LESSON 1.3

LESSON ORGANIZER

Objective Recognize and count sets of 10 through 20 objects; read and write numbers 10 through 20.

Resources Reteach, Practice, Enrichment, Problem Solving, Homework, English Learners, Transparencies, Math Center

Materials Workmats 1 and 2, counters, single and double ten frame transparency, grid paper (LT 29), number word card 18 (LT 13), number dot card 11 (LT 17), grid paper transparency

Activity

Warm-Up Activity
Modeling Counting

Whole Group	5 minutes	Auditory, Tactile

Materials: ***counters, double ten frame transparency***

1. Review counting 1–9. Have children count as you place counters on the ten frame.
2. Continue by counting from 10–20 as you fill two ten frames.
3. Empty the ten frames and call on volunteers. Have them pick up some of the counters, place them on a ten frame, and count the number.

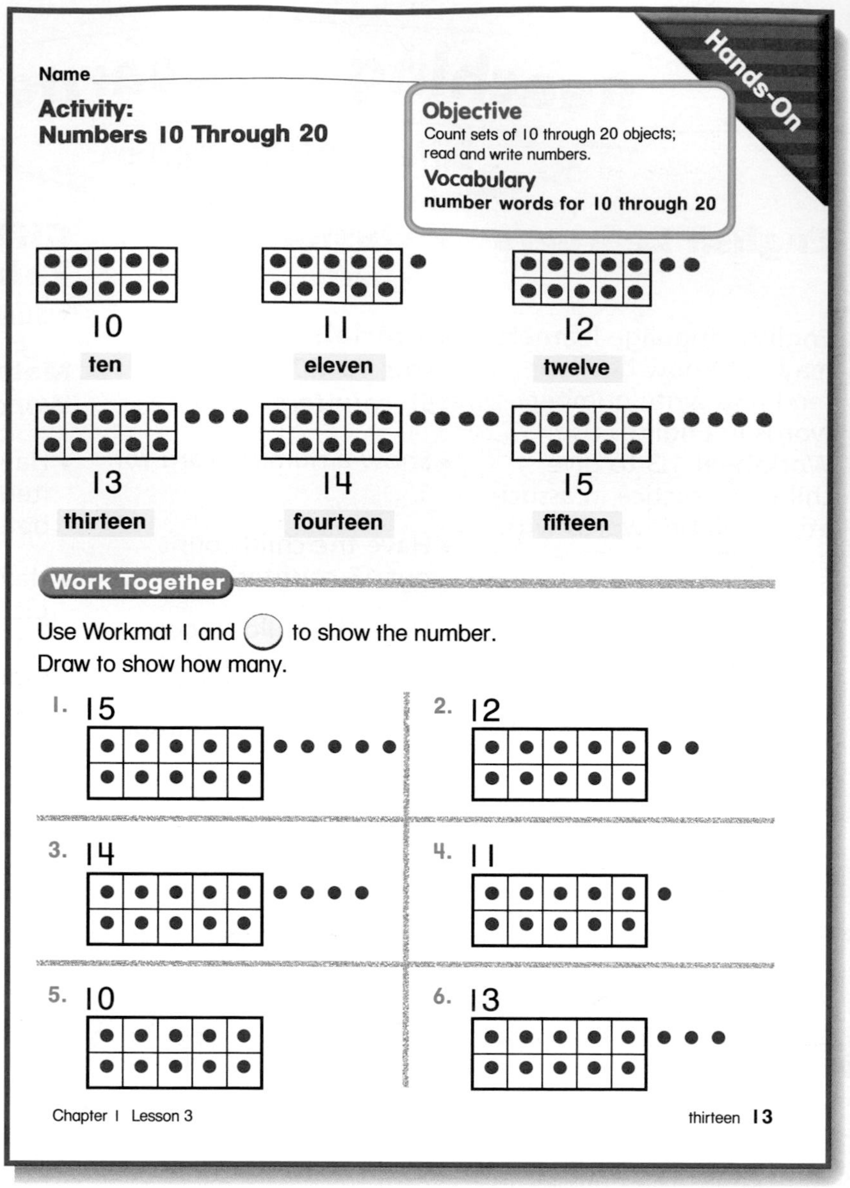
Name

Activity: Numbers 10 Through 20

Objective Count sets of 10 through 20 objects; read and write numbers.
Vocabulary number words for 10 through 20

Hands-On

10 ten
11 eleven
12 twelve
13 thirteen
14 fourteen
15 fifteen

Work Together

Use Workmat 1 and ◯ to show the number.
Draw to show how many.

1. 15
2. 12
3. 14
4. 11
5. 10
6. 13

Chapter 1 Lesson 3

thirteen 13

1 Introduce

Activity

Discuss Numbers 10 Through 20

Whole Group	10–15 minutes	Visual, Auditory

Materials: ***single and double ten frame transparency, Workmats 1 and 2, counters***

1. Display a single ten frame on the overhead. Write the number 10 and have a volunteer place 10 counters on the ten frame. Place 1 counter outside the ten frame. **How many counters?** (11) Have children show 11 with Workmat 1 and counters. Then, model writing the number 11 next to the number 10. Have children trace the number 11 in the air with their finger.
2. Continue to add one more counter and repeat the steps to introduce 12, 13, 14, and 15. Have children count from 10 through 15.
3. Then introduce the numbers 16, 17, 18, 19, and 20 in the same way using the double ten frame transparency and Workmat 2.

2 Develop

Guided Learning

Teaching Example Introduce the objective and vocabulary to the children. Guide children to see how the counters on the ten frame are used to help them read the numerals and the number words for ten through fifteen.

Work Together

Have children complete **Exercises 1–6** as you observe.

On Your Own

Count.
Write the number.

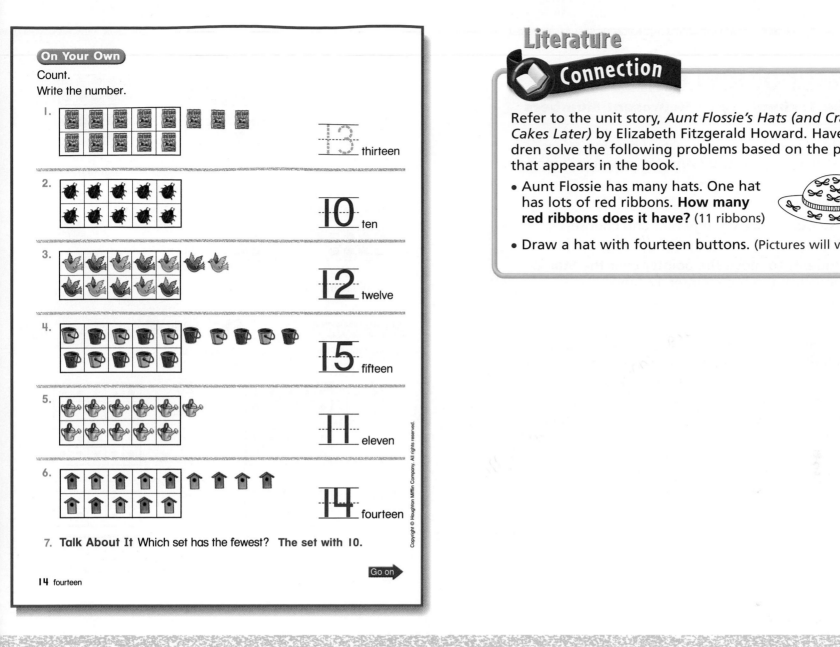

1. ¯I¯3 thirteen

2. ¯I¯0 ten

3. ¯I¯2 twelve

4. ¯I¯5 fifteen

5. ¯I¯I eleven

6. ¯I¯4 fourteen

7. **Talk About It** Which set has the fewest? **The set with 10.**

Go on

14 fourteen

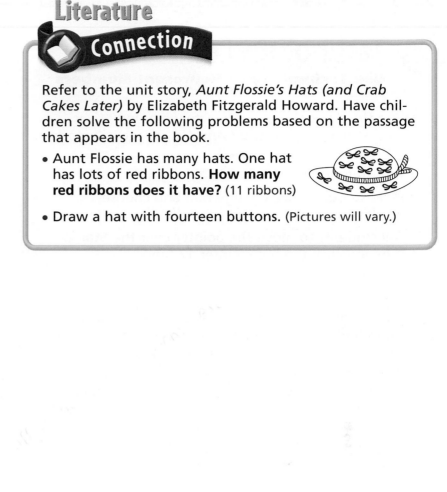

Literature Connection

Refer to the unit story, *Aunt Flossie's Hats (and Crab Cakes Later)* by Elizabeth Fitzgerald Howard. Have children solve the following problems based on the passage that appears in the book.

- Aunt Flossie has many hats. One hat has lots of red ribbons. **How many red ribbons does it have?** (11 ribbons)

- Draw a hat with fourteen buttons. (Pictures will vary.)

3 Practice

On Your Own

Children complete **Exercises 1–6** independently.

Use the **Talk About It** in **Exercise 7** to review the term fewest. Extend the discussion. **Which set has the most?** (15)

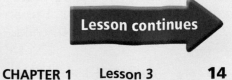

Lesson continues

TechnologyConnection
Use Technology to Represent Numbers

*Using the one-color counter virtual manipulatives found at **eduplace.com/kids/mw/,** students will model numbers between 10 and 20.*

Show students how to model 17.

- Have students click **Change Mat** and choose **Workmat.**

- Tell students to move the pointer over the **Stamp** tool and click the red counter 17 times.

- Have students click **Show How Much** to check their work.

Group students in pairs. Have one student choose a number between 10 and 20. Have the second student represent the number using the virtual manipulative. Then have students switch roles.

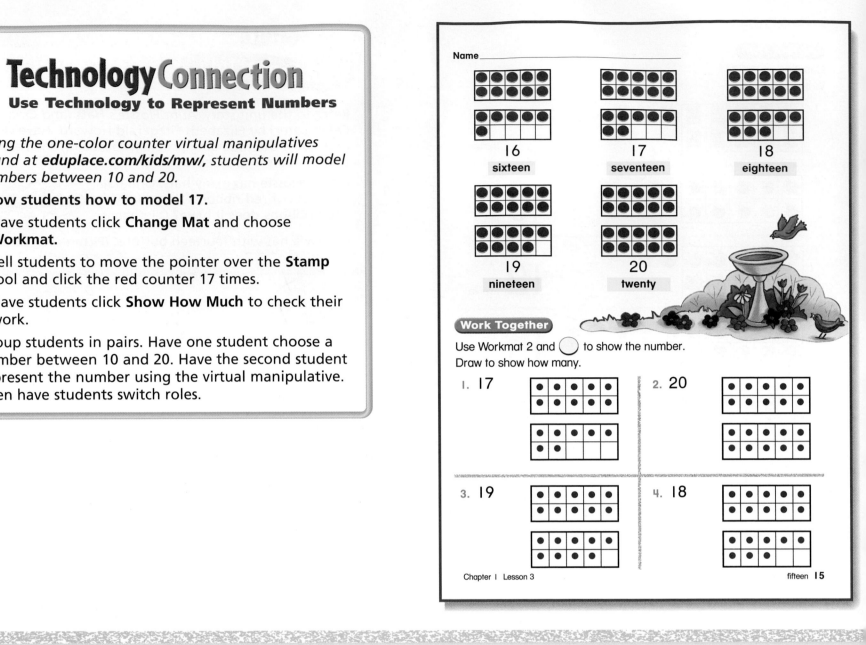

Name _____

16 — sixteen

17 — seventeen

18 — eighteen

19 — nineteen

20 — twenty

Work Together

Use Workmat 2 and ⬭ to show the number.
Draw to show how many.

1. 17

2. 20

3. 19

4. 18

Chapter 1 Lesson 3 — fifteen 15

3 Practice

Guide children to use counters to show each number and number word for 16 through 20.

Work Together

Have children complete **Exercises 1–4** as you observe.

On Your Own

Have children complete **Exercises 1–5** independently.

Use **Exercise 6** to review the term most. Extend the discussion. **Which set has the fewest counters?** (the set with 16)

Have children complete **Exercises 7–9** independently.

Common Error

Miscounts When Counting On From Ten
Child may not have progressed to counting from 10 and may have to count from 1 to arrive at a total. Practice counting both ways with child.

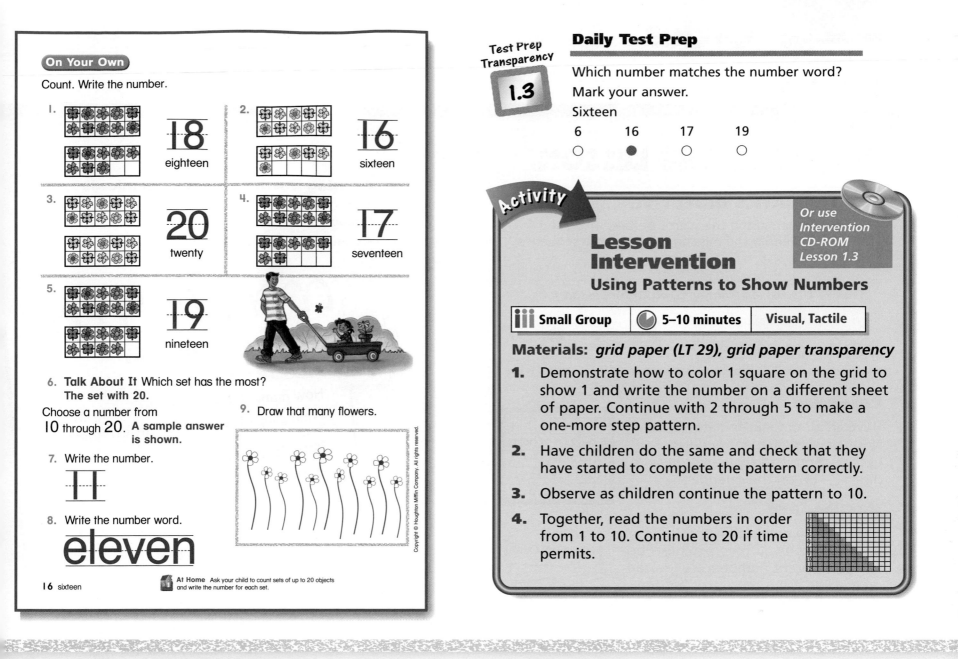

On Your Own

Count. Write the number.

1. 18 eighteen

2. 16 sixteen

3. 20 twenty

4. 17 seventeen

5. 19 nineteen

6. **Talk About It** Which set has the most?
The set with 20.

Choose a number from
10 through 20. A sample answer is shown.

7. Write the number.

11

8. Write the number word.

eleven

9. Draw that many flowers.

At Home Ask your child to count sets of up to 20 objects and write the number for each set.

16 sixteen

Copyright © Houghton Mifflin Company. All rights reserved.

Test Prep Transparency
1.3

Daily Test Prep

Which number matches the number word?
Mark your answer.
Sixteen

6   ● 16   17   19
○   ●   ○   ○

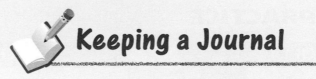 **Activity**

Lesson Intervention
Using Patterns to Show Numbers

Or use Intervention CD-ROM Lesson 1.3

| Small Group | 5–10 minutes | Visual, Tactile |

Materials: *grid paper (LT 29), grid paper transparency*

1. Demonstrate how to color 1 square on the grid to show 1 and write the number on a different sheet of paper. Continue with 2 through 5 to make a one-more step pattern.

2. Have children do the same and check that they have started to complete the pattern correctly.

3. Observe as children continue the pattern to 10.

4. Together, read the numbers in order from 1 to 10. Continue to 20 if time permits.

4 Assess and Close

Display a number word card for eighteen.
Write the number. (18)
Display a dot card with 11 dots.
How many dots? (11)
Have a volunteer write the number word on the board.
(eleven)

Keeping a Journal

Write a number from 10 through 20. Write the number word. Draw pictures to show the number.

CHAPTER 1   Lesson 3   **16**

Order

PLANNING THE LESSON

MATHEMATICS OBJECTIVE

Order numbers using the words *before, after,* and *between;* identify the missing numbers in a sequence; count backward.

Use Lesson Planner CD-ROM for Lesson 1.4.

Daily Routines

Calendar

Have children identify dates 1–19. Now, have them identify dates before, after, and between other dates (1–19) on the calendar.

Sunday	Monday	Tuesday	Wednesday	Thursday	Friday	Saturday
			1	2	3	4
5	6	7	8	9	10	11
12	13	14	15	16	17	18
19	20	21	22	23	24	25
26	27	28	29	30	31	

Vocabulary

Draw a 0–10 **number line** on the board. Call on volunteers to describe where different numbers are located on the line using the words **before, after,** and **between**.

Vocabulary Cards

Meeting North Carolina's Standards

1.01 Develop number sense for whole numbers through 99.

• Compare and order sets and numbers.

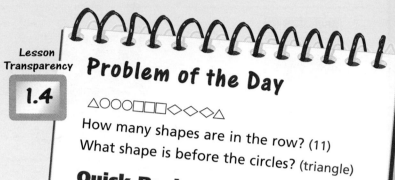

Lesson Transparency 1.4

Problem of the Day

△○○○□□□◇◇◇△

How many shapes are in the row? (11)
What shape is before the circles? (triangle)

Quick Review

Write the number.

(12)   (0)   (17)

Lesson Quiz

1. Which number is just before 17? (16)
2. Which number is between 9 and 11? (10)
3. Which number is just after 19? (20)

LEVELED PRACTICE

RETEACH 1.4

Name _____ Date _____

Reteach 1.4

Order

Number lines can help you put numbers in order.

0 1 2 3 4 5 6 7 8 9 10

11 12 13 14 15 16 17 18 19 20

3 is just before 4.   8 is between 7 and 9.   17 is just after 16.

Use the number lines.
Write the number.

1. Just before	2. Between	3. Just after
[7], 8, 9	13, [14], 15	9, 10, [11]
[16], 17, 18	3, [4], 5	4, 5, [6]
[15], 16, 17	12, [13], 14	18, 19, [20]

Use with text pages 17–18.

PRACTICE 1.4

Name _____ Date _____

Practice 1.4

Order

Write the numbers. Use the number lines.

0 1 2 3 4 5 6 7 8 9 10

11 12 13 14 15 16 17 18 19 20

1. Just before
[6], 7, 8
[13], 14, 15

2. Just after
9, 10, [11]
17, 18, [19]

3. Between
15, [16], 17
17, [18], 19

4. Just before and just after
[1], 2, [3]
[11], 12, [13]

Test Prep

Fill in the ○ for the correct answer. NH means Not Here.
Which number is missing?

5. 10, 11, 12, ☐
   12   13   14   NH
   ○   ○   ●   ○

6. ☐, 18, 19, 20
   15   16   17   NH
   ○   ●   ○   ○

Explain how you knew which number to fill in.

Possible response: I used the number line and looked at the numbers on it.

Use with text pages 17–18.

ENRICHMENT 1.4

Name _____ Date _____

Enrichment 1.4

Secret Numbers

Use the number line to help you guess the number.
Write the number.

0 1 2 3 4 5 6 7 8 9 10 11 12 13 14 15 16 17 18 19 20

1. I am a number after 10.
   I am just before 12.
   I am the number __11__.

2. I am a number between 15 and 17.
   I am the number __16__.

3. I am a number that comes after 7.
   I come before 9.
   I am the number __8__.

4. I am a number that comes after 19.
   I am the number __20__.

5. We are the numbers that come after 13 and before 17.
   We are the numbers __14__, __15__, __16__.

6. We are the numbers that come between 8 and 12.
   We are the numbers __9__, __10__, __11__.

Write About It What number comes just after 20? How do you know?

Possible answer: I see that 11 comes after 10, so 21 should come after 20.

Use with text pages 17–18.

Practice Workbook Page 4

Reaching All Learners

Differentiated Instruction

English Learners

English-language learners may not understand the words *before*, *after*, and *between*. They will need to understand these words in order to understand number lines. Use Worksheet 1.4 to introduce the concept of order and to teach children the corresponding words.

Special Needs
VISUAL, TACTILE

Materials: *cubes, number cards 1–10 (LT 14)*

- Help child picture order of numbers. Have child make cube towers for the numbers 1 through 10.
- Have child arrange the cube towers in order and label each tower with a number card.

Gifted and Talented
VISUAL, AUDITORY

Materials: *hundred chart (LT 7), counters*

- Have one child place a counter over a number on the chart.
- Have partner write the covered number. Then write the numbers that come just before and just after.
- Have partners switch roles and continue.

TECHNOLOGY

Spiral Review

You can prepare students for standardized tests with **customized** spiral review on key skills using the *Ways to Assess* CD-ROM.

Education Place

Recommend that parents visit **Education Place** at eduplace.com/parents/mw/ for parent support activities.

Literature Connection

Read *Can You Count Ten Toes? Count to 10 in 10 Different Languages* by Lezlie Evans.

Ask children what number comes before, after, or between other numbers in a different language.

MATH CENTER

Basic Skills Activity

Motivate children to build basic skills. Use this activity to address multiple learning styles using hands-on activities related to the skills of this lesson.

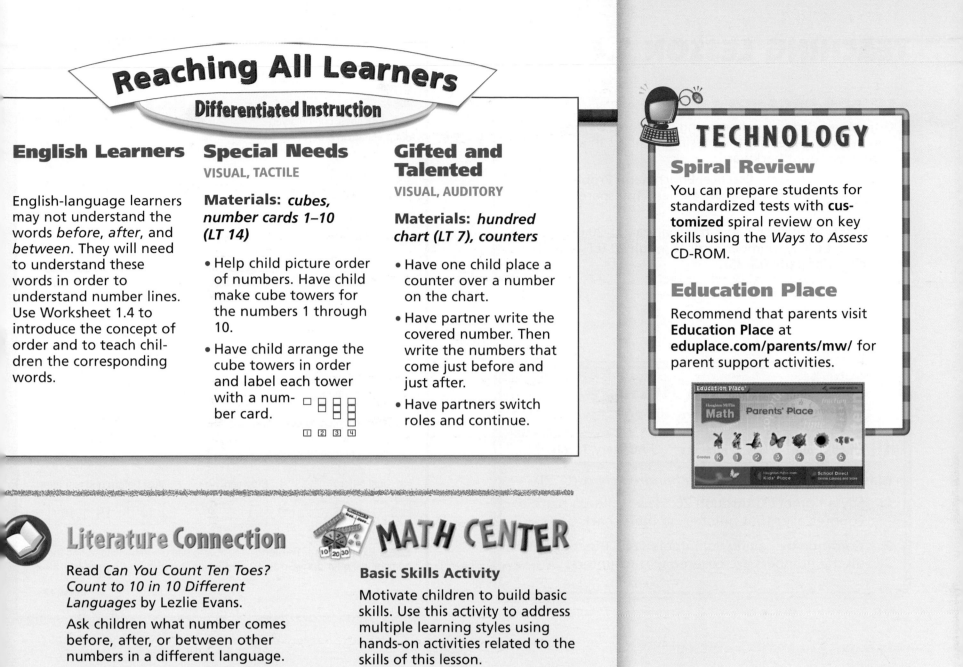

Homework Workbook Page 4

TEACHING LESSON 1.4

LESSON ORGANIZER

Objective Order numbers using the words *before, after,* and *between;* identify the missing numbers in a sequence; count backward.

Resources Reteach, Practice, Enrichment, Problem Solving, Homework, English Learners, Transparencies, Math Center

Materials Counters, blank transparency, 0–20 on hundred chart (LT 7), number cards through 20 (LT 14 and 15), calendar page (LT 35)

Activity

Warm-Up Activity
Numbers through 20

👥 Small Group	⏱ 5 minutes	Auditory, Tactile

Materials: *counters, 0–20 on hundred chart (LT 7)*

1. Say a number 0 through 20. Have children place a counter over that number on their chart.

2. Continue by having volunteers say a number until all the numbers are covered with counters.

Name _____

Order

🎧 MathTracks 1/3
Listen and Understand

Number lines can help you put numbers in order.

Objective
Order numbers using words.

Vocabulary
number line
before
after
between

6 is just **before** 7.

8 is just **after** 7.

7 is **between** 6 and 8.

← 0 1 2 3 4 5 6 7 8 9 10 →

11 is just before 12.

13 is just after 12.

12 is between 11 and 13.

← 11 12 13 14 15 16 17 18 19 20 →

Guided Practice

Write the numbers.

Think
Find 18 on the number line. Look at the number just before it.

1. Which number is just before 18? | 17 |

2. Which number is between 4 and 6? | 5 |

3. Just before
| 3 | , 4, 5

4. Between
0, | 1 | , 2

5. Just before and just after
| 13 | , 14, | 15 |

TEST TIPS **Explain Your Thinking** Tell how to use a number line to find the number just after 19. **Go to 19 and move forward one number to 20.**

Chapter 1 Lesson 4   seventeen **17**

---

1 Introduce
Discuss Order

👥 Whole Group	⏱ 5–10 minutes	Visual, Auditory

Materials: *counters, blank transparency*

1. Draw a 0–10 number line on the board. Ask children to count with you as you point to each number on the number line. Emphasize that as you move right on the line each number is 1 more than the previous number. Then count backwards using the line emphasizing that each number is 1 less than the previous number.

2. Draw a 0 to 10 number line on a blank transparency. Display it and place a counter on 5. **What number comes just before 5?** (4) Place a counter on 4. **What number comes just after 5?** (6) Place a counter on 6. **What number is between 4 and 6?** (5)

3. Continue by asking similar questions using different numbers on the number line. Call on volunteers to place counters on these numbers.

2 Develop

Guided Learning

Teaching Example Introduce the objective and vocabulary to the children. Guide them through the examples to review how to use a number line to identify numbers just before, just after, and between other numbers.

Guided Practice

Have children complete **Exercises 1–5** as you observe. Discuss children's responses to the Explain Your Thinking question.

Use the number lines.

Write the numbers.

1. Just after

10, 11, [12]

3, 4, [5]

2. Just before

[7], 8, 9

[17], 18, 19

3. Between

13, [14], 15

18, [19], 20

4. Just before and just after

[0], 1, [2]

[15], 16, [17]

Problem Solving ▶ Number Sense

Write the missing number.

5. Jon has 1 more.

Max	Jon
15	16

6. Ana has 1 less.

Mia	Ana
5	4

18 eighteen

At Home Open a book to a page between 0 and 20. Read the page number and ask your child to identify the numbers just before and just after that number.

Go on

ACHIEVING Mathematical Proficiency

Learning Number Names

Research indicates that English-language number names can sometimes interfere with children's understanding of the role of the number ten in our number system. It thus becomes crucial to **strengthen the connection children make between the base-ten organization underlying number names and how this relates to quantities of tens and ones.**

Names such as "eleven" and "fourteen" do not make clear to children that $11 = 10 + 1$ and $14 = 10 + 4$. Presenting objects or drawings that visually represent tens and ones and then linking them to number names and written numerals helps children acquire the necessary insight into the base-ten system.

Extensive practice with this type of conceptual support in the primary grades will build a foundation for understanding numbers in a meaningful way.

3 Practice

Independent Practice

Children complete **Exercises 1–4** independently.

Problem Solving

After children complete **Exercises 5 and 6**, call on volunteers to share their solutions. Also discuss how identifying 1 more than or 1 less than a number is similar to identifying numbers that come just before or just after a number.

Common Error

Counting in the Wrong Direction

Remind children that they must count back to find the number that comes just before and they must count forward to find the number that comes just after.

4 Assess and Close

What number comes just before 10? (9)
What number comes just after 10? (11)
What number comes between 9 and 11? (10)

Keeping a Journal

Have children copy a 0–20 number line from the board. Circle 16 in red. Circle the number just before in green. Circle the number just after in blue.

Lesson continues

Daily Test Prep

Mark the number that is just after 10.

9   12   11   20
○   ○   ●   ○

Activity

Lesson Intervention
Using Counting to Order Numbers

| 👤👤👤 Small Group | 🕐 10–15 minutes | Auditory, Visual |

Materials: *number cards through 20 (LT 14 and 15)*

1. Display two number cards. **Which number comes first?**

2. Have children count aloud with you until you reach one of the numbers shown. **This number comes before.** Place the other card next to it. **This number comes after.**

3. Display a new number card. Have children count to find where it belongs in relation to the other two numbers. Describe whether it comes before, after, or between the other numbers.

4. Continue until all the number cards are in order. Now, have children count back from 20 while you point to each card.

Name_____

Now Try This   Counting Forward and Backward

1. Write the missing numbers in order.

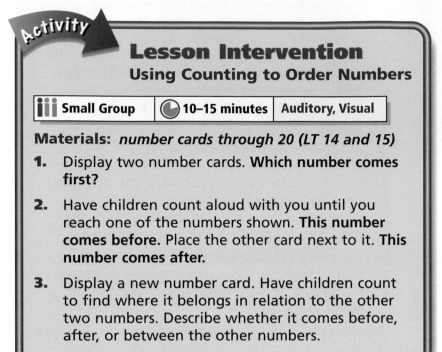

Count backward. Write the numbers.

2. 20, 19, _18_, _17_, _16_, _15_, _14_, _13_, _12_, _11_, _10_, _9_, _8_, _7_, _6_, _5_, _4_, _3_, _2_, _1_

3. **Talk About It** Take turns with a classmate. Pick a number between 10 and 20. Count backward to 0 from that number. **Answers may vary.**

Chapter 1 Lesson 4   nineteen **19**

Now Try This

Materials: *calendar page*

Introduce Ask children to count to 20 with you. As children count point to the dates (numbers) one at a time. **Do you see a number pattern?** Review that as you count forward each number is 1 more than, or just after, the previous number. Now count backward from 20 with children. Review that as you count backward each number is 1 less than, or just before, the previous number.

Develop Have children complete **Exercises 1–2** independently. Have children use the calendar page to count backward. Then pair children for the **Talk About It** activity **Exercise 3.**

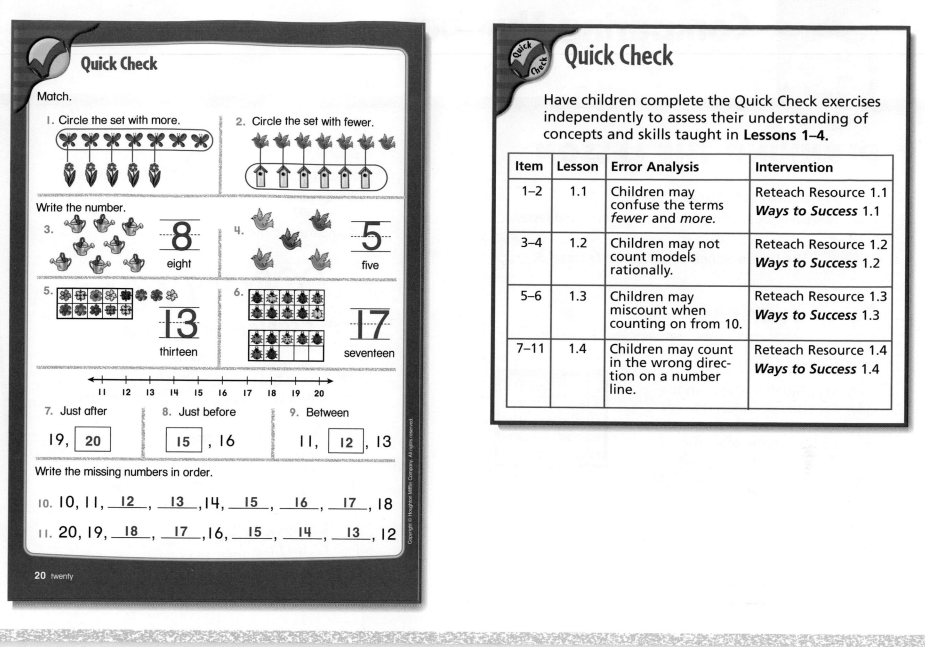

Quick Check

Match.

1. Circle the set with more.

2. Circle the set with fewer.

Write the number.

3. 8 eight

4. 5 five

5. 13 thirteen

6. 17 seventeen

11 12 13 14 15 16 17 18 19 20

7. Just after

19, 20

8. Just before

15 , 16

9. Between

11, 12 , 13

Write the missing numbers in order.

10. 10, 11, 12 , 13 ,14, 15 , 16 , 17 , 18

11. 20, 19, 18 , 17 ,16, 15 , 14 , 13 , 12

Quick Check

Have children complete the Quick Check exercises independently to assess their understanding of concepts and skills taught in **Lessons 1–4.**

Item	Lesson	Error Analysis	Intervention
1–2	1.1	Children may confuse the terms *fewer* and *more.*	Reteach Resource 1.1 *Ways to Success* 1.1
3–4	1.2	Children may not count models rationally.	Reteach Resource 1.2 *Ways to Success* 1.2
5–6	1.3	Children may miscount when counting on from 10.	Reteach Resource 1.3 *Ways to Success* 1.3
7–11	1.4	Children may count in the wrong direction on a number line.	Reteach Resource 1.4 *Ways to Success* 1.4

Comparing Numbers

PLANNING THE LESSON

MATHEMATICS OBJECTIVE
Compare numbers using the terms *greater* and *lesser*.

Use Lesson Planner CD-ROM for Lesson 1.5.

Daily Routines

Calendar
Point to a number (date) on the calendar and ask children to say a number that comes before and a number that comes after the number. Tell children the number is greater than or less than the first number.

Sunday	Monday	Tuesday	Wednesday	Thursday	Friday	Saturday
			1	2	3	4
5	6	7	8	9	10	11
12	13	14	15	16	17	18
19	20	21	22	23	24	25
26	27	28	29	30	31	

Vocabulary
Write two numbers, from 1 through 20, on the board. Lead children in making comparisons using the terms **greater than**, **less than**, and **equal to**.

Vocabulary Cards

Meeting North Carolina's Standards
1.01 Develop number sense for whole numbers through 99.
• Compare and order sets and numbers.

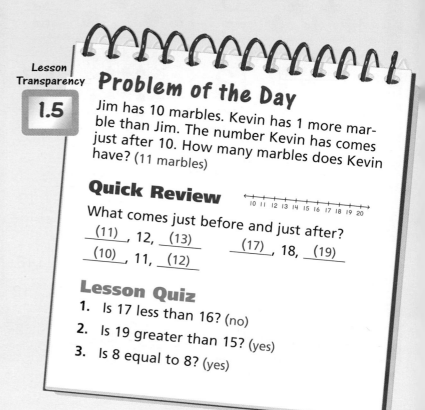

Lesson Transparency 1.5

Problem of the Day
Jim has 10 marbles. Kevin has 1 more marble than Jim. The number Kevin has comes just after 10. How many marbles does Kevin have? (11 marbles)

Quick Review
What comes just before and just after?
(11), 12, (13)   (17), 18, (19)
(10), 11, (12)

Lesson Quiz
1. Is 17 less than 16? (no)
2. Is 19 greater than 15? (yes)
3. Is 8 equal to 8? (yes)

LEVELED PRACTICE

RETEACH 1.5
Name _____ Date _____ **Reteach 1.5**

Comparing Numbers

You can count to compare numbers.

2 is less than 4.   6 is greater than 4.   4 is equal to 4.

Circle the words that make the sentence true.

1. 3 is greater than / (is less than) 5
2. 9 (is greater than) / is less than 5
3. 4 (is equal to) / is less than 4
4. 7 is equal to / (is greater than) 2

Use with text pages 21–22.

PRACTICE 1.5
Name _____ Date _____ **Practice 1.5**

Comparing Numbers
Count.
Write the numbers that make the sentence true.

1. 10 is less than 13   2. 18 is greater than 15

3. 12 is greater than 7   4. 14 is equal to 14

Test Prep
Fill in the ○ for the correct answer. NH means Not Here.

5. Which number is greater than 12?
7   10   ● 14   NH

6. Which number is less than 10?
18   11   15   NH

Explain how you knew which number to fill in.
Possible response: I looked at the number lines to see which numbers came after or which came before.

Use with text pages 21–22.

ENRICHMENT 1.5
Name _____ Date _____ **Enrichment 1.5**

Before and After

0 1 2 3 4 5 6 7 8 9 10 11 12 13 14 15 16 17 18 19 20

1. Color each ☆ that has a number greater than 10.
8   11   17   7   15

2. Color each ✿ that has a number greater than 15.
13   9   16   14   20

3. Color each ☆ that has a number less than 10.
4   12   15   4   11

4. Color each ✿ that has a number less than 15.
11   13   16   5   18

Write About It How can you use a number line to compare two numbers?
Possible answer: I can find both numbers on the number line and see which one is greater.

Use with text pages 21–22.

Practice Workbook Page 5

Reaching All Learners

Differentiated Instruction

English Learners

To compare numbers, English-language learners will need to understand the comparative terms *less than*, *greater than*, and *equal to*. Use Worksheet 1.5 to help develop understanding of these terms.

Inclusion
VISUAL, AUDITORY

Materials: *number cards 0–10 (LT 14), dot cards 1–10 (LT 17)*

- Display a pair of dot cards.
- Have the child show the matching numeral cards. Then have the child count aloud to the numbers. Place the numbers in order. Then ask the child which of the two numbers is greater, and which number is less.
- Repeat the activity.

Early Finishers
AUDITORY, VISUAL

Materials: *number cards 0–20 (LT 14 and 15)*

- Have one partner display a number card and say "is greater than," "is less than," or "is equal to."
- Have the partner show a number card that completes the statement accurately.
- Partners switch roles and continue.

TECHNOLOGY

Spiral Review

Create **customized** spiral review worksheets for individual students using the *Ways to Assess* CD-ROM.

Lesson Planner

You can customize your teaching plan or meet your curriculum requirements with the **Lesson Planner CD-ROM**.

eBook

An electronic version of this lesson can be found in **eMathBook**.

Science Connection

Have children draw groups of items they might find at the seashore. Have them write the number of items on the page. Compare the numbers using the terms greater than, less than, or equal to.

MATH CENTER

Vocabulary Activity

This vocabulary-building activity helps children understand and remember new words. Encourage children to use the words in math discussion.

PROBLEM SOLVING 1.5

Name _____ Date _____   Problem Solving 1.5

Comparing Numbers

0 1 2 3 4 5 6 7 8 9 10 11 12 13 14 15 16 17 18 19 20

Draw or write to explain.

1. Jan is looking for a number that is less than 15. Circle the number that is less than 15.
   17   15   (11)

2. Dazee is looking for a number that is greater than 12. Circle the number that is greater than 12.
   9   12   (15)

3. Ryan is looking for a number that is less than 2. Circle the number that is less than 2.
   (1)   2   3

4. Keli is looking for a number that is greater than 9. Circle the number that is greater than 9.
   (10)   8   6

Use with text pages 21–22.

HOMEWORK 1.5

Name _____ Date _____   Homework 1.5

Comparing Numbers

You can compare numbers using the words greater than and less than.

12 is _greater than_ 4.   6 is _less than_ 10.

Write greater than or less than to make the sentence true.

1. 15 is _greater than_ 13.   2. 11 is _less than_ 14.

3. 17 is _less than_ 20.   4. 15 is _greater than_ 8.

5. Write any numbers from 8 through 18 under My Number in the chart.

   Then fill in the other columns.

A Number Less Than	My Number	A Number Greater Than

Use with text pages 21–22.

ENGLISH LEARNERS 1.5

Name _____ Date _____   English Learners 1.5

Comparing Numbers

5 cats are **more than** 3 cats. 5 is **greater than** 3.

2 cats are **fewer than** 3 cats. 2 is **less than** 3.   3 cats are the **same as** three cats. 3 is **equal to** 3.

Circle the correct words.

1. 3 is (less than) greater than 5.

2. 8 is less than (equal to) 8.

To the Teacher: Use the illustrations and the sentences at the top of the page to help children understand the terms *greater than*, *less than*, and *equal to*. Then read the sentences with children and have them circle the words to complete each sentence.

Use with text pages 21–22.

Homework Workbook Page 5

TEACHING LESSON 1.5

LESSON ORGANIZER

Objective Compare numbers using the terms *greater* and *lesser*.

Resources Reteach, Practice, Enrichment, Problem Solving, Homework, English Learners, Transparencies, Math Center

Materials Dot cards (LT 17), blank transparencies, cubes

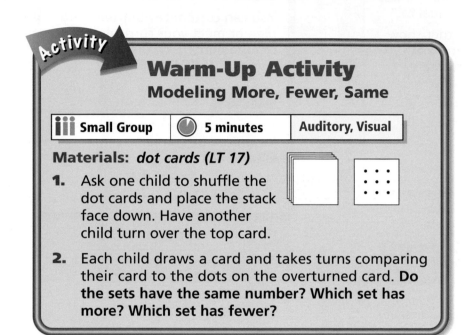

Warm-Up Activity
Modeling More, Fewer, Same

| iii Small Group | 🕐 5 minutes | Auditory, Visual |

Materials: *dot cards (LT 17)*

1. Ask one child to shuffle the dot cards and place the stack face down. Have another child turn over the top card.

2. Each child draws a card and takes turns comparing their card to the dots on the overturned card. **Do the sets have the same number? Which set has more? Which set has fewer?**

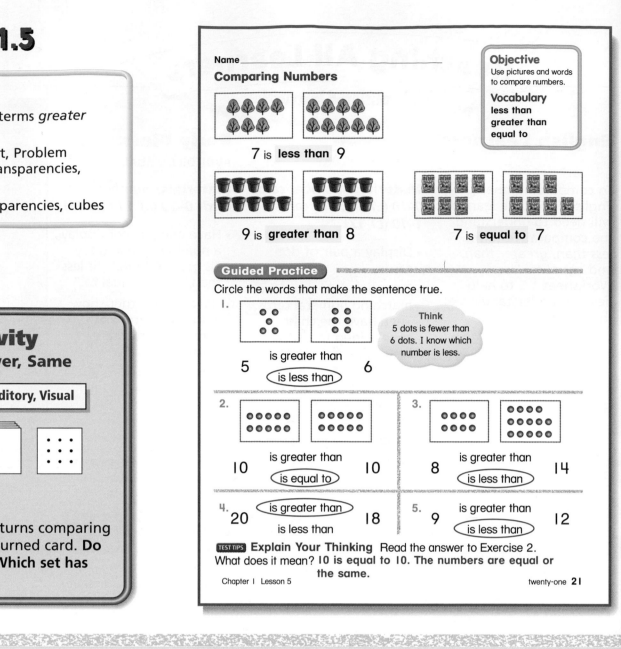

Name_____

Comparing Numbers

Objective Use pictures and words to compare numbers.

Vocabulary
less than
greater than
equal to

7 is **less than** 9

9 is **greater than** 8

7 is **equal to** 7

Guided Practice
Circle the words that make the sentence true.

1.
5 is greater than / **is less than** 6

Think
5 dots is fewer than 6 dots. I know which number is less.

2.
10 is greater than / **is equal to** 10

3.
8 is greater than / **is less than** 14

4.
20 **is greater than** / is less than 18

5.
9 is greater than / **is less than** 12

TEST TIPS Explain Your Thinking Read the answer to Exercise 2. What does it mean? 10 is equal to 10. The numbers are equal or the same.

Chapter 1 Lesson 5   twenty-one **21**

① Introduce
Discuss Comparing Numbers

| iiii Whole Group | 🕐 5–10 minutes | Visual, Auditory |

Materials: *dot cards (LT 17), blank transparencies*

1. Use a blank transparency to make overhead dot cards.

2. Display the dot card for 12 on the overhead. **What is the number?** (12) Write 12 beneath the card. Display the dot card for 9 next to it. **What is the number?** (9) Write 9 beneath it. **Which number is greater?** (12) **How do you know?** (There are more dots.) Write *12 is greater than 9*. Read the sentence with children.

3. Repeat the activity with different dot cards to introduce the terms **less than** and **equal to**.

② Develop

Guided Learning

Teaching Example Read the objective and vocabulary with children. Guide them through each example showing them how each set of items relates, to the number. Then explain how the numbers relate to the sentence.

Guided Practice

Have children complete **Exercises 1–5** as you observe. Discuss children's responses to the Explain Your Thinking question.

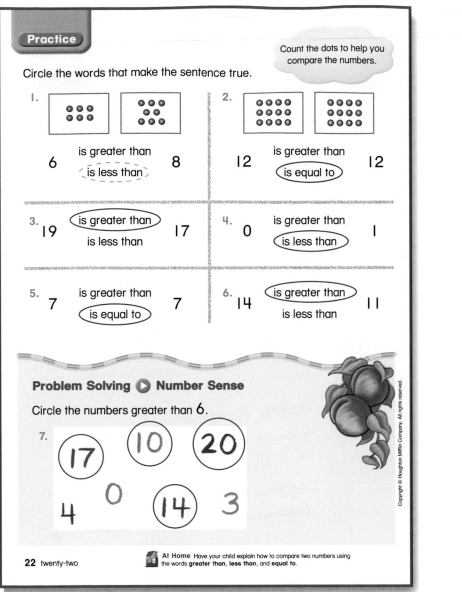

Practice

Circle the words that make the sentence true.

> Count the dots to help you compare the numbers.

1. 6 is greater than (is less than) 8

2. 12 is greater than (is equal to) 12

3. 19 (is greater than) is less than 17

4. 0 is greater than (is less than) 1

5. 7 is greater than (is equal to) 7

6. 14 (is greater than) is less than 11

Problem Solving ▶ Number Sense

Circle the numbers greater than 6.

7. (17) (10) (20) 4 0 (14) 3

22 twenty-two

At Home Have your child explain how to compare two numbers using the words **greater than, less than,** and **equal to.**

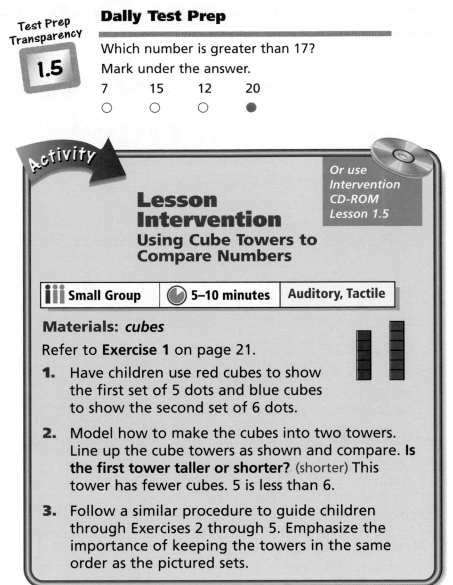

Dally Test Prep

Which number is greater than 17?
Mark under the answer.

7   15   12   20
○   ○   ○   ●

Activity

Or use Intervention CD-ROM Lesson 1.5

Lesson Intervention
Using Cube Towers to Compare Numbers

| ▮▮▮ Small Group | ◷ 5–10 minutes | Auditory, Tactile |

Materials: *cubes*

Refer to **Exercise 1** on page 21.

1. Have children use red cubes to show the first set of 5 dots and blue cubes to show the second set of 6 dots.

2. Model how to make the cubes into two towers. Line up the cube towers as shown and compare. **Is the first tower taller or shorter?** (shorter) This tower has fewer cubes. 5 is less than 6.

3. Follow a similar procedure to guide children through Exercises 2 through 5. Emphasize the importance of keeping the towers in the same order as the pictured sets.

❸ Practice

Independent Practice

Children complete **Exercises 1–6** independently.

Problem Solving

After children complete **Exercise 7,** call on volunteers to share their solutions.

Common Error

May Confuse Terms

Have children who confuse *greater than* and *less than* use picture cards labeled with the terms. Have children use the cards to relate *greater than* to a set with more and *less than* to a set with fewer.

❹ Assess and Close

Is 9 greater than 14? (no)
Is 7 less than 8? (yes)
What number is equal to 5? (5)

✎ Keeping a Journal

Use the numbers 15 and 16.

Write 3 numbers that are greater than 15.

Write 3 numbers that are less than 16.

Write one number that is equal to 15.

Greater Than, Less Than

PLANNING THE LESSON

MATHEMATICS OBJECTIVE
Use a number line to compare numbers.

Use Lesson Planner CD-ROM for Lesson 1.6.

Daily Routines

Calendar

Point to a number (date), 20 or less, on the calendar and have children say the numbers that come before.

Sunday	Monday	Tuesday	Wednesday	Thursday	Friday	Saturday
			1	2	3	4
5	6	7	8	9	10	11
12	13	14	15	16	17	18
19	20	21	22	23	24	25
26	27	28	29	30	31	

Vocabulary

Review compare. Write pairs of numbers, 1 through 20, on the board. Remind children that they need at least two numbers to compare. Have children compare by saying **greater than** or **less than** when you point to one of the two numbers in a pair.

Vocabulary Cards

Meeting North Carolina's Standards

1.01 Develop number sense for whole numbers through 99.

• Compare and order sets and numbers.

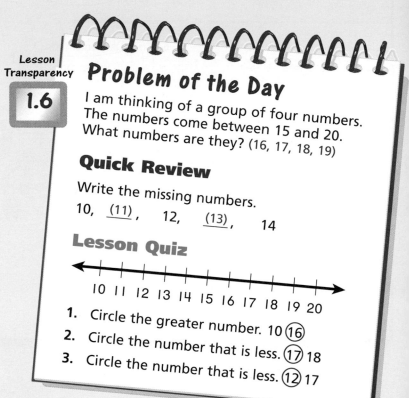

Lesson Transparency 1.6

Problem of the Day

I am thinking of a group of four numbers. The numbers come between 15 and 20. What numbers are they? (16, 17, 18, 19)

Quick Review

Write the missing numbers.
10, (11), 12, (13), 14

Lesson Quiz

10 11 12 13 14 15 16 17 18 19 20

1. Circle the greater number. 10 (16)
2. Circle the number that is less. (17) 18
3. Circle the number that is less. (12) 17

LEVELED PRACTICE

RETEACH 1.6

Name _____ Date _____ Reteach 1.6

Greater Than, Less Than

When you compare two numbers, use the words greater than and less than.

0 1 2 3 4 5 6 7 8 9 10 → 9 is greater than 7.

11 12 13 14 15 16 17 18 19 20 → 16 is less than 18.

Use the number lines.
Circle the greater number.

1. (10) 5
2. (13) 3
3. 1 (2)
4. 8 (11)
5. 15 (16)
6. (20) 19

Use the number lines.
Circle the number that is less.

7. (9) 12
8. 18 (14)
9. (5) 15
10. (16) 19
11. (0) 4
12. (10) 19

Use with text pages 23–24.

PRACTICE 1.6

Name _____ Date _____ Practice 1.6

Greater Than, Less Than

0 1 2 3 4 5 6 7 8 9 10
11 12 13 14 15 16 17 18 19 20

Use the number lines.
Circle the greater number.

1. 12 (15)
2. (18) 8
3. 0 (1)

Use the number lines.
Circle the lesser number.

4. (7) 11
5. (13) 14
6. (6) 7

Test Prep

7. Fill in the ○ for the correct answer. NH means Not Here.
   Which set is true?

• • • • • • • •	• • • • • •	• • • • • • •	
less than 8	greater than 7	less than 3	NH
○	○	○	●

Use with text pages 23–24.

ENRICHMENT 1.6

Name _____ Date _____ Enrichment 1.6

Which Means More?

Write greater than, equal to, or less than to make the sentence true.

8   11
10   12

1. 12 is __greater than__ 8.
2. 10 is __equal to__ 10.
3. 11 is __less than__ 12.
4. 12 is __equal to__ 12.

Write About It How could you use counters to show that 11 is equal to 11?

Possible answer: I could make two rows of 11 counters.

Use with text pages 23–24.

Practice Workbook Page 6

Reaching All Learners
Differentiated Instruction

English Learners

English-language learners will need to have an understanding of the comparative terms *greater than* and *less than* in order to compare numbers on a number line. Use Worksheet 1.6 to develop children's ability to understand and use these terms.

Special Needs
VISUAL, TACTILE

Materials: *number lines 0–20 (LT 8)*

Circle a number on a number line. Then ask the child to highlight all the numbers that come before in one color and all the numbers that come after in a different color. Relate the circled number to the highlighted numbers using the terms *greater than* and *less than*.

| Less than 4 | Greater than 4 |

Gifted and Talented
VISUAL, AUDITORY

- Have children write number riddles. Example: I am the number that comes before 5. I am greater than 3. What number am I? (4)

- Have children share the riddles they created. Have them solve the riddles as a class.

Social Studies Connection

Discuss items that are sold in quantities of 3, 6 and so on. Explain that knowing how to compare numbers is helpful in finding which package contains a greater or lesser number of items.

MATH CENTER

Vocabulary Activity

This vocabulary-building activity helps children understand and remember new words. Encourage children to use the words in math discussion.

TECHNOLOGY

Spiral Review

Using the *Ways to Assess* CD-ROM, you can create **customized** spiral review worksheets covering any lessons you choose.

Lesson Planner

You can customize your teaching plan or meet your curriculum requirements with the **Lesson Planner CD-ROM.**

Games

Students can practice their math vocabulary using the Math Lingo game, available on the *Ways to Success* CD-ROM.

Math Lingo

median	equally likely	outcome
range	predict	less likely
survey	mode	more likely

On this spinner, the ___ can be red, blue, or yellow.

PROBLEM SOLVING 1.6

Name _____ Date _____

Problem Solving 1.6

Greater Than, Less Than

0 1 2 3 4 5 6 7 8 9 10 11 12 13 14 15 16 17 18 19 20

Answer the question. Write the numbers that make the sentence true.

1. Joe has 13 models in his collection. Trish has 12. Who has the greater number? **Joe**
   __13__ is greater than __12__

Draw or write to explain.

2. Rita has 9 coins. Dick has 6 coins. Who has the number that is less? **Dick**
   __6__ is less than __9__

3. Nikki has 16 action figures. Alec has 16 action figures. Do they have the same number? **Yes**
   __16__ is equal to __16__

4. Beth has 12 stuffed bears. Randy has 15 stuffed bears. Who has the greater number? **Randy**
   __15__ is greater than __12__

Use with text pages 23–24.

HOMEWORK 1.6

Name _____ Date _____

Homework 1.6

Greater Than, Less Than

You can use a number line to compare numbers.

0 1 2 3 4 5 6 7 8 9 10

7 is greater than 3.

11 12 13 14 15 16 17 18 19 20

13 is less than 18.

Use the number lines. Circle the number that is greater.

1. (9) 4   2. (17) 13   3. 11 (19)

Use the number lines. Circle the number that is less.

4. 15 (12)   5. (6) 10   6. (8) 17

Use the number lines.

7. Write a number that is greater than 14.
   _____ is greater than 14.

8. Write a number that is less than 9.
   _____ is less than 9.

9. Find numbers in magazines and newspapers. Make your own greater than and less than sentences.

Draw or write here.

Use with text pages 23–24.

Homework Workbook Page 6

ENGLISH LEARNERS 1.6

Name _____ Date _____

English Learners 1.6

Greater Than, Less Than

16 is **greater** than 14.   10 is **less** than 14.

Count the dots and write the number next to the box. Then circle the correct words.

1. ___ 12   ___ 9
   12 is less than (greater than) 9.

2. ___ 7   ___ 8
   7 is (less than) greater than 8.

Use with text pages 23–24.

TEACHING LESSON 1.6

LESSON ORGANIZER

Objective Use a number line to compare numbers.

Resources Reteach, Practice, Enrichment, Problem Solving, Homework, English Learners, Transparencies, Math Center

Materials blank transparency, counters, number cards 0–10 (LT 14)

Activity

Warm-Up Activity
Modeling Order on a Number Line

| 👥 Small Group | ⏱ 5 minutes | Auditory, Visual |

Materials: *blank transparency, counters*

1. Draw a 0 to 10 number line on the transparency. Review with children that as you move right or forward on the line, each number is 1 greater than the previous number. As you move left or back on the line, each number is 1 less than the previous number.

2. Place a counter on the number 5. **What numbers come before 5?** (0, 1, 2, 3, 4) **What numbers come**

Name_____

Greater Than, Less Than
MathTracks 1/4
Listen and Understand

Objective Use a number line to compare numbers.

Compare 10 and 6.

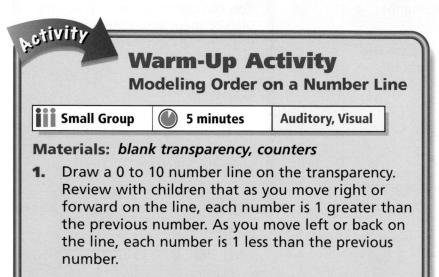

(10 is greater than 6.)

Compare 13 and 17.

(13 is less than 17.)

Guided Practice

Use the number lines.
Circle the greater number.

Think 6 comes after 2 on the number line.

1. 2 ⑥   2. ④ 0

3. 9 ⑩   4. ⑰ 11   5. 14 ⑳

Use the number lines.
Circle the number that is less.

6. ⑥ 7   7. ③ 5   8. 5 ④

9. 16 ⑫   10. ⑪ 15   11. ⑱ 19

TEST TIPS **Explain Your Thinking** Which is greater, 10 or 20? How do you know? **20; because it is after 10 on the number line.**

Chapter 1 Lesson 6   twenty-three **23**

---

1 Introduce
Discuss Greater Than, Less Than

| 👥 Whole Group | ⏱ 10–15 minutes | Visual, Auditory |

Materials: *blank transparency, counters*

1. **Compare 5 and 8.** Draw a 0 through 10 number line on the overhead. Place a counter on the number 5. **What numbers come before 5 on the number line?** (0, 1, 2, 3, 4) **These numbers are less than 5. What numbers come after 5?** (6, 7, 8, 9, 10) **These numbers are greater than 5.**

2. Keep the counter on the number 5 and place a counter on the number 8. **Which number comes first, 5 or 8?** (5) **5 is less than 8. Which number comes after the other number?** (8) **8 is greater than 5.**

3. Call on volunteers to place counters on two numbers and then use the number line to tell which number is greater and which number is less.

2 Develop

Guided Learning

Teaching Example Introduce the objective to the children. Guide them through the examples to show how to use a number line to compare numbers.

Guided Practice

Have children complete **Exercises 1–11** as you observe. Discuss children's responses to the Explain Your Thinking question.

23   **CHAPTER 1   Lesson 6**

Practice

Find the numbers on the number line.

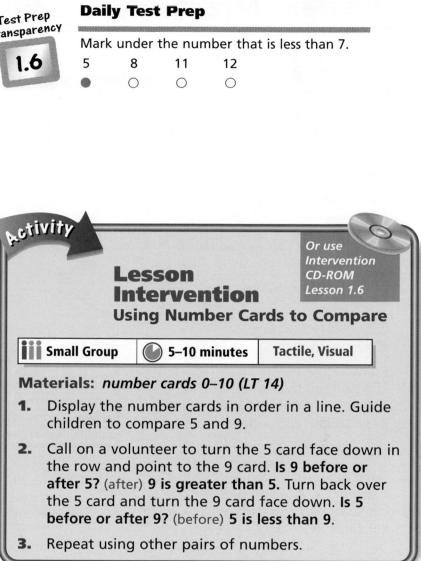

Use the number lines. Circle the greater number.

1. 14   (16)
2. (10)   8
3. 15   (19)
4. (10)   0
5. 16   (17)
6. 13   11

Use the number lines. Circle the number that is less.

7. (0)   1
8. 18   (14)
9. 9   (7)
10. (11)   12
11. 10   (2)
12. (16)   20

Problem Solving ▶ Number Sense   Answers may vary.

13. Write two numbers that are greater than 10 but less than 20.

14. Write two numbers that are less than 10.

When you compare three or more numbers you use the words **greatest** and **least**.   Answers will depend on answers to 13 and 14.

15. **Write About It** Put the four numbers you wrote above in order from greatest to least.

24 twenty-four

At Home   Name two numbers less than 20. Have your child tell which is greater. Repeat with two other numbers and ask your child which is less.

Daily Test Prep

Mark under the number that is less than 7.

5   8   11   12

●   ○   ○   ○

Activity

Or use Intervention CD-ROM Lesson 1.6

Lesson Intervention
Using Number Cards to Compare

| 👥 Small Group | ⏱ 5–10 minutes | Tactile, Visual |

Materials: *number cards 0–10 (LT 14)*

1. Display the number cards in order in a line. Guide children to compare 5 and 9.

2. Call on a volunteer to turn the 5 card face down in the row and point to the 9 card. **Is 9 before or after 5?** (after) **9 is greater than 5.** Turn back over the 5 card and turn the 9 card face down. **Is 5 before or after 9?** (before) **5 is less than 9.**

3. Repeat using other pairs of numbers.

---

3 Practice

Independent Practice

Children complete **Exercises 1–12** independently.

Problem Solving

After children complete **Exercises 13–14**, call on volunteers to share their solutions. Use the **Write About It** in **Exercise 15** to note children's ability to compare and order more than two numbers using the terms *greatest* and *least*.

Common Error

Wrong Direction

Children may read the numbers in the wrong direction on the number line. Review with children that numbers to the left of a number on a number line are less and that numbers to the right of a number are greater.

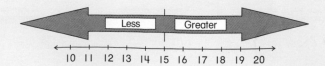

4 Assess and Close

Name two numbers that are greater than 8. (Answers will vary. Possible answers: 9, 12)

Name two numbers that are less than 10. (Answers will vary. Possible answers: 1, 5)

Keeping a Journal

Draw a 0 to 10 number line.

Compare 8 and 5. Tell what number is greater and what number is less. Compare two different numbers.

Problem Solving: Draw a Picture

Lesson 1.7

PLANNING THE LESSON

MATHEMATICS OBJECTIVE
Draw pictures to solve problems.

Use Lesson Planner CD-ROM for Lesson 1.7.

Daily Routines

Calendar
Point to the current date. Have children say the date and then the date just before and just after. Repeat with other dates.

Sunday	Monday	Tuesday	Wednesday	Thursday	Friday	Saturday
			1	2	3	4
5	6	7	8	9	10	11
12	13	14	15	16	17	18
19	20	21	22	23	24	25
26	27	28	29	30	31	

Vocabulary
Review **more, fewer,** and **same number** by showing pairs of dot cards and having children say which card has more dots, or fewer dots, or if they have they same number of dots.

Vocabulary Cards

Meeting North Carolina's Standards
1.01 Develop number sense for whole numbers through 99.
• Connect the model, number word, and number using a variety of representations.

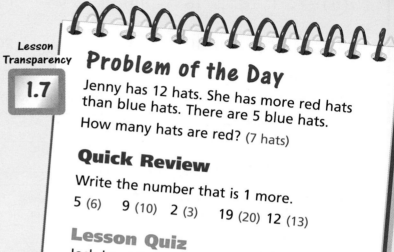

Lesson Transparency 1.7

Problem of the Day
Jenny has 12 hats. She has more red hats than blue hats. There are 5 blue hats.
How many hats are red? (7 hats)

Quick Review
Write the number that is 1 more.
5 (6)   9 (10)   2 (3)   19 (20) 12 (13)

Lesson Quiz
Josh has 10 stickers. Lucy has 1 sticker fewer than Josh. Nina has 1 more than Lucy.
How many stickers does Lucy have? (9 stickers)
How many stickers does Nina have? (10 stickers)

LEVELED PRACTICE

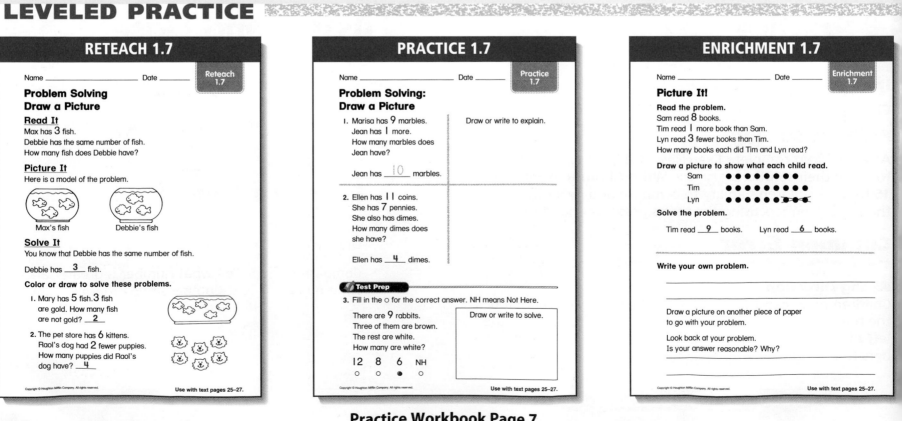

RETEACH 1.7

Name _____ Date _____   Reteach 1.7

**Problem Solving
Draw a Picture**

Read It
Max has 3 fish.
Debbie has the same number of fish.
How many fish does Debbie have?

Picture It
Here is a model of the problem.

Max's fish   Debbie's fish

Solve It
You know that Debbie has the same number of fish.

Debbie has __3__ fish.

Color or draw to solve these problems.

1. Mary has 5 fish. 3 fish are gold. How many fish are not gold? __2__

2. The pet store has 6 kittens. Raol's dog had 2 fewer puppies. How many puppies did Raol's dog have? __4__

Copyright © Houghton Mifflin Company. All rights reserved.   Use with text pages 25–27.

PRACTICE 1.7

Name _____ Date _____   Practice 1.7

**Problem Solving:
Draw a Picture**

1. Marisa has 9 marbles. Jean has 1 more. How many marbles does Jean have?

   Jean has __10__ marbles.

   Draw or write to explain.

2. Ellen has 11 coins. She has 7 pennies. She also has dimes. How many dimes does she have?

   Ellen has __4__ dimes.

▶ **Test Prep**

3. Fill in the ○ for the correct answer. NH means Not Here.

   There are 9 rabbits. Three of them are brown. The rest are white. How many are white?

   12   8   6   NH
   ○   ○   ●   ○

   Draw or write to solve.

Copyright © Houghton Mifflin Company. All rights reserved.   Use with text pages 25–27.

ENRICHMENT 1.7

Name _____ Date _____   Enrichment 1.7

Picture It!

Read the problem.
Sam read 8 books.
Tim read 1 more book than Sam.
Lyn read 3 fewer books than Tim.
How many books each did Tim and Lyn read?

Draw a picture to show what each child read.
Sam ●●●●●●●●
Tim ●●●●●●●●●
Lyn ●●●●●●~~●●●~~

Solve the problem.

Tim read __9__ books.   Lyn read __6__ books.

Write your own problem.

_____

Draw a picture on another piece of paper to go with your problem.

Look back at your problem.
Is your answer reasonable? Why?

_____

Copyright © Houghton Mifflin Company. All rights reserved.   Use with text pages 25–27.

Practice Workbook Page 7

Reaching All Learners
Differentiated Instruction

English Learners

Worksheet 1.7 develops understanding of the terms *1 more*, *1 fewer*, and *the same number as*. Children will need to understand these terms in order to draw pictures and to solve word problems.

Special Needs
AUDITORY, TACTILE

Materials: *cubes*

- Have the child use cubes to model the problem: Dawn has 5 blocks. Pete has 1 more block than Dawn. How many blocks does Pete have? (6)

- Continue with similar problems.

Early Finishers
VISUAL, AUDITORY

- Draw 6 kites on the board.

- Ask children to make up their own word problems where the answer is 6 kites.

- Have them share their word problem with a classmate.

Art Connection

Have children draw pictures of themselves playing with two groups of their favorite toys. Display the pictures and use them as a source to create oral problems that can be solved by looking at the pictures.

MATH CENTER

Number of the Week Activity

Display the Number of the Week to motivate children to use their problem-solving skills. The exercises cover topics across all math strands.

TECHNOLOGY

Spiral Review

To reinforce skills on lessons taught earlier, create **customized** spiral review worksheets using the *Ways to Assess* CD-ROM.

Lesson Planner

You can use the **Lesson Planner CD-ROM** to create a report of the lessons and standards you have taught.

eBook

eMathBook allows students to review lessons and do homework without carrying their textbooks home.

Intervention

Use the *Ways to Success* CD-ROM intervention software to support students who need more help in understanding the concepts and skills taught in this chapter.

PROBLEM SOLVING 1.7

Name _____ Date _____

Problem Solving 1.7

Draw a Picture

There are 12 balls and 8 of them are blue.
All the other balls are red.
How many balls are red?

UNDERSTAND

| What do I need to find out? | how many balls are red |
| What do I know that can help me? | I know there are 12 balls. I know 8 are blue. |

PLAN

| Will I count the balls or will I draw a picture? | |

SOLVE

| Color 8 balls blue. How many are left? How many balls are red? | 4 balls |

LOOK BACK

| Does my answer make sense? | Yes, because I counted the balls that I did not color blue. |

Copyright © Houghton Mifflin Company. All rights reserved.   Use with text pages 25–27.

HOMEWORK 1.7

Name _____ Date _____

Homework 1.7

Problem Solving Draw a Picture

Jackie has 4 hats. Josh has 1 more hat than Jackie.
Haley has 2 fewer hats than Josh.
How many hats does Josh have?
How many hats does Haley have?

What do I know?
Jackie has __4__ hats.
Josh has __1__ more hat than Jackie.
Haley has __2__ fewer hats than Josh.

Plan
Start with Jackie's hats.
Jackie has __4__ hats.

Solve   Draw here.
Draw Jackie's hats.
Draw 1 more hat to show Josh's hats.
Draw 2 fewer hats than Josh to show Haley's hats.
Josh has __5__ hats.
Haley has __3__ hats.

Look Back
Does my answer make sense?

Copyright © Houghton Mifflin Company. All rights reserved.   Use with text pages 25–27.

Homework Workbook Page 7

ENGLISH LEARNERS 1.7

Name _____ Date _____

English Learners 1.7

Draw a Picture

Larry has 6 apples.

| 1 **more** apple | 1 **fewer** apple | **same number** of apples |
| 7 apples | 5 apples | 6 apples |

1. Here are 2 apples.   Draw 1 more than 2.

          Drawing of 3 apples

2. Here are 5 apples.   Draw 1 fewer than 5.

          Drawing of 4 apples

3. Here are 3 apples.   Draw the same number as 3.

          Drawing of 3 apples

To the Teacher: Use the example at the top of the page to demonstrate the meaning of the terms *1 more*, *1 fewer*, and *same as*. Then read the sentences with children and have them draw a picture in the boxes.

Copyright © Houghton Mifflin Company. All rights reserved.   Use with text pages 25–27.

TEACHING LESSON 1.7

LESSON ORGANIZER

Objective Draw pictures to solve problems.

Resources Reteach, Practice, Enrichment, Problem Solving, Homework, English Learners

Materials Counters, blank transparency

Activity

Warm-Up Activity
Modeling Problems

👤👤👤👤 Whole Group	🕐 5 minutes	Auditory, Tactile

Materials: *counters, blank transparency*

1. Model a problem on the overhead as you go through each step. **I have 5 counters. Show 5 counters.**

2. Call on a volunteer. **(Child's name) has more counters than I have.** (Child shows more than 5 counters.) Ask how many counters the child shows. Call on another volunteer. **(Child's name) has fewer counters than I have.** (Child shows fewer than 5 counters.) Ask how many counters child shows. (Answers will vary.)

3. Review the number of counters the two children have shown. Relate the answers to the counters as a way to check. **How can you solve this problem if you do not have counters?** Guide children to the idea of drawing the counters.

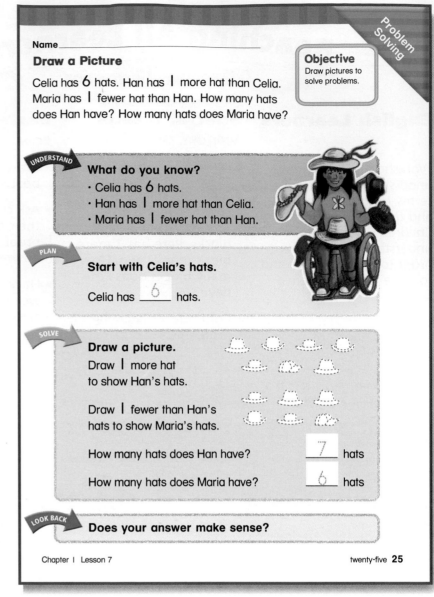

Draw a Picture

Objective Draw pictures to solve problems.

Celia has 6 hats. Han has 1 more hat than Celia. Maria has 1 fewer hat than Han. How many hats does Han have? How many hats does Maria have?

UNDERSTAND

What do you know?
· Celia has 6 hats.
· Han has 1 more hat than Celia.
· Maria has 1 fewer hat than Han.

PLAN

Start with Celia's hats.

Celia has ___6___ hats.

SOLVE

Draw a picture.
Draw 1 more hat to show Han's hats.

Draw 1 fewer than Han's hats to show Maria's hats.

How many hats does Han have? ___7___ hats

How many hats does Maria have? ___6___ hats

LOOK BACK

Does your answer make sense?

---

① Introduce

Discuss Drawing a Picture to Solve

👤👤👤👤 Whole Group	🕐 10–15 minutes	Visual, Auditory

Materials: *blank transparency*

1. *Draw a picture.* Write the problem on the transparency.

   Liz has 5 buttons. Sean has 1 more button than Liz. Mei has 1 more button than Sean.

2. Draw 5 buttons and say **Liz has 5 buttons. Does Sean have more or fewer buttons than Liz?** (more) **How many more?** (1) **How many buttons should I draw for Sean?** (5 and 1 more, or 6) Draw 6 buttons.

3. **Does Mei have more buttons than Sean or Liz?** (Both Sean and Liz) **How many more?** (1) **How many buttons should I draw for Mei?** (6 and 1 more, or 7) Draw 7 buttons.

4. Reread the questions and have children give the answers based on the pictures.

② Develop

Guided Learning

Teaching Example Discuss the objective with the children. Guide them through the example to show how to find that Han has 7 hats and Maria has 6 hats. Allow time for children to share why their answers make sense.

Guided Practice

Have children complete **Exercises 1–2** on page 26 as you observe. Give children the opportunity to share their solutions.

Guided Practice

Remember:
► Understand
► Plan
► Solve
► Look Back

Draw a picture to solve.

1. There are 10 flowers. There is the same number of red flowers as orange flowers. How many flowers are there of each color?

   Ⓡ Ⓡ Ⓡ Ⓡ Ⓡ
   Ⓞ Ⓞ Ⓞ Ⓞ Ⓞ

   Think
   Draw 1 red flower and 1 orange flower until you have drawn 10 flowers.

   __5__ red
   __5__ orange

2. Amy has 9 bugs. Erin has 1 fewer bug than Amy. Mike has 1 more bug than Erin. How many bugs does Erin have? How many bugs does Mike have?

   ○○○○○ ○○○○○
   ○○○○○ ○○○○

   Erin   Mike

   Think
   Start with Amy's 9 bugs.

   Erin has __8__ bugs.

   Mike has __9__ bugs.

Practice

3. There are 8 birds. There is the same number of blue birds as yellow birds. How many birds are there of each color?

   ○○○○ blue
   ○○○○ yellow

   __4__ blue
   __4__ yellow

4. Abby has 7 pots. Jan has 1 more pot than Abby. Luis has 1 fewer pot than Jan. How many pots does Jan have? How many pots does Luis have?

   □□□□ □□□□
   □□□□ □□□
   Jan   Luis

   Jan has __8__ pots.

   Luis has __7__ pots.

   Go on

26 twenty-six

Play "In Between Math"

Materials: *For each pair of children:* **set of number cards, 1–20 (LT 14 and 15)**

How to Play

• Shuffle cards and place face down between the two players.

• Each player takes two cards. Have the child arrange the cards in order.

• Then each player draws a third card. The player scores 1 point if the third card is in between the first two cards.

• The game ends when 10 points are scored.

ACHIEVING
Mathematical Proficiency

What Is Problem Solving?

Research emphatically demonstrates that if children can count, they can begin to use their counting skills to solve word problems. **These in turn give children opportunities to demonstrate counting proficiency and to build a set of procedures for computation.**

Children have the most success solving problems that are phrased simply and that involve the use of counters or other concrete objects for modeling. Children can also learn to model problems by drawing a picture. For instance, **word problems that require children to develop a plan and then draw a picture to solve should also give them the option to use counters to solve.**

Combining strategies further expands children's abilities. Becoming **strategically competent in the use of problem-solving strategies** allows children to move beyond superficial understanding.

---

3 Practice

Independent Practice

Children complete **Exercises 3–4** on page 26 independently.

Daily Test Prep

Kate has 7 balloons. Jose has 1 more balloon than Kate. How many balloons does Jose have?

1   6   7   8
○   ○   ○   ●

Activity

Lesson Intervention
Drawing to Solve a Problem

Or use Intervention CD-ROM Lesson 1.7

| 👥 Small Group | 🕐 5–10 minutes | Auditory, Tactile |

Materials: *counters*

1. Have children use counters to model problems. Then have them draw or trace the counters to show their solutions.

2. **David has 6 beach balls. How many counters will you show?** (6) **Show 6 counters then draw them. These show David's beach balls. Casey has 1 more beach ball than David. How many counters will you show and then draw?** (6 and 1 more, or 7) Guide children to see that they can also show and then draw 1 counter next to the picture of 6 counters and get the same answer.

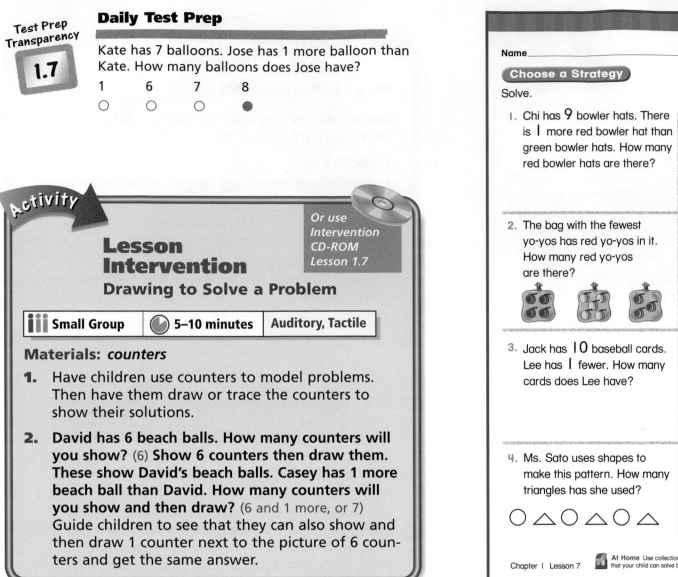

Name _____

Strategies
Act It Out With Models
Draw a Picture

Choose a Strategy

Solve.

1. Chi has 9 bowler hats. There is 1 more red bowler hat than green bowler hats. How many red bowler hats are there?

   Draw or write to explain.
   Allow children to use any strategy or method they want.

   __5__ red bowlers   bowler

2. The bag with the fewest yo-yos has red yo-yos in it. How many red yo-yos are there?

   __3__ red yo-yos   yo-yo

3. Jack has 10 baseball cards. Lee has 1 fewer. How many cards does Lee have?

   __9__ cards   baseball card

4. Ms. Sato uses shapes to make this pattern. How many triangles has she used?

   ○ △ ○ △ ○ △

   __3__ triangles   shapes

Chapter 1 Lesson 7   **At Home** Use collections to create problems that your child can solve by drawing a picture.   twenty-seven **27**

3 Practice

Mixed Strategy Practice

Read the problem-solving strategies on page 27 and discuss them with the class. Be sure children can read and comprehend the problems in **Exercises 1–4**. If necessary, pair more proficient readers with less proficient readers.

Common Error

Using the Wrong Picture to Find the Answer
Children may confuse the pictures if they do not draw one below the other. Provide grids to help children organize their pictures.

4 Assess and Close

Clara has 8 bells. Norm has 1 bell fewer than Clara. Steve has 1 bell more than Norm. How many bells does Norm have? (7) **How many bells does Steve have?** (8)

✍ Keeping a Journal

Finish this problem and show how to solve it.

Tom has 5 fish. Paul has _____ more fish than Tom. How many fish does Paul have? (Answers will vary.)

Listen to your teacher read the problem. Solve.

1. There are 10 balls in a box. Some of the balls are red. 6 of the balls are blue. How many red balls are in the box?

Show your work using pictures, numbers, or words.

_4_ red balls

2. Tad has 8 blocks in a bag. Ramón has 2 fewer blocks than Tad. How many blocks does Ramón have?

_6_ blocks

Listen to your teacher read the problem. Choose the correct answer.

3. 5   7   8   9
    ○   ○   ○   ●

4. 12   10   9   2
    ○   ●   ○   ○

This page provides children practice with the oral problem-solving format used in some standardized test items.

You may want to read each item only once to mimic the style of oral tests.

Use with Items 1 and 2

Listening Strategy: Listen for important facts and details as the teacher reads.

- *Listen to the question so you will know how to use the numbers.*
- *Use the numbers to find the answer. You can draw a picture if you want.*
- *Do not start writing until I finish reading.*

Use with Item 3

Listening Strategy: Listen to the problem and then look at the picture.

- *Look at me when I read a problem that is not on the page.*

  Mei is counting the buttons on her shirt. She has counted to 7 and there are two more buttons to count. How many buttons are on Mei's shirt?

- *Look at the picture. Mark your answer.*

Use with Item 4

Listening Strategy: Listen for important facts.

- *Listen to the problem so that you will know how to use the picture.*

  Doug has 12 pencils in his desk. Billy has 2 pencils fewer than Doug. How many pencils does Billy have?

- *You can use the picture to find the answer to the question. Mark your answer.*

Quick Check

Have children complete the Quick Check exercises independently to assess their understanding of concepts and skills taught in **Lessons 5–7**.

Item	Lesson	Error Analysis	Intervention
1–2	1.5	Children confuse terms greater than and less than.	Reteach Resource 1.5 ***Ways to Success*** 1.5
3–8	1.6	Children may go in wrong direction when using a number line.	Reteach Resource 1.6 ***Ways to Success*** 1.6
9	1.7	Children may use the wrong picture to find an answer.	Reteach Resource 1.7 ***Ways to Success*** 1.7

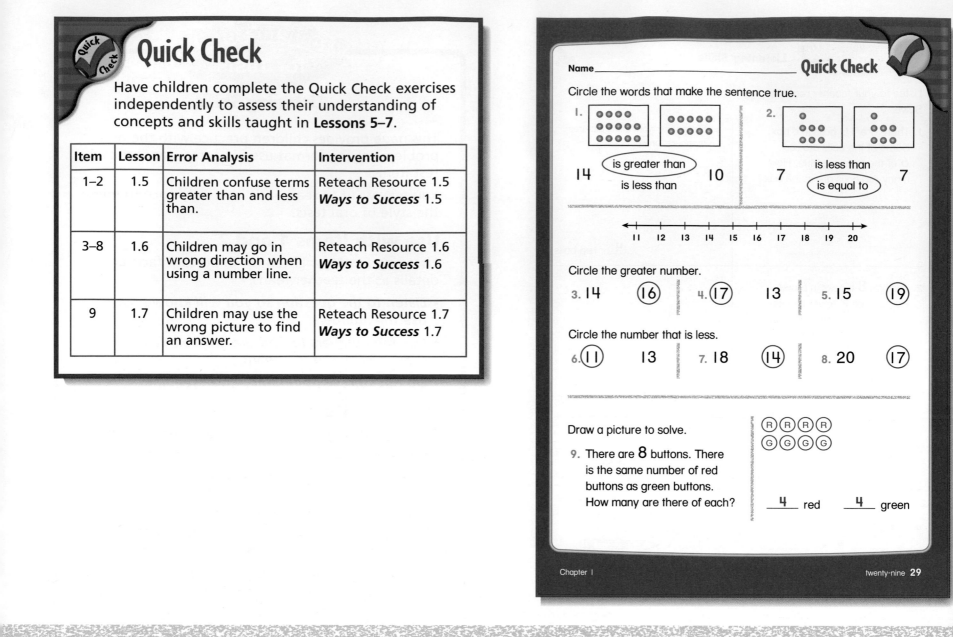

Name _____ Quick Check

Circle the words that make the sentence true.

1. 14 (is greater than) / is less than 10

2. 7 is less than / (is equal to) 7

11 12 13 14 15 16 17 18 19 20

Circle the greater number.

3. 14 (16)   4. (17) 13   5. 15 (19)

Circle the number that is less.

6. (11) 13   7. 18 (14)   8. 20 (17)

Draw a picture to solve.

9. There are 8 buttons. There is the same number of red buttons as green buttons. How many are there of each?

Ⓡ Ⓡ Ⓡ Ⓡ
Ⓖ Ⓖ Ⓖ Ⓖ

__4__ red   __4__ green

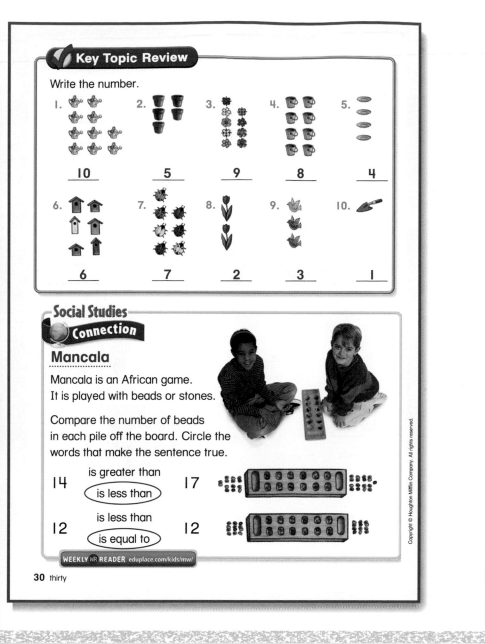

Key Topic Review

Write the number.

1. 10
2. 5
3. 9
4. 8
5. 4
6. 6
7. 7
8. 2
9. 3
10. 1

Social Studies Connection

Mancala

Mancala is an African game.
It is played with beads or stones.

Compare the number of beads in each pile off the board. Circle the words that make the sentence true.

14 is greater than / (is less than) 17

12 is less than / (is equal to) 12

WEEKLY WR READER eduplace.com/kids/mw/

30 thirty

Key Topic Review

This assessment provides a review of skills and concepts taught in this chapter.

Check to be sure that children:

• count all the objects.

• do not reverse numbers when writing.

• are able to write the number.

Social Studies Connection

Mancala

Mancala (man KAH luh) is an African game. Point to the gameboard. The players add and count the beads as they move them around the board. Children play to see who gets the most beads in his or her long space at the end of the board.

How to Play:

• Place three beads in each compartment of the board.

• Players take turns picking up all the beads from one of the compartments on their side of the board. Moving counterclockwise, add one bead to each compartment.

• If your last bead lands in your end space, play again.

• If your last bead lands in an empty compartment on your side of the board, take all the beads from the opposite compartment. Add them to your end space.

• When one player's compartments are all empty, the game is over. That player takes the remaining beads in the other player's compartments and adds them to his or her end space. After counting their beads, the player with the highest score starts the next game.

Monitoring Student Progress

Purpose: This test provides an informal assessment of the Chapter 1 objectives.

Chapter Test Items 1–20

To assign a numerical grade for this Chapter Test, use 5 points for each test item.

Check Understanding

Use children's work on word problems to informally assess progress on chapter content.

Customizing Your Instruction

For children who have not yet mastered these objectives, you can use the reteaching resources listed in the chart below.

 Assessment Options

A summary test for this chapter is also provided in the Unit Resource Folder.

Chapter Review/Test

Name _____

Vocabulary *e* Glossary

Write the words to complete the sentence.

| greater than |
| less than |
| equal to |

1. 5 is ___less than___ _____ 7.

2. 6 is ___greater than___ _____ 3.

Concepts and Skills

Match. Circle the set that has fewer.

3. [cups and saucers]

Count.
Write the number.

4. [dots] ___8___   5. [hands] ___9___

6. [ten frame] ___12___   7. [ten frames] ___19___

8. Just after   9. Just before   10. Between

13, [14]   [19], 20   9, [10], 11

Chapter 1   thirty-one **31**

Reteaching Support

Chapter Test Items	Summary Test Items	Chapter Objectives Tested	TE Pages	Use These Reteaching Resources
1–3	1–2	**1A** Develop and use math vocabulary relating to number concepts through 20.	23A–24	Reteach Resource and *Ways to Success* CD: 1.6 Skillsheet 3
4–7	3–5	**1B** Read and write numbers through 20.	9A–16	Reteach Resources and *Ways to Success* CD: 1.2, 1.3, 1.6 Skillsheet 4
8–19	6–8	**1C** Recognize, count, compare, and order sets through 20 using pictures, words, and number lines.	17A–18, 21A–22	Reteach Resources and *Ways to Success* CD: 1.4, 1.5 Skillsheets 5–6
20	9–10	**1D** Draw pictures to solve problems.	25A–28	Reteach Resource and *Ways to Success* CD: 1.7 Skillsheet 7

CHAPTER SUMMARY TEST

Name _____ Date _____

Chapter 1 Test

Match.
Circle the set that has more.

Match.
Circle the set that has fewer.

1. [stars and circles]   2. [balls]

Circle the words that make the sentence true.

3. [flowers] [pumpkins]
8 (is less than / is greater than) 9

4. [drops] [circles]
10 (is less than / is equal to) 10

5. [apples] [tomatoes]
7 (is greater than / is less than) 9

Copyright © Houghton Mifflin Company. All rights reserved.

Go on

Chapter Review/Test

11. Write the missing numbers in order.

11, __12__, __13__, 14, __15__, __16__, 17, __18__, 19

Circle the words that make the sentence true.

12. 12   is greater than   12
    (is equal to)

13. 5   (is greater than)   3
    is less than

← 11 12 13 14 15 16 17 18 19 20 →

Use the number line.
Circle the greater number.

14. 11   (12)

15. 13   (14)

16. (18)   15

Use the number line.
Circle the number that is less.

17. (11)   13

18. 16   (14)

19. (17)   20

Problem Solving
Draw a picture to solve.

20. There are 6 pots. There is the same number of green pots as yellow pots. How many pots are there of each color?

| G | G | G |
| Y | Y | Y |

__3__ green

__3__ yellow

32 thirty-two

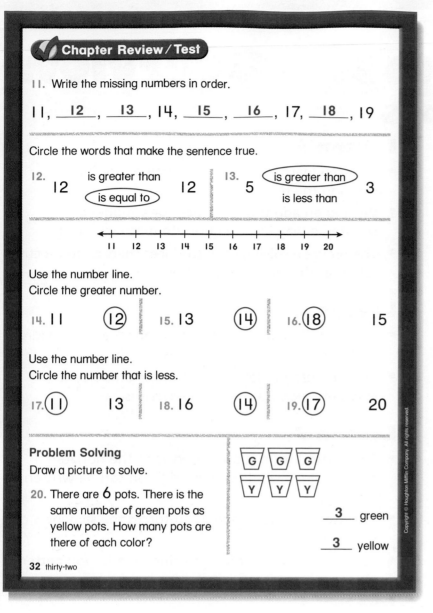

Adequate Yearly Progress

CHAPTER SUMMARY TEST

Name _____ Date _____

Chapter 1 Test continued

Write the number.

6. Just after   7. Just before   8. Between

9, [10]   [2], 3   0, [1], 2

Circle the picture that helps solve the problem.

9. Eric has 4 blocks. Anna has 1 more block than Eric. Rico has 2 fewer blocks than Anna. How many blocks does Anna have?

Anna has

10. Felix eats 4 small pancakes. Jodie eats 2 more pancakes than Felix. Malcolm eats 1 fewer pancake than Jodie. How many pancakes does Malcolm eat?

Malcolm eats

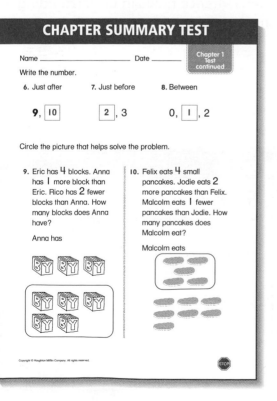

Lesson by Lesson Overview
Addition Concepts

Lesson 1

- Children are introduced to the concept of addition through oral problems, which they act out.
- Learning addition in a context helps children understand the concept.
- The initial introduction to addition uses increasing, or joining, which most children can understand.

Lesson 2

- Using a part-part-whole workmat and counters provides children with a physical representation of that aspect of addition.
- This model reappears in Chapter 3 to develop subtraction and is also used later in problem solving.

Lesson 3

- This lesson introduces addition sentences.
- Pictorial representations provide a visual for finding sums.
- The use of + and = takes children to the symbolic level of addition.

Lesson 4

- Adding with zero can be difficult for some children.
- Pictures help children visualize the idea of a group of zero, or nothing, being added to a group with some number of objects.
- Children create and solve their own problems as they interpret a picture problem.

Lesson 5

- Children learn the order property of addition through the use of cube trains.
- Writing an addition sentence for a model gives children a way to communicate mathematically.
- The problem-solving set introduces children to function tables as they practice addition.

Lesson 6

- Finding different ways to make 7 and 8 allows children to discover facts for these sums.
- Children use models and the order property to complete algebra readiness exercises.

Lesson 7

- The vertical form is presented with the horizontal form to show children that addition can be written two ways.
- The use of a single model reinforces the sameness of the two forms.
- Children use vertical form to find an addition pattern.

Lesson 8

- Children learn to write an addition sentence to solve a story problem.
- Writing a number sentence helps in understanding as well as in solving a problem.

SKILLS TRACE: ADDITION CONCEPTS

Grade K	Grade 1	Grade 2
• model addition (ch. 13)	• model addition as increasing	• use the addition properties (ch. 2)
• complete addition sentences (ch. 13)	• model addition as part-part-whole	
• add 1 to 0 through 9 (ch. 13)	• find the sum of an addition sentence	
• add 2 to 0 through 8 (ch. 13)	• add with zero	
	• use the Order Property of Addition	
	• add in vertical form	

Chapter Planner

Lesson	Objective	Vocabulary	Materials	✓ NCTM Standards
2.1 **Addition Stories** **(Hands-On)** p. 35A	Model the concept of addition.		number cards 1–6 (Learning Tool (LT) 14), counters, 2 number cubes labeled with 1–3 dots	Count with understanding and recognize "how many" in sets of objects.
2.2 **Model Addition** **(Hands-On)** p. 37A	Model the concept of addition as putting together.	add part whole	two-color counters part-part-whole transparency, dried beans, paper cups, overhead 2-color counters, Workmat 3	Develop and use strategies for whole-number computations, with a focus on addition and subtraction.
2.3 **Use Symbols to Add** p. 39A	Solve addition sentences using + and =.	plus sign equal sign addition sentence sum	two-color counters, number cards 1–6 (LT 14), cards with plus and equal signs (LT 15), blank transparency	Develop and use strategies for whole-number computations, with a focus on addition and subtraction.
2.4 **Add with Zero** p. 41A	Solve addition problems with zero.	zero	two-color counters, number cards 1–5 (LT 14), cards with + and = (LT 15), number cube with numbers 1–5, counters, teacher-made direction cards, paper bag	Develop and use strategies for whole-number computations, with a focus on addition and subtraction.
2.5 **Add in Any Order** **(Hands-On)** p. 45A	Understand the order property of addition.	order addend	cubes in two colors, number cards 1–3 (LT 14), grid paper (LT 29)	Develop and use strategies for whole-number computations, with a focus on addition and subtraction.
2.6 **Ways to Make 7 and 8** p. 47A	Complete addition sentences with the sums of 7 and 8.		cubes	Develop and use strategies for whole-number computations, with a focus on addition and subtraction.
2.7 **Add in Vertical Form** p. 49A	Write addition sentences in vertical format.		number dot cards 1–4 (LT 17), blank transparency, cubes	Develop and use strategies for whole-number computations, with a focus on addition and subtraction.
2.8 **Problem Solving: Write a Number Sentence** p. 51A	Write addition sentences for problem situations.		2-color cubes	Develop and use strategies for whole-number computations with a focus on addition and subtraction.

Resources For Reaching All Learners

LESSON RESOURCES: Reteach, Practice, Enrichment, Problem Solving, Homework, English Learners, Daily Routines, Transparencies, Math Center.

ADDITIONAL RESOURCES FROM HOUGHTON MIFFLIN: Chapter Challenges, Combination Classroom Planning Guide, Every Day Counts, Math to Learn (Student Handbook).

Every Day Counts
The Daily Depositor, Numbers Stories, and Counting Tape Activities in Every Day Counts support the math in this chapter.

Assessing Prior Knowledge

Before beginning the chapter, you can assess student understandings in order to assist you in differentiating instruction.

Complete Chapter Pretest in Unit Resource Folder

Use this test to assess both prerequisite skills (**Are You Ready?** — one page) and chapter content (**Check What You Know** — two pages).

Chapter 2 Prerequisite Skills Pretest

Chapter 2 New Content Pretest

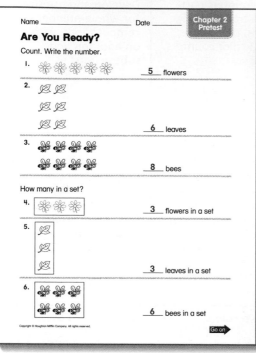

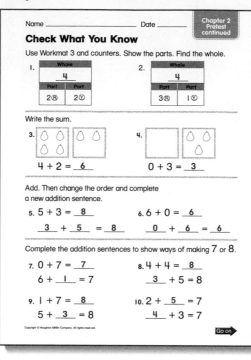

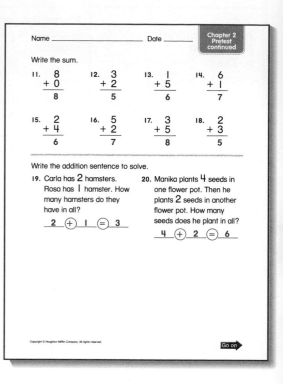

Customizing Instruction

For Students Having Difficulty

Items	Prerequisites	*Ways to Success*
1–3	Count and write numbers to 10.	CD: 1.2 Skillsheet 8
4–6	Understand the concept of a set.	CD: 1.2 Skillsheet 9

Ways to Success: Intervention for every concept and skill (CD-ROM or Chapter Intervention Skillsheets).

For Students Having Success

Items	Objectives	Resources
1–2	2A Use vocabulary relating to addition concepts.	Enrichment 2.3
3–8, 5–20	2B Solve addition problems horizontally and vertically through 8.	Enrichment 2.1–2.4, 2.6, 2.7
11–14	2C Understand the order property of addition.	Enrichment 2.5
9–10	2D Write number sentences to solve story problems.	Enrichment 2.8

Use **Chapter Challenges** with any students who have success with all new chapter content.

Other Pretest Options

Informal Pretest

The pretest assesses vocabulary and prerequisite skills needed for success in this chapter.

***Ways to Success* CD-ROM**

The ***Ways to Success*** chapter pretest has automatic assignment of appropriate review lessons.

Chapter Resources

Professional Resources Handbook

Activity

Assessing Prior Knowledge

"Take Inventory" in a Class Store (count to 20)

- A classroom store can be a popular addition to your classroom. Designate an area of the room to be used as a store. Equip the store with common classroom items such as pencils, erasers, paint brushes and markers in quantities of 1 to 20.
- Explain that an important job of storekeepers is to take inventory, or count how many of each item they have. Have children take a daily inventory of the items in the store as you add and remove items.

Activity

Ongoing Skill Activity

Adding Animals (write addition sentences)

- Make available a collection of books that show animals and their babies.
- Encourage children to study the photographs and count the animals in these groups.
- Then have them write addition sentences that tell how many in all. Remind them to use + and = signs.

Activity

Connecting to the Unit Project

- Tell children the following addition story. Encourage them to model the story with counters.
- **There are 4 red apples. There are 3 green apples. How many apples are there in all?** (7 apples)

Teacher Support

Professional Resources Handbook

Research, Mathematics Content, and Language Intervention

Research-Based Teaching

In teaching basic facts, a focus on speed and memorization can be harmful. Children can find number facts meaningless words to be memorized. Demanding quick and correct responses to number fact problems can create unwanted pressure or anxiety in children. Such anxiety may hinder understanding, interfere with ability to calculate, discourage the use of available principles, as well as develop a negative attitude towards mathematics (Ginsburg, 1989). See *Professional Resources Handbook, Grade 1,* Unit 1.

For more ideas relating to Unit 1, see the Teacher Support Handbook at the back of this Teacher's Edition.

Language Intervention

In China, the basic addition facts are taught using an approach that reinforces the importance of 10 as a special organizer of our number system. Children learn thoroughly all of the different ways to compose and decompose numbers less than or equal to 10. For further explanation, see "Mathematical Language and Addition Facts" in the *Professional Resources Handbook Grade 1.*

Technology

Time-Saving Technology Support
Ways to Assess Customized Spiral Review Test Generator CD
Lesson Planner CD-ROM
Ways to Success Intervention CD-ROM
MathTracks CD-ROM
Education Place: www.eduplace.com/math/mw
Houghton Mifflin Math eBook CD-ROM
eManipulatives
eGames

Starting Chapter 2
Addition Concepts

CHAPTER OBJECTIVES

2A Develop and use math vocabulary relating to addition concepts.

2B Solve addition problems horizontally and vertically through 8 using + and =, including problems with 0 as an addend.

2C Understand the order property of addition.

2D Write number sentences to solve story problems.

Math Background

Addition Concepts

Addition is one of the four basic operations that form the foundation of arithmetic and is an essential part of the computation work of the elementary school grades. The definition of addition is based on the union of disjoint sets (sets with no common items). The general form of an addition sentence is written as $a + b = c$, where a, b, and c are whole numbers.

$3 + 2 = 5$ indicates that $3 + 2$ is the same as the number 5, or that $3 + 2$ is another way to name the number 5. In general $a + b = c$ can also be written as

$$\begin{array}{r} a \\ + b \\ \hline c \end{array}$$

Another way to represent addition is to use a number line model.

There are properties of addition that lay a foundation for the study of algebra and also make computation easier. The Commutative Property of Addition states that numbers can be added in any order and the sum will be the same. The Identity Property of Addition states that the sum of any number and zero is equal to that number.

Addition Concepts

INVESTIGATION

How many cats and dogs do you see altogether?

Chapter 2   thirty-three **33**

Using The Investigation

- Hold up 3 pencils in one hand and 1 pencil in the other hand. **How many pencils are in each group?** (3 and 1) **The 3 and 1 are called** *addends*. **How many pencils do I have in all?** (4 pencils) **4 is called the** *sum*.

- Have children find groups of items around the classroom that they can combine for sums through 4.

- Read the directions to children. **Look at the groups of cats and dogs in the picture. Put the groups together. How many cats and dogs do you see altogether?** (2 + 1 = 3)

 For more information about projects and investigations, visit Education Place. **eduplace.com/math/mw/**

Around Town

This is a parade route.

school

library

3 blocks

1 block

2 blocks

grocery store

2 blocks

fire station

bakery

1 block

Use the parade route to answer the question.

1. How many blocks is it from the  to the ?

   __4__ blocks

2. How many blocks is it from the to the ?

   __4__ blocks

For Mathematically Promising Students

Math

CHAPTER
Challenges

The *Chapter Challenges* resource book provides blackline masters for activities that explore, extend, and connect the mathematics in every chapter. To support this independent work, see the Teacher Notes for each activity.

Explore: Adding More Ducks, page 7, after Lesson 1
Extend: Shell Graph, page 9, after Lesson 3
Connect: Using Patterns, page 11, after Lesson 5

Using This Page

- Tell children that they are looking at a map of a parade route. Ask the children to share about some parades they have seen.
- Identify the different buildings along the route.
- **Put your pencil on the school and add the number of blocks to the library. How many blocks?** (3 blocks + 1 block = 4 blocks) **Put your pencil on the grocery store and add the number of the blocks to the fire station. How many blocks?** (2 blocks + 2 blocks = 4 blocks)
- Have children make up questions adding the number of blocks between other buildings along the parade route.

Children's Math Worlds

NSF

Using *Children's Math Worlds* helps develop student communication skills because of the daily work with Math Talk, a teaching practice that can be used with all lessons. The emphasis on building a helping community will also enhance student participation in all classroom discussion.

Hands-On: Addition Stories

Lesson 2.1

PLANNING THE LESSON

MATHEMATICS OBJECTIVE
Model the concept of addition.

Use Lesson Planner CD-ROM for Lesson 2.1.

Meeting North Carolina's Standards
1.03 Develop fluency with single-digit addition and corresponding differences using strategies such as modeling, composing and decomposing quantities, using doubles, and making tens.

Also 1.04

Daily Routines

Calendar
Point to the first full week of the month and have children tell how many days are in one week. Then point to the Sunday of the next week and ask how many days are in one week and one day.

Sunday	Monday	Tuesday	Wednesday	Thursday	Friday	Saturday
				1	2	3	4
5	6	7	8	9	10	11
12	13	14	15	16	17	18
19	20	21	22	23	24	25
26	27	28	29	30	31	

Vocabulary
Discuss the concept of *putting together* to find *how many in all.* Provide examples by having children act out simple joining situations.

Vocabulary Cards

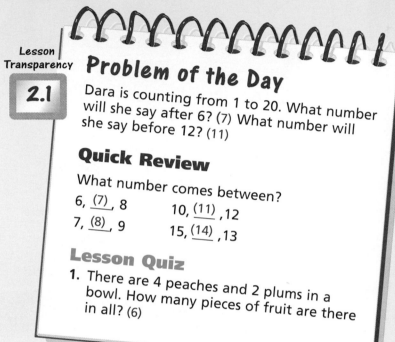

Lesson Transparency 2.1

Problem of the Day
Dara is counting from 1 to 20. What number will she say after 6? (7) What number will she say before 12? (11)

Quick Review
What number comes between?

6, __(7)__, 8   10, __(11)__, 12

7, __(8)__, 9   15, __(14)__, 13

Lesson Quiz
1. There are 4 peaches and 2 plums in a bowl. How many pieces of fruit are there in all? (6)

LEVELED PRACTICE

RETEACH 2.1

Name _____ Date _____

Reteach 2.1

Addition Stories

You can use counters to show the numbers in a story.

Callie's cat had 3 kittens.   Julio's cat had 2 kittens.

You can write the numbers in a story.
You can count to tell how many in all.

__3__   __2__   __5__ kittens in all

Make up a story about adding numbers.
Show the story with ⬭ ⬭.
Write the numbers.

Maria has 2 books.   Joseph has 4 books.

Use counters to show the story.

Write the numbers and tell how many in all.

__2__   __4__   __6__ books in all

Copyright © Houghton Mifflin Company. All rights reserved.   **Use with text pages 35–36.**

PRACTICE 2.1

Name _____ Date _____

Practice 2.1

Addition Stories

Tell a story about 🐑🐑🐑 and 🐑🐑.
You can use two different colored counters.
If you work with a partner you can each tell a different part of the story.
Write the numbers.

1.

__3__   __2__   __5__ in all

or: __2__   __3__   __5__ in all

Test Prep

Fill in the ○ for the correct answer. NH means Not Here.

2. The counters and numbers should match.

Which set of counters match the numbers?

4   2   6   NH

Copyright © Houghton Mifflin Company. All rights reserved.   **Use with text pages 35–36.**

ENRICHMENT 2.1

Name _____ Date _____

Enrichment 2.1

Tell an Adding Story

Make up a story about the picture.
Show the story with ○ ●.
Write the numbers.

1.

__1__   __3__   __4__ in all

2.

__2__   __3__   __5__ in all

3.

__1__   __2__   __3__ in all

4.

__4__   __2__   __6__ in all

Write About It   How do counters help you tell a story?

__I can use one counter for each animal. Then I__
__can count how many in all.__

Copyright © Houghton Mifflin Company. All rights reserved.   **Use with text pages 35–36.**

Practice Workbook Page 8

35A   **CHAPTER 2**   **Lesson 1**

Reaching All Learners
Differentiated Instruction

English Learners

Children will need to understand the term *in all* to understand the concept of addition. Use Worksheet 2.1 to introduce the term to English-language learners.

Inclusion
VISUAL, TACTILE

Materials: *number cards 1–6 (LT 14), counters*

- Show a number card for 1. Have child put down 1 counter. Now, show the number card for 2. Have child add one more counter to show 2. Ask child to count and write how many in all.

- Continue the activity with number cards 3–6.

Gifted and Talented
TACTILE, VISUAL

- Have children work in pairs to make a picture of a park scene. Have them show groups of 1, 2, 3, and 4 different animals.

- Then have children create questions such as: How many squirrels and birds do you see? How many rabbits and ducks are there?

- Have pairs share their scene with the class.

TECHNOLOGY

Spiral Review
Help students remember skills they learned earlier by creating **customized** spiral review worksheets using the *Ways to Assess* CD-ROM.

Lesson Planner
Use the **Lesson Planner CD-ROM** to see how lesson objectives for this chapter are correlated to standards.

eBook
An electronic version of this lesson can be found in **eMathBook**.

Manipulatives
Interactive Counters with several workmats are available on the *Ways to Success* CD-ROM.

Social Studies Connection

Discuss different jobs that people have in your school. Write the names of each job on the board. For example: teacher, librarian, or nurse. Then tell addition stories about the school workers for children to solve.

MATH CENTER

Cross-Curricular Activity

As you use this activity to relate the mathematics of this lesson to another curriculum area, children will see how math can help them with other subjects.

PROBLEM SOLVING 2.1

Name _____ Date _____
Problem Solving 2.1

Addition Stories

Show the story with counters.

There are 2 horses in the field. 2 more horses run to them. How many horses are there in all?

___4___ horses in all

Draw or write to explain.

1. Jana has 2 books. Her sister gives her 1 more book. How many books does Jana have in all?

   ___3___ books

2. There are 3 plates on the table. Mom puts 2 more plates on the table. How many plates are there in all?

   ___5___ plates

3. Declan has 4 trading cards. His dad gives him 1 more. How many trading cards does Declan have?

   ___5___ cards

Use with text pages 35–36.

HOMEWORK 2.1

Name _____ Date _____
Homework 2.1

Addition Stories

There are 3 white dogs. There are 2 black dogs. Show the story with small items such as buttons, coins, or macaroni.

Count the items you have and write the numbers.

___3___   ___2___   ___5___ in all

Write the numbers.

1. There are 4 ladybugs on a leaf. Then 1 ladybug joins them.

   ___4___   ___1___   ___5___ in all

2. Make up a story of your own. Write the numbers in your story.

   ___   ___   ___

Use with text pages 35–36.

Homework Workbook Page 8

ENGLISH LEARNERS 2.1

Name _____ Date _____
English Learners 2.1

Addition Stories

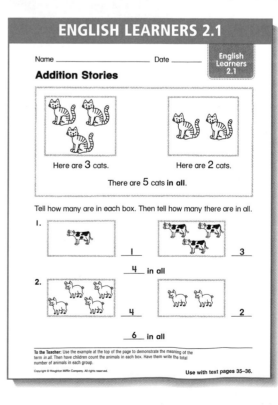

Here are 3 cats.   Here are 2 cats.
There are 5 cats **in all**.

Tell how many are in each box. Then tell how many there are in all.

1.   ___1___   ___3___
       ___4___ in all

2.   ___4___   ___2___
       ___6___ in all

To the Teacher: Use the example at the top of the page to demonstrate the meaning of the term *in all*. Then have children count the animals in each box. Have them write the total number of animals in each group.

Use with text pages 35–36.

TEACHING LESSON 2.1

LESSON ORGANIZER

Objective Model the concept of addition as increasing.

Resources Reteach, Practice, Enrichment, Problem Solving, Homework, English Learners, Transparencies, Math Center

Materials Counters, number cards 1–6 (Learning Tool (LT) 14), 2 number cubes labeled with 1–3 dots

Warm-Up Activity
Counting

iii Small Group	⏱ 5 minutes	Visual, Tactile

Materials: *counters, number cards 1–6 (LT 14)*

1. Review counting by giving each group 6 counters and number cards 1–6. Have children place cards face down in a pile. Ask one child to turn over the top card and take counters to show that number. Have another child check to see if the number of counters matches the number on the card.

2. **How can we check to see if the counters match the number on the card?** (Count the counters.)

3. Have other children match counters to different number cards.

Name_____

Activity: Addition Stories

Objective Model the concept of addition as increasing.

Work Together

Listen to the story.
Show the story with ⬭ .

1.

Children should place the correct number of counters to match the numbers in the story.

2. **Talk About It** How do you know if your answer is correct? **I can count all of the counters on the page.**

Chapter 2 Lesson 1

thirty-five **35**

1 Introduce

Discuss Modeling Addition

iiii Whole Group	⏱ 10–15 minutes	Visual, Tactile

Materials: *counters*

1. *Add 1 to 4.* Tell a story. **There are 4 children in the room.** Ask children to use counters to show 4. **One more child comes into the room.** Have them add 1 counter to the group. **How many children are now in the room?** (5) Have children count to find out how many in all.

2. **What happens when you put more counters in a group? Do you have more or fewer in all?** (more) Explain that when you put more into a group, you are adding.

2 Develop

Work Together

Give counters to children and have them complete **Exercise 1** as you say: **There are 3 children marching in the parade.** Have children place 3 counters on their page. Explain that each counter stands for one child in the parade. **The parade stops and 2 more children join in.** Have them place counters to show that 2 more join the parade. **How many children are in the parade in all?** (5) Children can draw to show their answer.

Encourage children to make up other stories about the children marching in the parade. Help children understand that each time they put more in a group, they are adding to find how many in all. Ask children to show other words that mean adding such as *joining* and *combining*.

Use the **Talk About It** question in **Exercise 2** to discuss how you can check if your answer is correct.

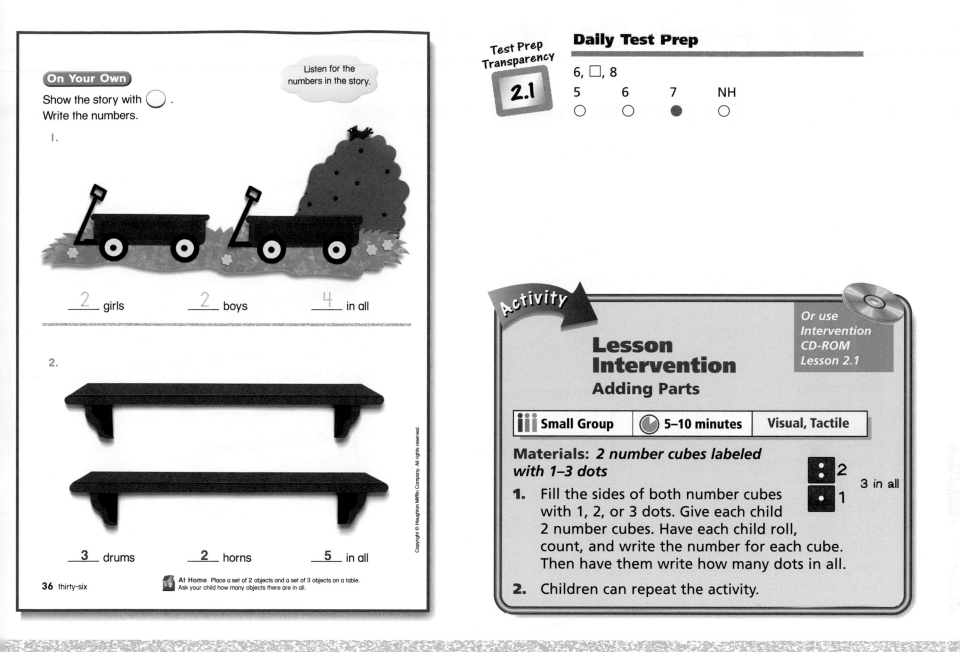

On Your Own

Listen for the numbers in the story.

Show the story with ◯.
Write the numbers.

1.

___2___ girls ___2___ boys ___4___ in all

2.

___3___ drums ___2___ horns ___5___ in all

36 thirty-six

At Home Place a set of 2 objects and a set of 3 objects on a table. Ask your child how many objects there are in all.

Daily Test Prep

6, ☐, 8

5 ◯ 6 ◯ 7 ● NH ◯

Activity

Lesson Intervention
Adding Parts

Or use Intervention CD-ROM Lesson 2.1

| iii Small Group | ◷ 5–10 minutes | Visual, Tactile |

Materials: *2 number cubes labeled with 1–3 dots*

⚁ 2
⚀ 1
3 in all

1. Fill the sides of both number cubes with 1, 2, or 3 dots. Give each child 2 number cubes. Have each child roll, count, and write the number for each cube. Then have them write how many dots in all.

2. Children can repeat the activity.

➌ Practice

On Your Own

Have children look at the wagons as you tell this story: **There are 2 girls in one wagon.** Have children place 2 counters on one of the wagons in the picture. Remind them that the counters are representing the girls. **Two boys climb in the other wagon.** Now have children put 2 counters in the other wagon. **How many children are there in the wagons?** Have children write the numbers to show how many girls, how many boys, and how many in all. (2 girls, 2 boys, 4 in all)

Continue with the next picture. **Jan put 3 drums on the top shelf.** Make sure children place 3 counters on the top shelf. **Then Jan put 2 horns on the bottom shelf. How many instruments are on the shelves?** (3 drums, 2 horns, 5 in all) Have children write the numbers.

Common Error

Trouble Following Directions

Children may show the same number for the second addend as the first. Provide practice with showing and counting aloud different numbers of counters.

➍ Assess and Close

When you add, what are you doing? (putting things together to find how many in all)

You have 3 pennies in your bank. You find 2 pennies and put them in your bank. Do you now have more pennies or fewer? (more) **How many do you have in all?** (5)

Keeping a Journal

Draw a picture of a story about dogs and cats. Write numbers to show how many in each group and how many in all.

CHAPTER 2   Lesson 1   36

Hands-On: Model Addition

Lesson 2.2

PLANNING THE LESSON

MATHEMATICS OBJECTIVE
Model the concept of addition as putting together.

Use Lesson Planner CD-ROM for Lesson 2.2.

Meeting North Carolina's Standards

1.03 Develop fluency with single-digit addition and corresponding differences using strategies such as modeling, composing and decomposing quantities, using doubles, and making tens.

Daily Routines

Calendar
After discussing today's day and date, ask children to find what the date will be in 2 days. Repeat the activity several times using different starting dates.

Sunday	Monday	Tuesday	Wednesday	Thursday	Friday	Saturday
			1	2	3	4
5	6	7	8	9	10	11
12	13	14	15	16	17	18
19	20	21	22	23	24	25
26	27	28	29	30	31	

Vocabulary
Demonstrate part-part-whole, emphasizing the language. There is a **part** with 2 and a **part** with 1. **Add** the parts together to find the **whole**.

Vocabulary Cards

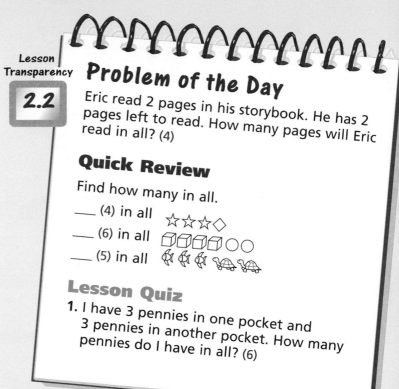

Lesson Transparency 2.2

Problem of the Day
Eric read 2 pages in his storybook. He has 2 pages left to read. How many pages will Eric read in all? (4)

Quick Review
Find how many in all.

— (4) in all ☆☆☆◇
— (6) in all ▱▱▱◯◯
— (5) in all 🐟🐟🐟🐢🐢

Lesson Quiz
1. I have 3 pennies in one pocket and 3 pennies in another pocket. How many pennies do I have in all? (6)

LEVELED PRACTICE

RETEACH 2.2

Name _____ Date _____ **Reteach 2.2**

Model Addition

You can show parts with counters.
You can add the parts to find the whole.

Workmat 3
Whole

Part	Part
●	◯◯

Use Workmat 3 and ● ◯.
Show the parts. Find the whole.

1. Whole **7**

Part	Part
3●	2◯

2. Whole **8**

Part	Part
1●	1◯

3. Whole **4**

Part	Part
1●	3◯

4. Whole **9**

Part	Part
2●	2◯

Use with text pages 37–38.

PRACTICE 2.2

Name _____ Date _____ **Practice 2.2**

Model Addition

Use Workmat 3 and two different colored counters.
Show the parts. Find the whole.

1. Whole **2**

Part	Part
1 ●	1 ◯

2. Whole **5**

Part	Part
3 ●	2 ◯

Test Prep

Fill in the ◯ for the correct answer. NH means Not Here.

3. Find the whole.

Whole

Part	Part
3 ●	1 ◯

3   5   4   NH
◯   ◯   ●   ◯

Explain how you used the counters to add.

<u>Possible response: I counted all the counters to</u>
<u>get the right answer.</u>

Use with text pages 37–38.

ENRICHMENT 2.2

Name _____ Date _____ **Enrichment 2.2**

How Many In All?

Make up addition stories.
Draw pictures to show the parts.
Write how many in each part.
Write how many in all.

Draw hats.

_____ _____ _____ hats

Draw gifts.

_____ _____ _____ gifts

Write About It How can you use counters to show how many in all? **Possible Answer:**

<u>I can use red and yellow counters to show the</u>

<u>parts. I can count the parts to show the whole.</u>

Use with text pages 37–38.

Practice Workbook Page 9

Reaching All Learners
Differentiated Instruction

English Learners

Worksheet 2.2 will introduce English-language learners to the relationship of parts to the whole. Children will need to understand this relationship in order to understand the concept of addition.

Special Needs
VISUAL, TACTILE

Materials: *number cube 1–3, counters*

- Fill the sides of the cube with 1, 2, and 3.
- Have child roll the cube. Place that many counters of one color on the table. Have the child write the number. Repeat with another roll.
- Now have child count all the counters and write how many in all.

Gifted and Talented
VISUAL, TACTILE

Materials: *2 number cubes 1–3, counters*

- Fill the sides of the cubes with 1, 2, and 3.
- Children work in pairs. Each child rolls two number cubes. Show the two parts with counters.
- Partners count their 2 parts to find the whole.
- The greater number scores 1 point. Play until one child has 5 points.

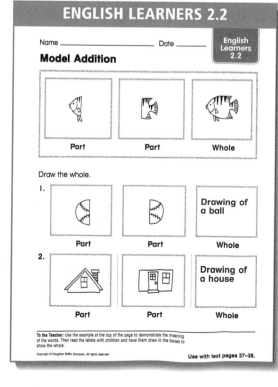

TECHNOLOGY

Spiral Review

You can prepare students for standardized tests with **customized** spiral review on key skills using the *Ways to Assess* CD-ROM.

Lesson Planner

You can use the **Lesson Planner CD-ROM** to create a report of the lessons and standards you have taught.

Education Place

Encourage students to visit **Education Place** at **eduplace.com/kids/mw/** for more student activities.

Manipulatives

Interactive Counters with several workmats are available on the *Ways to Success* CD-ROM.

Science Connection

Tell children that plants need soil, sunlight, and water. Have pairs plant bean seeds. Give each child 3 seeds, a paper cup, and soil. Have pairs tell how many seeds they planted in all.

MATH CENTER

Basic Skills Activity

Motivate children to build basic skills. Use this activity to address multiple learning styles using hands-on activities related to the skills of this lesson.

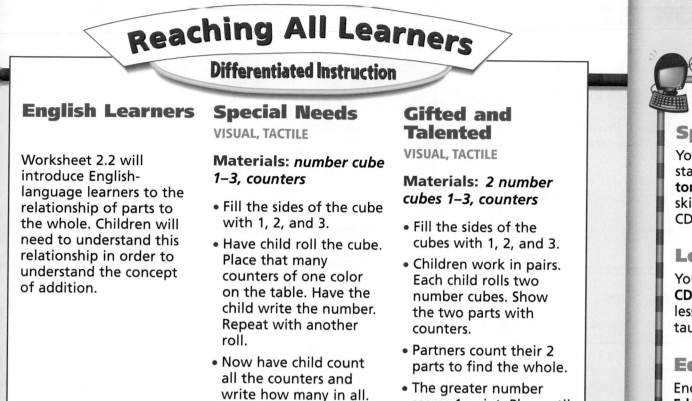

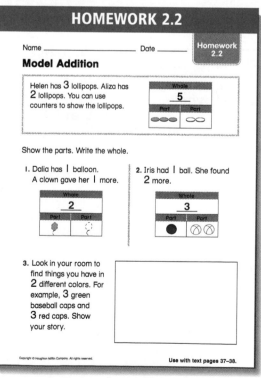

Homework Workbook Page 9

TEACHING LESSON 2.2

LESSON ORGANIZER

Objective Model the concept of addition as putting together.

Resources Reteach, Practice, Enrichment, Problem Solving, Homework, English Learners, Transparencies, Math Center

Materials Two-color counters, part-part-whole transparency, overhead two-color counters, Workmat 3, dried beans, paper cups

Activity

Prior Knowledge
Modeling Addition Stories

| iiii Small Group | ⏲ 5 minutes | Auditory, Kinesthetic |

Materials: *two-color counters (red and yellow)*

1. Review modeling addition stories. Give each group two-color counters. **Sara has 2 red ribbons. She buys 2 yellow ribbons. How many ribbons does she have in all?** (4)

2. Have children use counters to show the number of red ribbons, the number of yellow ribbons, and the number of ribbons in all. Children can check each other's work.

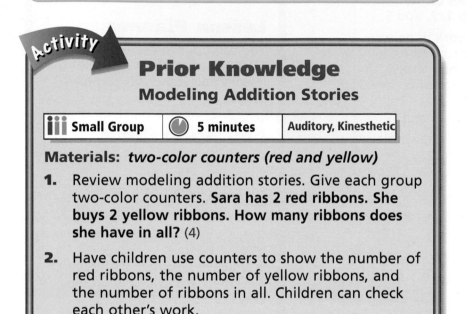

Name _____

Model Addition

🔘 MathTracks 1 / 5
Listen and Understand

You **add** the **parts** to find the **whole**.

Objective
Model the concept of addition as part-part-whole.

Vocabulary
add   part   whole

Guided Practice

Use Workmat 3 and ◯ .
Show the parts. Find the whole.

Think
I add 1 and 3
to find the whole.

TEST TIPS **Explain Your Thinking** What does the word **add** mean?
Possible answers: You put groups together; you find how many in all.

Chapter 2 Lesson 2   thirty-seven **37**

---

1 Introduce
Model Part-Part-Whole

| iiii Whole Group | ⏲ 10–15 minutes | Visual, Tactile |

Materials: *overhead two-color counters, part-part-whole transparency*

1. *Add 4 and 2.* Place 4 counters on one part of the mat and 2 counters on the other part.

2. Point to the first part. **How many counters are in this part?** (4) Record 4 in the space. Point to the other part. **How many counters are in this part?** (2) Write 2 in the space. Move the counters from both parts to the whole section. **How many counters in all?** (6) Write 6 in the whole section of the mat.

3. Point to each part on the mat and explain that each number is part of the whole. **You add when you put two parts together to find the whole.**

2 Develop

Guided Learning

Teaching Example Introduce the objective and vocabulary to the children. Guide them through the example to show that when you put a group of 3 counters and a group of 2 counters together, there are 5 counters in all. When you add 3 and 2 you get 5.

Guided Practice

Have children complete **Exercises 1–2** as you observe. Discuss children's responses to the Explain Your Thinking question.

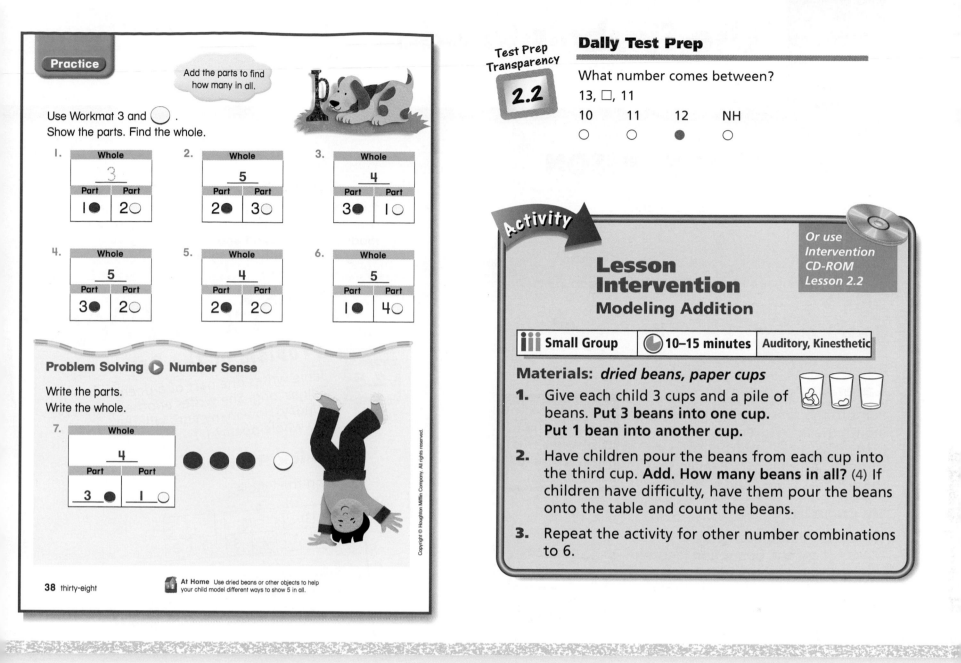

Practice

Add the parts to find how many in all.

Use Workmat 3 and ◯.
Show the parts. Find the whole.

1.
Whole	
3	
Part	Part
1●	2◯

2.
Whole	
5	
Part	Part
2●	3◯

3.
Whole	
4	
Part	Part
3●	1◯

4.
Whole	
5	
Part	Part
3●	2◯

5.
Whole	
4	
Part	Part
2●	2◯

6.
Whole	
5	
Part	Part
1●	4◯

Problem Solving ▶ Number Sense

Write the parts.
Write the whole.

7.
Whole	
4	
Part	Part
3 ●	1 ◯

● ● ● ◯

38 thirty-eight

At Home Use dried beans or other objects to help your child model different ways to show 5 in all.

Test Prep Transparency 2.2

Daily Test Prep

What number comes between?

13, ☐, 11

10   11   12   NH
◯   ◯   ●   ◯

Activity

Or use Intervention CD-ROM Lesson 2.2

Lesson Intervention
Modeling Addition

| 👥 Small Group | 🕐 10–15 minutes | Auditory, Kinesthetic |

Materials: *dried beans, paper cups*

1. Give each child 3 cups and a pile of beans. **Put 3 beans into one cup. Put 1 bean into another cup.**

2. Have children pour the beans from each cup into the third cup. **Add. How many beans in all?** (4) If children have difficulty, have them pour the beans onto the table and count the beans.

3. Repeat the activity for other number combinations to 6.

3 Practice

Independent Practice

Children complete **Exercises 1–6** independently.

Problem Solving

After children complete **Exercise 7**, call on volunteers to share their solutions.

Common Error

Miscounting Counters

Children may lose count when placing counters on a workmat. Encourage children to recount the counters in each part again to make sure the parts match the numbers in the exercise.

4 Assess and Close

There are 2 goldfish in one bag. There are 3 goldfish in another bag. You put all the goldfish into one fishbowl. How many goldfish are in the bowl in all? (5)

There are 2 big dishes on the table. There are 2 small dishes on the table. How many dishes in all? (4)

Keeping a Journal

Draw a picture to show a part with 3 and a part with 1. Write how many in all.

Use Symbols to Add

Lesson 2.3

PLANNING THE LESSON

Solve addition sentences using + and =.

Use Lesson Planner CD-ROM for Lesson 2.3.

Meeting North Carolina's Standards

1.03 Develop fluency with single-digit addition and corresponding differences using strategies such as modeling, composing and decomposing quantities, using doubles, and making tens.

Daily Routines

Calendar

Point to the first Sunday of the month. Have children count how many days there are from Sunday through Saturday? (7). Explain that there 5 days from Sunday to Friday.

Sunday	Monday	Tuesday	Wednesday	Thursday	Friday	Saturday
				1	2	3	4
5	6	7	8	9	10	11
12	13	14	15	16	17	18
19	20	21	22	23	24	25
26	27	28	29	30	31	

Vocabulary

Write the **addition sentence** 2 + 3 = 5 on the board and identify the **plus sign** and the **equal sign**. Explain that the number that tells how many in all is the **sum**.

Vocabulary Cards

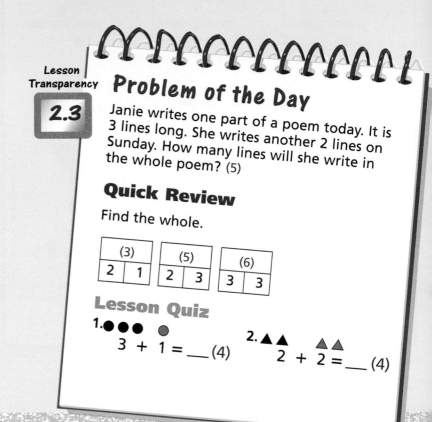

Lesson Transparency 2.3

Problem of the Day

Janie writes one part of a poem today. It is 3 lines long. She writes another 2 lines on Sunday. How many lines will she write in the whole poem? (5)

Quick Review

Find the whole.

(3)		(5)		(6)	
2	1	2	3	3	3

Lesson Quiz

1. ● ● ● ○
   3 + 1 = ___ (4)

2. ▲ ▲   ▲ ▲
   2 + 2 = ___ (4)

LEVELED PRACTICE

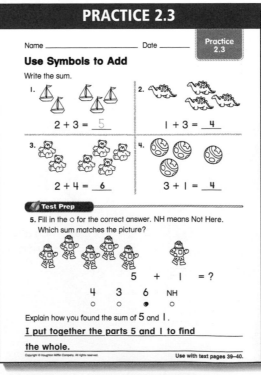

RETEACH 2.3

Name _____ Date _____ **Reteach 2.3**

Use Symbols to Add

You can use the plus sign and the equal sign to write an addition sentence.

3 + 3 = __3__ ← sum

plus sign   equal sign

Write the sum.

1. 2 + 1 = __3__
2. 1 + 3 = __4__
3. 4 + 2 = __6__
4. 3 + 2 = __5__

Copyright © Houghton Mifflin Company. All rights reserved.   Use with text pages 39–40.

PRACTICE 2.3

Name _____ Date _____ **Practice 2.3**

Use Symbols to Add

Write the sum.

1. 2 + 3 = __5__
2. 1 + 3 = __4__
3. 2 + 4 = __6__
4. 3 + 1 = __4__

Test Prep

5. Fill in the ○ for the correct answer. NH means Not Here. Which sum matches the picture?

   5 + 1 = ?

   4   3   6   NH
   ○   ○   ●   ○

Explain how you found the sum of 5 and 1.

I put together the parts 5 and 1 to find the whole.

Copyright © Houghton Mifflin Company. All rights reserved.   Use with text pages 39–40.

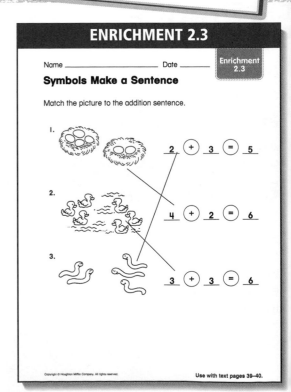

ENRICHMENT 2.3

Name _____ Date _____ **Enrichment 2.3**

Symbols Make a Sentence

Match the picture to the addition sentence.

1. 2 + 3 = 5
2. 4 + 2 = 6
3. 3 + 3 = 6

Copyright © Houghton Mifflin Company. All rights reserved.   Use with text pages 39–40.

Practice Workbook Page 10

39A   **CHAPTER 2   Lesson 3**

Reaching All Learners

Differentiated Instruction

English Learners

In order to read and write addition sentences with 1 and 2 signs, children will have to understand addition sentences using complete words. Use Worksheet 2.3 to develop understanding of the language used in addition sentences.

Special Needs
TACTILE, VISUAL

Materials: *cubes*

• Have the child build a train of 6 cubes. Model breaking the train into parts and describe. For example, a part with 4 and a part with 2. Put the parts together and say, 6 in all.

• Repeat for other combinations of six. Have the child write the parts and the whole.

Early Finishers
VISUAL, TACTILE

Materials: *number cards 1–5 (LT 14)*

• Children work in pairs. One child chooses 2 cards.

• The partner writes a number sentence using the two numbers and the symbols + and =. Partners find the sum.

• Children take turns writing numbers and addition sentences.

TECHNOLOGY

Spiral Review

Create **customized** spiral review worksheets for individual students using the *Ways to Assess* CD-ROM.

eBook

eMathBook allows students to review lessons and do homework without carrying their textbooks home.

Education Place

You can visit **Education Place** at **eduplace.com/math/mw/** for teacher support materials.

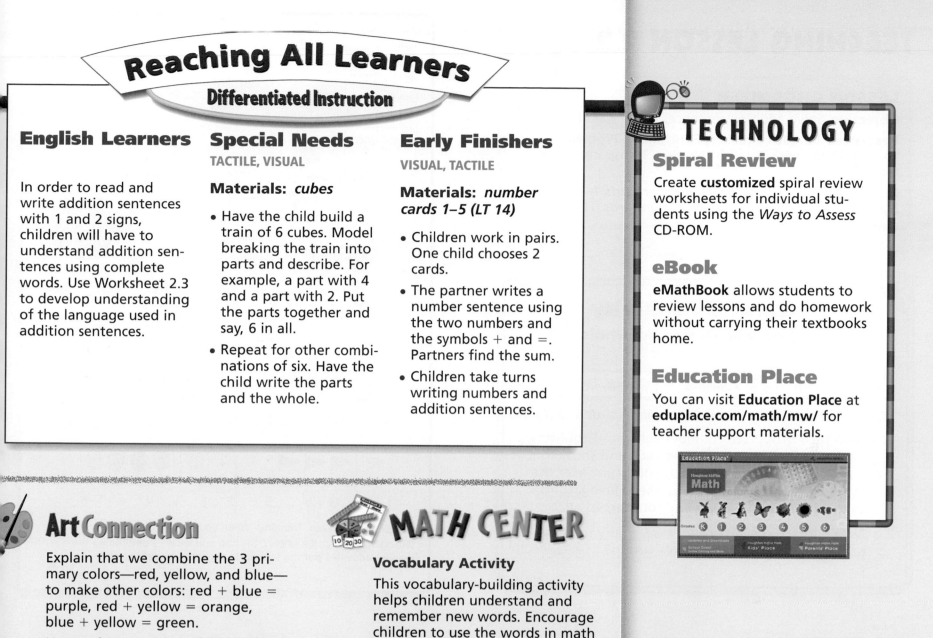

Art Connection

Explain that we combine the 3 primary colors—red, yellow, and blue—to make other colors: red + blue = purple, red + yellow = orange, blue + yellow = green.

Use markers to write addition sentences.

MATH CENTER

Vocabulary Activity

This vocabulary-building activity helps children understand and remember new words. Encourage children to use the words in math discussion.

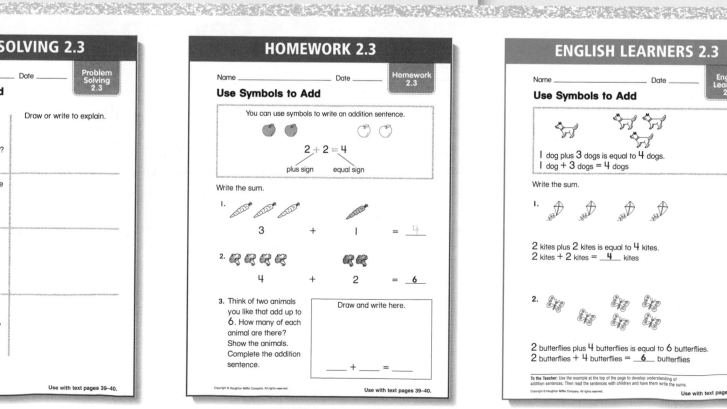

Homework Workbook Page 10

TEACHING LESSON 2.3

LESSON ORGANIZER

Objective Solve addition sentences using + and =.

Resources Reteach, Practice, Enrichment, Problem Solving, Homework, English Learners, Transparencies, Math Center

Materials *two-color counters, number cards 1–6 (LT 14), blank transparency, plus and equal sign cards (LT 15)*

Activity

Warm-Up Activity
Modeling Parts and Whole

👤👤👤 Small Group	⏱ 5 minutes	Visual, Tactile

Materials: *two-color counters, number cards 1–6 (LT 14)*

1. Give each group two number cards and counters. Have one child turn over one card and show that many counters. Have another child turn over the other card and show that number. Have a third child count to tell how many counters in all.

2. Ask children in each group, **How many in each part? How many in the whole group?** (Answers will vary.)

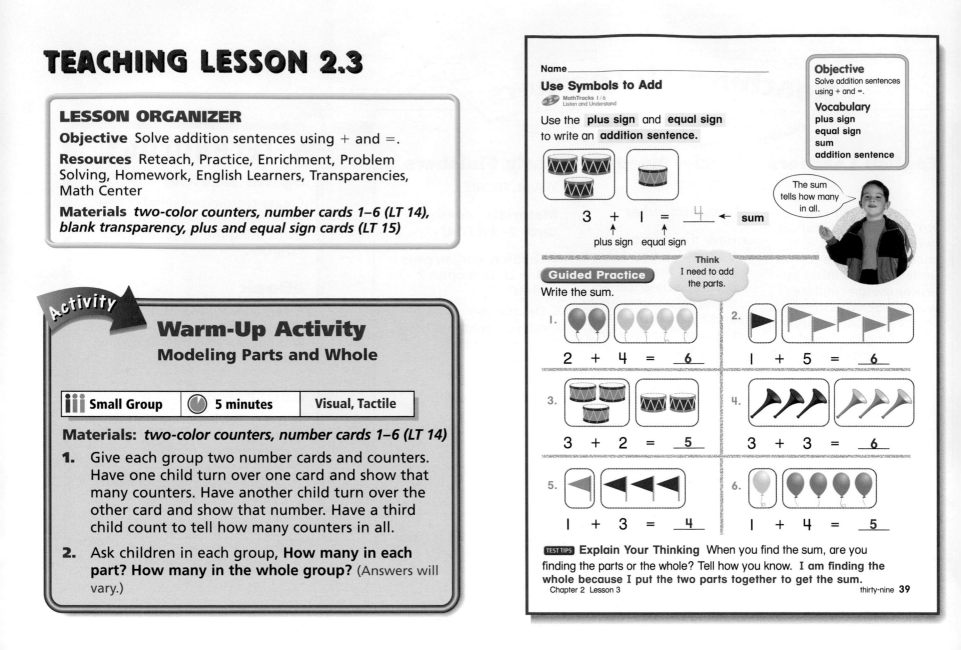

Name_____

Use Symbols to Add

🎵 MathTracks 1 / 6
Listen and Understand

Use the **plus sign** and **equal sign** to write an **addition sentence.**

$$3 + 1 = \underline{4} \leftarrow \text{sum}$$

↑ plus sign   ↑ equal sign

The sum tells how many in all.

Objective
Solve addition sentences using + and =.

Vocabulary
plus sign
equal sign
sum
addition sentence

Think I need to add the parts.

Guided Practice
Write the sum.

1. $2 + 4 = \underline{6}$

2. $1 + 5 = \underline{6}$

3. $3 + 2 = \underline{5}$

4. $3 + 3 = \underline{6}$

5. $1 + 3 = \underline{4}$

6. $1 + 4 = \underline{5}$

TEST TIPS **Explain Your Thinking** When you find the sum, are you finding the parts or the whole? Tell how you know. **I am finding the whole because I put the two parts together to get the sum.**

Chapter 2 Lesson 3   thirty-nine **39**

---

1 Introduce
Model Addition with Symbols

👤👤👤👤 Whole Group	⏱ 5–10 minutes	Visual, Auditory

Materials: *blank transparency*

1. Draw 2 triangles. Then draw 1 diamond. **How many triangles?** (2) **How many diamonds?** (1) **How many shapes in all?** (3)

2. Under the drawings, write the addition sentence $2 + 1 = 3$. Point to each number and symbol as you say **2 plus 1 equals 3**. Identify 3 as the sum.

3. Have children recite with you, 2 plus 1 equals 3. Ask a volunteer to tell the sum.

2 Develop

Guided Learning

Teaching Example Read the objective and vocabulary with children. Guide them through the example to show how to use the plus and equal signs to read an addition sentence.

Guided Practice

Have children complete **Exercises 1–6** as you observe. Discuss the children's responses to the Explain Your Thinking questions, reminding them that we combine the parts to find the whole, or sum.

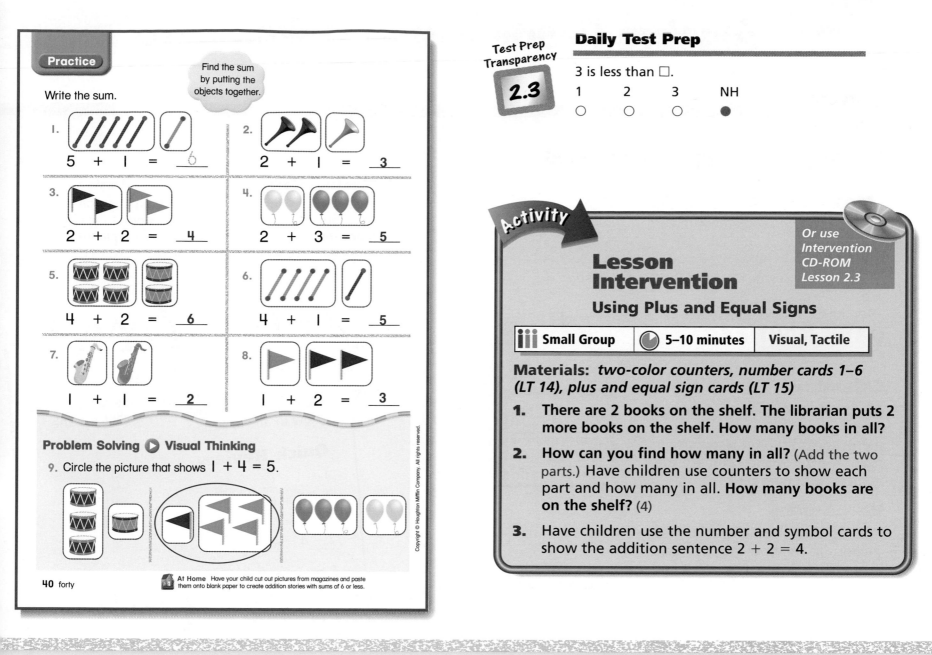

Practice

Write the sum.

Find the sum by putting the objects together.

1. $5 + 1 = \underline{6}$

2. $2 + 1 = \underline{3}$

3. $2 + 2 = \underline{4}$

4. $2 + 3 = \underline{5}$

5. $4 + 2 = \underline{6}$

6. $4 + 1 = \underline{5}$

7. $1 + 1 = \underline{2}$

8. $1 + 2 = \underline{3}$

Problem Solving ▶ Visual Thinking

9. Circle the picture that shows $1 + 4 = 5$.

40 forty

At Home Have your child cut out pictures from magazines and paste them onto blank paper to create addition stories with sums of 6 or less.

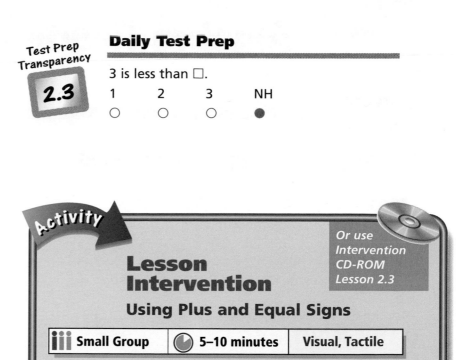

Daily Test Prep

3 is less than □.

1   2   3   NH
○   ○   ○   ●

Activity

Or use Intervention CD-ROM Lesson 2.3

Lesson Intervention

Using Plus and Equal Signs

| 👥 Small Group | 🕐 5–10 minutes | Visual, Tactile |

Materials: *two-color counters, number cards 1–6 (LT 14), plus and equal sign cards (LT 15)*

1. There are 2 books on the shelf. The librarian puts 2 more books on the shelf. How many books in all?

2. **How can you find how many in all?** (Add the two parts.) Have children use counters to show each part and how many in all. **How many books are on the shelf?** (4)

3. Have children use the number and symbol cards to show the addition sentence $2 + 2 = 4$.

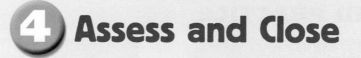

3 Practice

Independent Practice

Children complete **Exercises 1–8** independently.

Problem Solving

After children complete **Exercise 9**, call on volunteers to share their solutions.

Common Error

Counting Pictured Objects More Than Once
Suggest that children draw a line through each object as they count it.

4 Assess and Close

What is the sum of 3 and 2? (5)

Use the words *plus* **and** *equals* **to say 3 and 1 is 4.** (3 plus 1 equals 4)

Keeping a Journal

Write an addition sentence for the numbers 4 and 2. Remember to use the plus and equal signs.

Algebra Readiness: Add With Zero

PLANNING THE LESSON

MATHEMATICS OBJECTIVE
Solve addition problems with zero.

Use Lesson Planner CD-ROM for Lesson 2.4.

Meeting North Carolina's Standards

1.03 Develop fluency with single-digit addition and corresponding differences using strategies such as modeling, composing and decomposing quantities, using doubles, and making tens.

Daily Routines

Calendar
Ask children to guess how many dates in the month have zeros in them. Record their guesses. Then, count the zeros and compare the number to their guesses.

Sunday	Monday	Tuesday	Wednesday	Thursday	Friday	Saturday
			1	2	3	4
5	6	7	8	9	10	11
12	13	14	15	16	17	18
19	20	21	22	23	24	25
26	27	28	29	30	31	

Vocabulary
Hold up your hand with five fingers spread out. Ask children to tell how many fingers they see. (5) Then make a fist and ask how many fingers children see. (none) Tell children that we use the word **zero** to mean none.

Vocabulary Cards

Lesson Transparency 2.4

Problem of the Day
Erin grew 3 inches last year. She grew 2 inches this year. How many inches did she grow in all? (5 inches)

Quick Review
$1 + 1 = \underline{(2)}$
$2 + 3 = \underline{(5)}$
$3 + 1 = \underline{(4)}$
$2 + 4 = \underline{(6)}$

Lesson Quiz
1. $5 + 0 = \underline{(5)}$
2. $3 + 2 = \underline{(5)}$
3. $0 + 6 = \underline{(6)}$
4. $3 + 0 = \underline{(3)}$

LEVELED PRACTICE

RETEACH 2.4

Name _____ Date _____ **Reteach 2.4**

Add With Zero

When you add zero and a number, the sum is the number.

There are 3 frogs.   There are no frogs added.

$$\underline{3} + \underline{0} = \underline{3}$$

There are still 3 frogs.

Complete the addition sentence.

1. $\underline{2} + \underline{0} = 2$
2. $\underline{0} + \underline{4} = 4$
3. $\underline{5} + \underline{0} = 5$
4. $\underline{0} + \underline{3} = 3$

Use with text pages 41–42.

PRACTICE 2.4

Name _____ Date _____ **Practice 2.4**

Add With Zero

Write the sum.

1. $2 + 0 = \underline{2}$
2. $2 + 4 = \underline{6}$
3. $1 + 5 = \underline{6}$
4. $2 + 3 = \underline{5}$
5. $0 + 1 = \underline{1}$
6. $5 + 0 = \underline{5}$
7. $0 + 3 = \underline{3}$
8. $4 + 0 = \underline{4}$
9. $1 + 4 = \underline{5}$
10. $3 + 3 = \underline{6}$
11. $2 + 4 = \underline{6}$
12. $6 + 0 = \underline{6}$

Test Prep

Fill in the ○ for the correct answer. NH means Not Here.

13. $0 + 5 = ?$

    0   3   5   NH
    ○   ○   ●   ○

Explain what happened when you added 0 and 5.

I got the sum of 5 because 0 stands for nothing to add.

Use with text pages 41–42.

ENRICHMENT 2.4

Name _____ Date _____ **Enrichment 2.4**

Stories With Zero

Draw pictures to show how many of each flower or leaf you want.
Write the number and add zero.
Write the sum.

1. $\underline{2} + 0 = \underline{2}$
2. $\underline{1} + 0 = \underline{1}$
3. $0 + \underline{3} = \underline{3}$
4. $\underline{4} + 0 = \underline{4}$
5. $\underline{1} + 0 = \underline{1}$
6. $0 + \underline{1} = \underline{1}$

Write About It What happens to a number when you add zero to it?

Possible answer: Nothing happens. The number stays the same.

Use with text pages 41–42.

Practice Workbook Page 11

Reaching All Learners
Differentiated Instruction

English Learners

English-language learners will need to understand the word *none* in order to solve problems that involve adding zero. Use Worksheet 2.4 to develop understanding of the related words *no* and *none*.

Inclusion
KINESTHETIC, AUDITORY

Materials: *clay, number cards 1–5 (LT 14)*

- Have the child make plus and equal signs with clay.
- Say addition stories with sums to 6. Have the child model the addition with number cards and clay signs.
- Have the child point to each part as you read the number sentence aloud.

Gifted and Talented
VISUAL, TACTILE

Materials: *number cards 0–3 (LT 14) (4 sets)*

- Have partners shuffle the number cards and place face down. One child turns over 2 cards. The other child writes a number sentence using the 2 numbers and symbols.
- Partners switch roles.
- Have children continue until all cards have been played.

Literature Connection

Refer to the story, *Fish Eyes* by Lois Ehlert. Write the phrases "four striped fish" and "five spotted fish" on the board. Have children write addition sentences with sums of 4 and 5 to describe groups of 4 striped fish and 5 spotted fish.

MATH CENTER

Real-Life Activity

Help children understand the usefulness of mathematics. This activity makes math come alive by connecting the lesson skills to a real-life situation.

TECHNOLOGY

Spiral Review

Using the *Ways to Assess* CD-ROM, you can create **customized** spiral review worksheets covering any lessons you choose.

Lesson Planner

You can customize your teaching plan or meet your curriculum requirements with the **Lesson Planner CD-ROM.**

Education Place

Recommend that parents visit **Education Place** at eduplace.com/parents/mw/ for parent support activities.

PROBLEM SOLVING 2.4

Name _____ Date _____   Problem Solving 2.4

Add With Zero

Write the sum.

Draw or write to explain.

1. There are 6 apples in one basket. There are no apples in the other basket. How many apples are there in all?
   __6__ in all

2. There were 4 worms in the can. No more worms were added. How many worms were there in all?
   __4__ in all

3. There were no flowers in the vase. Marco added 3 flowers. How many flowers were there in all?
   __3__ in all

4. Kip has 5 pennies in his bank. Kim has no pennies in her bank. How many pennies do they have in all?
   __5__ in all

Use with text pages 41–42.

HOMEWORK 2.4

Name _____ Date _____   Homework 2.4

Add With Zero

When you add zero and a number, you get the number.

$$3 + 0 = 3$$

Write the sum.

1. $2 + 0 = \underline{2}$ 2. $0 + 1 = \underline{1}$
3. $0 + 7 = \underline{7}$ 4. $0 + 4 = \underline{4}$
5. $6 + 0 = \underline{6}$ 6. $5 + 0 = \underline{5}$
7. $0 + 3 = \underline{3}$ 8. $0 + 0 = \underline{0}$
9. $0 + 8 = \underline{8}$ 10. $0 + 2 = \underline{2}$

11. Tell a story in which nothing is added to a certain number of things. Draw pictures to show your story. Write an addition sentence to show the sum.

$0 + \underline{} = \underline{}$

Use with text pages 41–42.

ENGLISH LEARNERS 2.4

Name _____ Date _____   English Learners 2.4

Add With Zero

4 ants
four

no ants
none

Circle the correct answer.

1. (no mittens)   3 mittens

2. (2 mittens)   none

3. none   (3 umbrellas)

4. (no umbrellas)   2 umbrellas

To the Teacher: Use the examples at the top of the page to help children understand the meaning of the word *none*. Then read the labels with children and have them write the correct word to tell about the pictures.

Use with text pages 41–43.

Homework Workbook Page 11

TEACHING LESSON 2.4

LESSON ORGANIZER

Objective Solve addition problems with zero.

Resources Reteach, Practice, Enrichment, Problem Solving, Homework, English Learners, Transparencies, Math Center

Materials Two-color counters, number cards 1–5 (LT 14), + and = cards (LT 15), number cube with 0–5, teacher-made direction cards, paper bag

Activity

Warm-Up Activity
Modeling Using Symbols

👥 Small Group	🕐 5 minutes	Auditory, Tactile

Materials: *two-color counters, number cards 1–5 (LT 14), + and = cards (LT 15)*

1. Distribute counters, number cards, and sign cards to each group. Say **I saw 5 sailboats and 1 motor boat. How many boats did I see in all?** Have children show the addition story with counters.

2. **Use the number cards and the addition symbols. Make a number sentence for the story.** (5 + 1 = 6) Repeat with other addition stories.

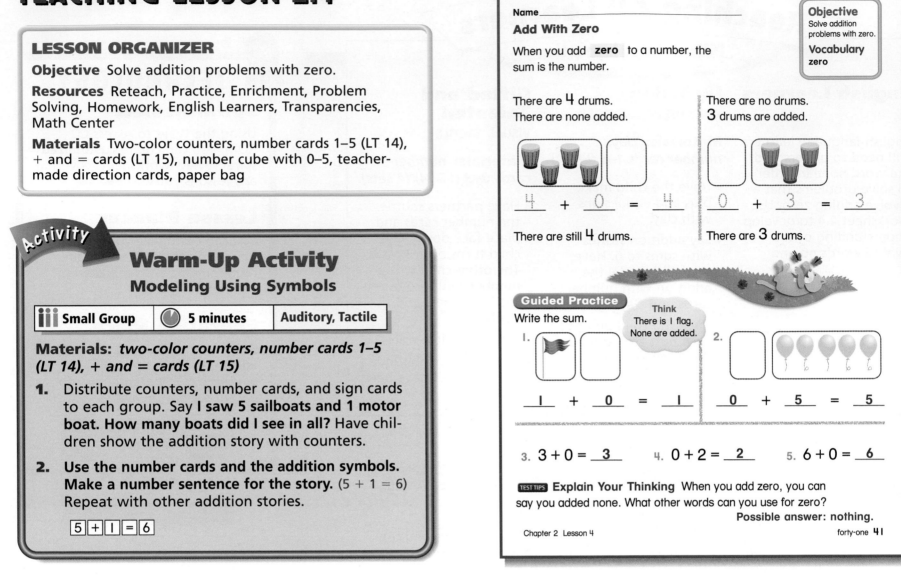

Add With Zero

When you add **zero** to a number, the sum is the number.

There are 4 drums.
There are none added.

There are no drums.
3 drums are added.

$$\underline{4} + \underline{0} = \underline{4}$$

$$\underline{0} + \underline{3} = \underline{3}$$

There are still 4 drums.

There are 3 drums.

Guided Practice

Write the sum.

Think
There is 1 flag.
None are added.

1. $$\underline{1} + \underline{0} = \underline{1}$$

2. $$\underline{0} + \underline{5} = \underline{5}$$

3. $3 + 0 = \underline{3}$ 4. $0 + 2 = \underline{2}$ 5. $6 + 0 = \underline{6}$

TEST TIPS Explain Your Thinking When you add zero, you can say you added none. What other words can you use for zero?

Possible answer: nothing.

---

① Introduce

Activity

Model Addition with Zero

👥 Whole Group	🕐 5–10 minutes	Auditory, Tactile

Materials: *two-color counters*

1. **Add 4 + 0.** Have children model this story with counters. **4 kittens are in a basket.** Explain that counters are used to show the kittens. **No more kittens got in the basket. How many kittens are there in all?** (4)

2. Write the addition sentence 4 + 0 = 4 on the board. Have children recite the addition sentence with you. **4 plus 0 equals 4.**

3. Point out that zero stands for none or no more.

② Develop

Guided Learning

Teaching Example Introduce the objective and vocabulary to the children. Guide them through the example to show that there are 4 drums and none are added, so there are still 4 drums. If there are no drums and 3 are added, there are 3 drums.

Guided Practice

Have children complete **Exercises 1–5** as you observe. Discuss children's responses to the Explain Your Thinking question with the class.

Practice

Write the sum.

1. 3 + 0 = _3_

2. 0 + 2 = _2_

3. 4 + 0 = _4_   4. 2 + 3 = _5_   5. 0 + 4 = _4_

6. 2 + 1 = _3_   7. 5 + 0 = _5_   8. 3 + 3 = _6_

9. 2 + 4 = _6_   10. 0 + 6 = _6_   11. 1 + 4 = _5_

12. 0 + 1 = _1_   13. 2 + 2 = _4_   14. 5 + 1 = _6_

15. 3 + 1 = _4_   16. 4 + 2 = _6_   17. 0 + 0 = _0_

18. 1 + 1 = _2_   19. 2 + 0 = _2_   20. 3 + 2 = _5_

Reading Math ▶ Vocabulary

Write the addition sentence.

21. Four plus two equals six.   _4_ (+) _2_ (=) _6_

22. Three plus zero equals three.   _3_ (+) _0_ (=) _3_

42 forty-two

At Home Ask your child to explain what happens when you add zero to a number.

Go on

Daily Test Prep

5 is greater than □.

4   5   8   NH

●   ○   ○   ○

Activity

Lesson Intervention

Modeling Adding with Zero

Or use Intervention CD-ROM Lesson 2.4

| Small Group | 5–10 minutes | Visual, Auditory |

Materials: *number cube with numbers 0–5, counters, teacher-made direction cards, paper bag*

1. Provide each group with a number cube, counters, and direction cards *Add 1 more. Add no more.* Place the cards in a paper bag. Have one child roll the number cube, make a group of counters, and choose a card from the bag. The child follows the direction on the card and tells the sum. Another child checks the answer.

2. Children take turns rolling the cube, choosing a direction card, and finding how many in all.

3. **Is adding no more the same as adding zero?** (yes)

---

3 Practice

Independent Practice

Children complete **Exercises 1–20** independently.

Reading Math

After children complete **Exercises 21 and 22,** allow time for them to share their addition sentences.

Common Error

Mistaking Zero as the Sum Instead of an Addend.

Have children use counters to show each group and count to find the sum.

---

4 Assess and Close

Is 6 the sum of six and zero? (yes)

When you add zero to a number, what is the sum? (the number)

Keeping a Journal

Draw an addition story to show 4 and 0. Then write an addition sentence for your story.

ACHIEVING Mathematical Proficiency

Learning Basic Facts

Educators know that children use a variety of methods to solve single-digit addition problems. Recent research points out that **children move through a progression of different methods as they learn to add single-digit numbers.**

Initially, children count objects in sets to determine how many in all. Specifically, they learn to use the part-part-whole method. They count out objects for the first part or addend, count out objects for the second part or addend, and then count the whole, or all of the objects.

In this chapter, **children use a part-part-whole workmat and counters to find the sum of single-digit numbers. They learn that the "whole" tells how many in all.**

Becoming proficient in this method of adding forms a basis for children's progression to more conceptual methods, such as counting on to add.

Writing Math: Create and Solve

Discuss the picture for **Exercise 1** to be sure children understand that it shows a group of children joining another group. After children write their story, they write an addition sentence for **Exercise 2**. Invite several children to share their addition story.

Explain that for **Exercises 3 and 4,** children will write an addition story to match the number sentence. Then they draw a picture to show the story. Allow time for children to share their pictures and stories as the group checks their sum.

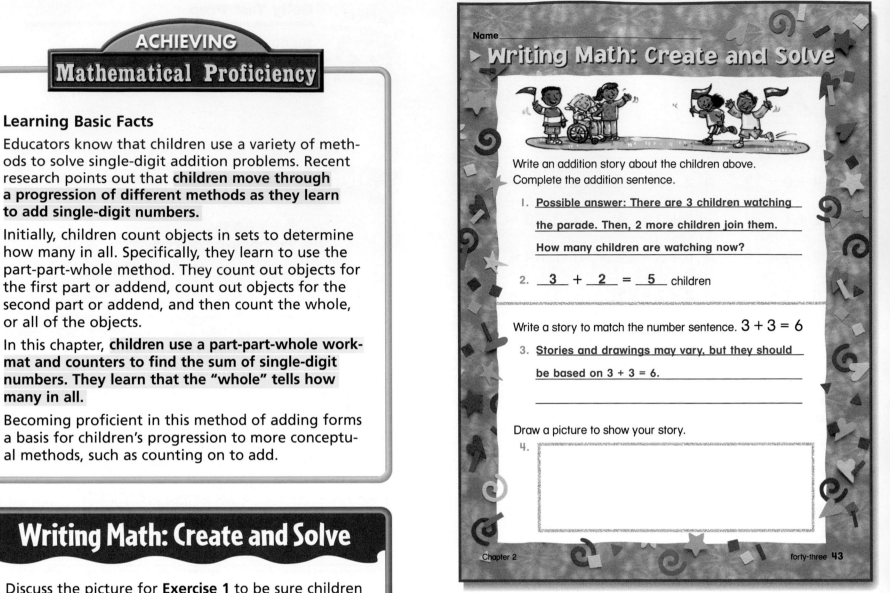

Name _____

Writing Math: Create and Solve

Write an addition story about the children above. Complete the addition sentence.

1. <u>Possible answer: There are 3 children watching</u> <u>the parade. Then, 2 more children join them.</u> <u>How many children are watching now?</u>

2. __3__ + __2__ = __5__ children

Write a story to match the number sentence. $3 + 3 = 6$

3. <u>Stories and drawings may vary, but they should</u> <u>be based on 3 + 3 = 6.</u>

_____

Draw a picture to show your story.

4. [empty box]

Quick Check

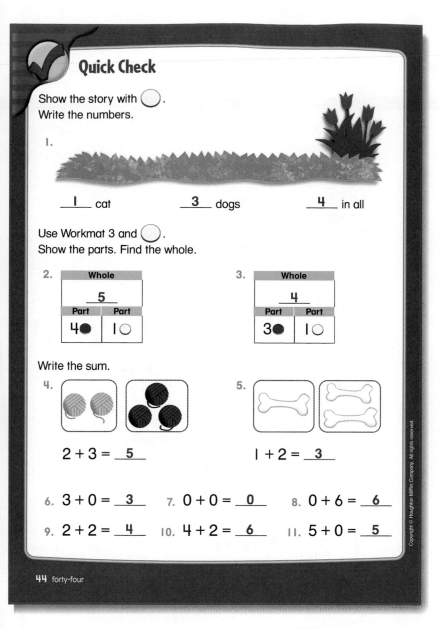

Show the story with ◯.
Write the numbers.

1.

___1___ cat   ___3___ dogs   ___4___ in all

Use Workmat 3 and ◯.
Show the parts. Find the whole.

2.

Whole
5

Part	Part
4●	1○

3.

Whole
4

Part	Part
3●	1○

Write the sum.

4. $2 + 3 = \underline{\ 5\ }$

5. $1 + 2 = \underline{\ 3\ }$

6. $3 + 0 = \underline{\ 3\ }$ 7. $0 + 0 = \underline{\ 0\ }$ 8. $0 + 6 = \underline{\ 6\ }$

9. $2 + 2 = \underline{\ 4\ }$ 10. $4 + 2 = \underline{\ 6\ }$ 11. $5 + 0 = \underline{\ 5\ }$

Quick Check

Have children complete the Quick Check exercises independently to assess their understanding of concepts and skills taught in **Lessons 1–4**.

Read the following story for Item 1:

There is 1 cat playing. Children place 1 counter on the grass. **Three dogs join the cats to play.** Children put 3 counters on the grass. **How many animals are there in all?** (4) Children write the numbers on the lines to show how many cats, how many dogs, and how many pets in all.

Item	Lesson	Error Analysis	Intervention
1	2.1	Children may not listen for the second number, and repeat the first.	Reteach Resource 2.1 *Ways to Success* 2.1
2–3	2.2	Children may lose count when placing counters on a workmat.	Reteach Resource 2.2 *Ways to Success* 2.2
4–5	2.3	Children may count pictured objects more than once.	Reteach Resource 2.3 *Ways to Success* 2.3
6–11	2.4	Children may misunderstand the rule for adding zero.	Reteach Resource 2.4 *Ways to Success* 2.4

Hands-On: Add in Any Order

PLANNING THE LESSON

MATHEMATICS OBJECTIVE
Understand the order property of addition.

Use Lesson Planner CD-ROM for Lesson 2.5.

Daily Routines

Calendar
Direct children's attention to today's date. Then ask children to add 0 to the number. Continue with different dates. Ask children to tell what all the sums have in common. (All the sums are the same as the beginning number.)

Sunday	Monday	Tuesday	Wednesday	Thursday	Friday	Saturday
			1	2	3	4
5	6	7	8	9	10	11
12	13	14	15	16	17	18
19	20	21	22	23	24	25
26	27	28	29	30	31	

Vocabulary
Write 1 + 2 = 3 and 2 + 1 = 3 on the board. Point to each **addend** and identify it as such. Then call children's attention to the order of the addends.

Vocabulary Cards

Meeting North Carolina's Standards
1.03 Develop fluency with single-digit addition and corresponding differences using strategies such as modeling, composing and decomposing quantities, using doubles, and making tens.

Lesson Transparency 2.5

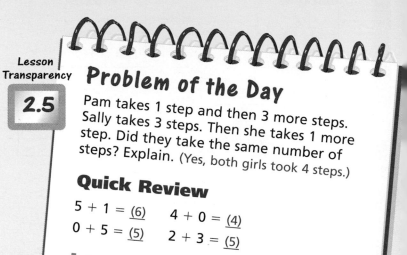

Problem of the Day
Pam takes 1 step and then 3 more steps. Sally takes 3 steps. Then she takes 1 more step. Did they take the same number of steps? Explain. (Yes, both girls took 4 steps.)

Quick Review
$5 + 1 = \underline{(6)}$ $4 + 0 = \underline{(4)}$
$0 + 5 = \underline{(5)}$ $2 + 3 = \underline{(5)}$

Lesson Quiz
Eric bought 3 red balloons and 2 blue balloons. Ted bought 2 blue balloons and 3 red balloons. How many balloons did each boy buy? (5 balloons)

LEVELED PRACTICE

RETEACH 2.5

Name _____ Date _____   Reteach 2.5

Add in Any Order
You can change the order of the addends and get the same sum.

Here are two cube trains.   Here is what happens if you turn the sentence around.

$\underline{4} + \underline{1} = \underline{5}$ $\underline{1} + \underline{4} = \underline{5}$

Use cubes in two colors. **Answers will vary.**
Make the train.
Complete the two addition sentences for the train.

1. Make a **3** train.	2. Make a **4** train.
___ + ___ = ___	___ + ___ = ___
___ + ___ = ___	___ + ___ = ___
3. Make a **6** train.	4. Make a **5** train.
___ + ___ = ___	___ + ___ = ___
___ + ___ = ___	___ + ___ = ___

Use with text pages 45–46.

PRACTICE 2.5

Name _____ Date _____   Practice 2.5

Add in Any Order
Use cubes in two colors. Make the train.
Complete the two addition sentences for the train.

1. Make a **5** train.

$\underline{2} + \underline{3} = \underline{5}$
$\underline{3} + \underline{2} = \underline{5}$

2. Make a **6** train.

$\underline{4} + \underline{2} = \underline{6}$
$\underline{2} + \underline{4} = \underline{6}$

Add. Then change the order and complete a new addition sentence.

3. $5 + 1 = \underline{6}$
   $\underline{1} + \underline{5} = \underline{6}$

4. $4 + 1 = \underline{5}$
   $\underline{1} + \underline{4} = \underline{5}$

5. $2 + 0 = \underline{2}$
   $\underline{0} + \underline{2} = \underline{2}$

6. $2 + 3 = \underline{5}$
   $\underline{3} + \underline{2} = \underline{5}$

Test Prep
Fill in the ○ for the correct answer. NH means Not Here.

7. $2 + 1 = 3$ $1 + 2 = ?$

   3 ●   0 ○   2 ○   NH ○

Use with text pages 45–46.

ENRICHMENT 2.5

Name _____ Date _____   Enrichment 2.5

Change the Order
Write the numbers in each box on the lines.
Write the sum.
Then, write the addition sentence another way.

1.

$\underline{2} + \underline{3} = \underline{5}$
I can also write the sentence as:
$\underline{3} + \underline{2} = \underline{5}$

2.

$\underline{6} + \underline{0} = \underline{6}$
I can also write the sentence as:
$\underline{0} + \underline{6} = \underline{6}$

3.

$\underline{4} + \underline{2} = \underline{6}$
I can also write the sentence as:
$\underline{2} + \underline{4} = \underline{6}$

4.

$\underline{6} + \underline{1} = \underline{7}$
I can also write the sentence as:
$\underline{1} + \underline{6} = \underline{7}$

Write About It If you add the same numbers in a different order, does the sum change? Why?

<u>Possible answer: No, because you are adding the</u>
<u>same numbers.</u>

Use with text pages 45–46.

Practice Workbook Page 12

Reaching All Learners
Differentiated Instruction

English Learners

Children will need to understand the concept of *order* to understand the order property of addition. Use Worksheet 2.5 to help children develop understanding of this concept.

Special Needs
TACTILE, AUDITORY

Materials: *counters, number cards 0–5 (LT 14), paper bag*

Place number cards face down. Have one child turn over the top card and take that many counters out of the bag. Record the number. Have the partner take the remaining counters out of the bag and record that number. Children write the number sentence using symbols.

Early Finishers
VISUAL, KINESTHETIC

Children work in pairs. Have one child put up fingers on both hands to make a sum of 6 or less. Have the partner write two addition sentences using the fingers on each hand as addends. Children check the addition sentences and switch roles.

TECHNOLOGY

Spiral Review

To reinforce skills on lessons taught earlier, create **customized** spiral review worksheets using the *Ways to Assess* CD-ROM.

Manipulatives

Interactive Connecting Cubes with several workmats are available on the *Ways to Success* CD-ROM.

Education Place

Encourage students to visit **Education Place** at eduplace.com/kids/mw/ for more student activities.

Literature Connection

Refer to the Literature selection *Fish Eyes* by Lois Ehlert. Point out that there are 2 jumping fish and 3 smiling fish. Ask children to write an addition sentence to show how many fish in all. Then have them change the order and write a new addition sentence.

MATH CENTER

Basic Skills Activity

Motivate children to build basic skills. Use this activity to address multiple learning styles using hands-on activities related to the skills of this lesson.

PROBLEM SOLVING 2.5

Name _____ Date _____
Problem Solving 2.5

Add in Any Order

Add. Then change the order and complete a new addition sentence. Use cubes if you wish.

Cindy has 1 blue marble and 4 red marbles. Nan has 4 blue marbles and 1 red marble. Do the girls have the same number of marbles?
___Yes___

$1 + 4 = 5$
$\underline{4} + \underline{1} = 5$

Draw or write to explain.

1. Brett has 3 green apples and 2 red apples. Alice has 2 green apples and 2 red apples. Do they have the same number of apples? __No__

$3 + 2 = \underline{5}$
$\underline{2} + \underline{2} = \underline{4}$

2. Jorja picked 5 red flowers and 1 yellow flower. Dina picked 1 red flower and 5 yellow flowers. Did the children pick the same number of flowers? __Yes__

$5 + 1 = \underline{6}$
$\underline{1} + \underline{5} = \underline{6}$

Use with text pages 45–46.

HOMEWORK 2.5

Name _____ Date _____
Homework 2.5

Add in Any Order

Look at the balloons. How many ways can you write an addition sentence about the balloons?

$3 + 2 = 5$ $2 + 3 = 5$

You can change the order of the addends and get the same sum.

Add. Write a new addition sentence for the one that is shown.

1. $2 + 1 = 3$
$\underline{1} + \underline{2} = \underline{3}$

2. $4 + 2 = 6$
$\underline{2} + \underline{4} = \underline{6}$

3. $1 + 4 = 5$
$\underline{4} + \underline{1} = \underline{5}$

4. $0 + 6 = 6$
$\underline{6} + \underline{0} = \underline{6}$

5. $1 + 5 = 6$
$\underline{5} + \underline{1} = \underline{6}$

6. $3 + 2 = 5$
$\underline{2} + \underline{3} = \underline{5}$

7. Amy has two pens. John gives her five more pens. Write two addition sentences to show how many pens Amy has.

Draw or write to explain.

Use with text pages 45–46.

Homework Workbook Page 12

ENGLISH LEARNERS 2.5

Name _____ Date _____
English Learners 2.5

Add in Any Order

The children are lined up in **order**.

Draw these in order.

1.
Drawing of boxes in order

2.
Drawing of balls in order

To the Teacher: Use the example at the top of the page to demonstrate the concept of *order*. Then have children draw the objects in order.

Use with text pages 45–46.

TEACHING LESSON 2.5

LESSON ORGANIZER

Objective Understand the order property of addition.

Resources Reteach, Practice, Enrichment, Problem Solving, Homework, English Learners, Transparencies, Math Center

Materials cubes in two colors, number cards 1–3 (LT 14), grid paper (LT 29)

Activity

Warm-Up Activity
Modeling Addition Sentences

| 👤 Small Group | ⏱ 5 minutes | Visual, Tactile |

Materials: *cubes, number cards 1–3 (LT 14)*

1. Provide each group with cubes and number cards. Tell children to place the cards face down in a pile. Have one child in each group pick a card and say the number. Have another child make a train of that many cubes. Ask another child to pick a card and use cubes of a second color to make a train. Have children put the two trains together.

2. Ask, **What addition sentence do the cubes show?** Have children write the sentence. (Answers will vary.)

3. Return the cards to the pile and continue.

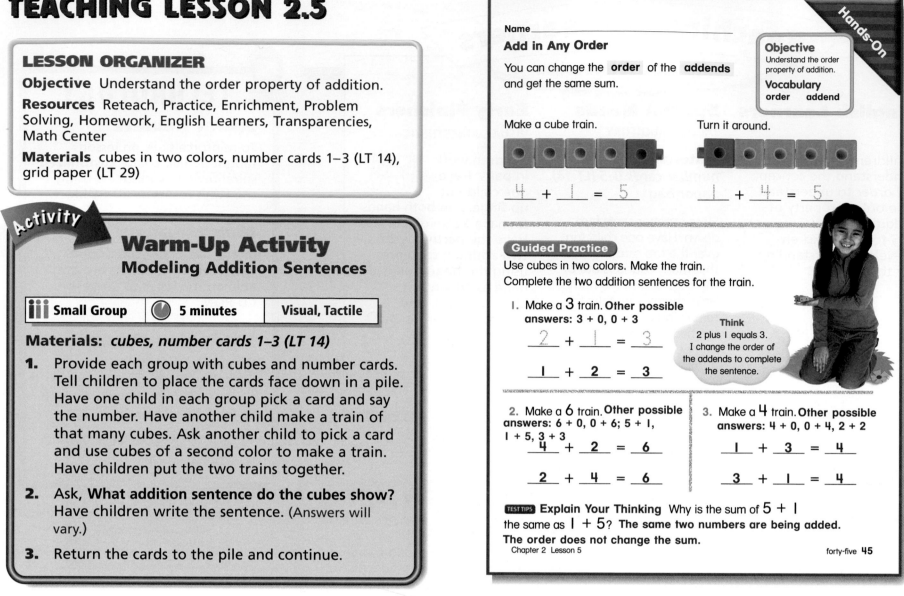

Name _____

Add in Any Order

Hands-On

You can change the **order** of the **addends** and get the same sum.

Objective Understand the order property of addition.

Vocabulary order   addend

Make a cube train.   Turn it around.

<u>4</u> + <u>1</u> = <u>5</u>   <u>1</u> + <u>4</u> = <u>5</u>

Guided Practice

Use cubes in two colors. Make the train.
Complete the two addition sentences for the train.

1. Make a 3 train. **Other possible answers:** 3 + 0, 0 + 3

   <u>2</u> + <u>1</u> = <u>3</u>

   <u>1</u> + <u>2</u> = <u>3</u>

   Think 2 plus 1 equals 3. I change the order of the addends to complete the sentence.

2. Make a 6 train. **Other possible answers:** 6 + 0, 0 + 6; 5 + 1, 1 + 5, 3 + 3

   <u>4</u> + <u>2</u> = <u>6</u>

   <u>2</u> + <u>4</u> = <u>6</u>

3. Make a 4 train. **Other possible answers:** 4 + 0, 0 + 4, 2 + 2

   <u>1</u> + <u>3</u> = <u>4</u>

   <u>3</u> + <u>1</u> = <u>4</u>

TEST TIPS **Explain Your Thinking** Why is the sum of 5 + 1 the same as 1 + 5? **The same two numbers are being added. The order does not change the sum.**

Chapter 2 Lesson 5

forty-five **45**

---

① Introduce ➤ Activity

Model Adding in Any Order

| 👤 Whole Group | ⏱ 5–10 minutes | Auditory, Tactile |

Materials: *cubes in two colors*

1. **Add 1 + 5 and 5 + 1.** Distribute cubes in two colors to each child. **Tell this story about a train. The train engine is on the track. Then, 5 more train cars are added to the train engine.** Have children use the connecting cubes of 2 colors to make a model of the train. **How many cars are on the train in all?** (6)

2. Invite a volunteer to come up to the board and write an addition sentence for the story. (1 + 5 = 6) Have him or her identify the addends 1 and 5.

3. Now, ask children to turn the cube train around to change the order. Have a volunteer change the order of the addends and write the addition sentence on the board. (5 + 1 = 6)

② Develop

Guided Learning

Teaching Example Introduce the objective and vocabulary to the children. Guide them through the example to show that 4 + 1 and 1 + 4 both equal 5. Reinforce that you can change the order of the addends and get the same sum.

Guided Practice

Have children complete **Exercises 1–3** as you observe. Allow time for children to share their addition sentences. Give several children the opportunity to answer the Explain Your Thinking question. Then discuss the responses with the class.

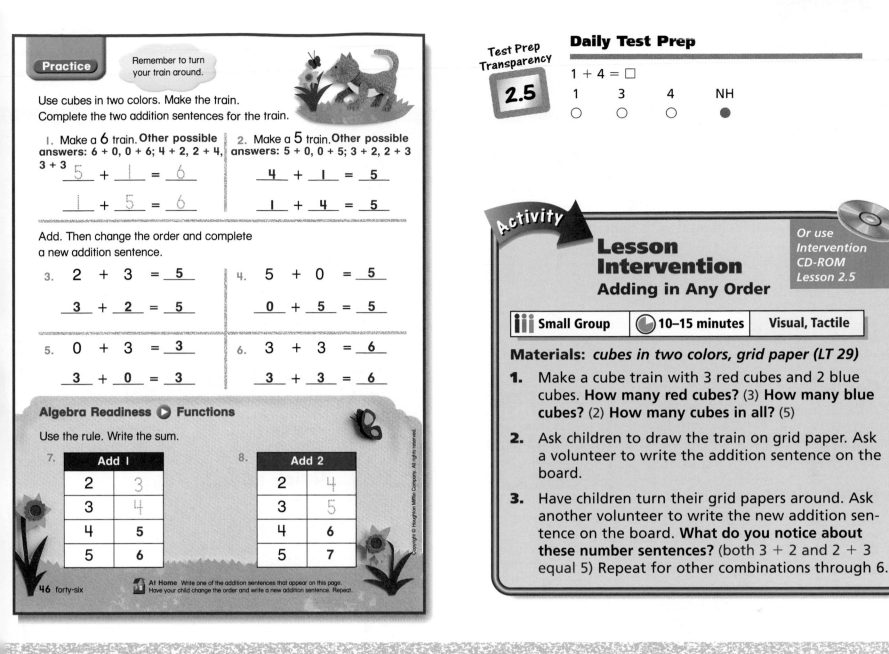

Practice

Remember to turn your train around.

Use cubes in two colors. Make the train.
Complete the two addition sentences for the train.

1. Make a **6** train. **Other possible answers: 6 + 0, 0 + 6; 4 + 2, 2 + 4, 3 + 3**

$$\underline{5} + \underline{1} = \underline{6}$$

$$\underline{1} + \underline{5} = \underline{6}$$

2. Make a **5** train. **Other possible answers: 5 + 0, 0 + 5; 3 + 2, 2 + 3**

$$\underline{4} + \underline{1} = \underline{5}$$

$$\underline{1} + \underline{4} = \underline{5}$$

Add. Then change the order and complete a new addition sentence.

3. $2 + 3 = \underline{5}$

   $\underline{3} + \underline{2} = \underline{5}$

4. $5 + 0 = \underline{5}$

   $\underline{0} + \underline{5} = \underline{5}$

5. $0 + 3 = \underline{3}$

   $\underline{3} + \underline{0} = \underline{3}$

6. $3 + 3 = \underline{6}$

   $\underline{3} + \underline{3} = \underline{6}$

Algebra Readiness ▶ Functions

Use the rule. Write the sum.

7.

Add 1	
2	3
3	4
4	5
5	6

8.

Add 2	
2	4
3	5
4	6
5	7

46 forty-six

At Home Write one of the addition sentences that appear on this page. Have your child change the order and write a new addition sentence. Repeat.

Activity

Lesson Intervention

Adding in Any Order

Or use Intervention CD-ROM Lesson 2.5

👤👤👤 Small Group	🕐 10–15 minutes	Visual, Tactile

Materials: *cubes in two colors, grid paper (LT 29)*

1. Make a cube train with 3 red cubes and 2 blue cubes. **How many red cubes?** (3) **How many blue cubes?** (2) **How many cubes in all?** (5)

2. Ask children to draw the train on grid paper. Ask a volunteer to write the addition sentence on the board.

3. Have children turn their grid papers around. Ask another volunteer to write the new addition sentence on the board. **What do you notice about these number sentences?** (both 3 + 2 and 2 + 3 equal 5) Repeat for other combinations through 6.

---

3 Practice

Independent Practice

Children complete **Exercises 1–6** independently.

Algebra Readiness

After children complete **Exercises 7 and 8**, call on volunteers to share their solutions. Ask children to identify the patterns they see in the tables.

Common Error

Writing the Same Addend in the Same Position

Have children check their addition sentences to make sure they have placed the addends in opposite positions.

4 Assess and Close

Why do 4 + 2 and 2 + 4 both equal 6? (The order in which numbers are added does not change the sum.)

Change the order of the addends in the addition sentence 2 + 3 = 5. What is the new addition sentence? (3 + 2 = 5)

Keeping a Journal

Write an addition sentence. Then change the order of the addends and write a new addition sentence.

Lesson 2.6
Ways to Make 7 and 8

PLANNING THE LESSON

MATHEMATICS OBJECTIVE
Complete addition sentences with sums of 7 and 8.

Use Lesson Planner CD-ROM for Lesson 2.6.

Meeting North Carolina's Standards
1.03 Develop fluency with single-digit addition and corresponding differences using strategies such as modeling, composing and decomposing quantities, using doubles, and making tens.

Daily Routines

Calendar
Ask children to find pairs of numbers on the calendar with a sum of 7. Repeat the activity for pairs of numbers with a sum of 8.

Sunday	Monday	Tuesday	Wednesday	Thursday	Friday	Saturday
			1	2	3	4
5	6	7	8	9	10	11
12	13	14	15	16	17	18
19	20	21	22	23	24	25
26	27	28	29	30	31	

Vocabulary
Write **addend** and **sum** on the board and read the words aloud. Remind children that you can change the order of the addends in an addition sentence and still get the same sum. Ask children to give examples of addition sentences while changing the order of the addends.

Vocabulary Cards

Lesson Transparency 2.6

Problem of the Day
Lisa has 3 goldfish. Drew has 2 goldfish. Lisa adds 2 new fish to her tank. Drew adds 3 new fish to his tank. Who has more fish now? (They have the same number of fish.)

Quick Review
$3 + 1 = \underline{(4)}$

$1 + 3 = \underline{(4)}$

$0 + 4 = \underline{(4)}$

$4 + 0 = \underline{(4)}$

Lesson Quiz
1. $4 + 4 = \underline{(8)}$

2. $2 + 5 = \underline{(7)}$

3. $5 + 3 = \underline{(8)}$

4. $6 + 1 = \underline{(7)}$

LEVELED PRACTICE

RETEACH 2.6
Name _____ Date _____   Reteach 2.6

Ways to Make 7 and 8

You can show 7 in different ways.
Here is one way.   Here is another way to show 7.

$2 + 5 = 7$ $4 + 3 = 7$

You can show 8 in different ways, too.

$4 + 4 = 8$ $3 + 5 = 8$

Use two colors to show another way to make 7.
Complete the addition sentence. **Answers may vary.**

1. $\underline{3} + \underline{4} = \underline{7}$

Use two colors to show another way to make 8.
Complete the addition sentence.

2. $\underline{2} + \underline{6} = \underline{8}$

Copyright © Houghton Mifflin Company. All rights reserved.   Use with text pages 47–48.

PRACTICE 2.6
Name _____ Date _____   Practice 2.6

Ways to Make 7 and 8

Use two colors to show a way to make 7.
Complete the addition sentence.

1. $\underline{1} + \underline{6} = \underline{7}$

Use two colors to show a way to make 8.   **Answers may vary.**
Complete the addition sentence.   **Possible answer shown.**

2. $\underline{2} + \underline{6} = \underline{8}$

Test Prep

Fill in the ○ for the correct answer. NH means Not Here.

3. $5 + 2 = ?$

5   7   4   NH
○   ●   ○   ○

Explain your answer.

Copyright © Houghton Mifflin Company. All rights reserved.   Use with text pages 47–48.

ENRICHMENT 2.6
Name _____ Date _____   Enrichment 2.6

So Many 7s and 8s

Use two different colored crayons.
Color the balloons to show different ways to make 7 and 8.
Complete the addition sentence. **Answers will vary.**

1. ___ + ___ = ___   2. ___ + ___ = ___

3. ___ + ___ = ___   4. ___ + ___ = ___

5. ___ + ___ = ___   6. ___ + ___ = ___

Write About It Why can you change the order of the addends and still get the same sum?

Possible answer: The addends are the same no matter what order they are in.

Copyright © Houghton Mifflin Company. All rights reserved.   Use with text pages 47–48.

Practice Workbook Page 13

47A   CHAPTER 2   Lesson 6

Reaching All Learners
Differentiated Instruction

English Learners

Worksheet 2.6 introduces the concept *same/different*. Children will need to understand this concept in order to understand that there are different ways you can make the same sum.

Inclusion
TACTILE, VISUAL

Materials: *cubes of 2 colors*

Make two cube trains with 3 red cubes and 1 blue cube in each. Ask the child how many red cubes, blue cubes, and how many cubes in all. Help child write the number sentence. Show the second cube train in the reverse order. Repeat the activity. Explain that $3 + 1$ and $1 + 3$ both equal 4. Repeat for other number combinations.

Gifted and Talented
TACTILE, VISUAL

Materials: *index cards*

Write addition facts with sums to 8 on index cards. Write the sums on another set of cards. Arrange all the cards face down in an array. One child turns over 2 cards and tries to match a fact with its sum. The child keeps a match but returns an unmatched pair. Play continues until all the cards are used.

Social Studies Connection

Discuss supermarkets, farm stands, and other places to buy food. Encourage children to share their experiences with food shopping. Then ask them to make shopping lists that equal 7 or 8 items.

MATH CENTER

Basic Skills Activity

Motivate children to build basic skills. Use this activity to address multiple learning styles using hands-on activities related to the skills of this lesson.

PROBLEM SOLVING 2.6

Name _____ Date _____ | Problem Solving 2.6

Ways to Make 7 and 8

Add. Show different ways to make 7 or 8.

1. Tanya has 7 apples. She has two bags. Write three addition sentences to show how she could put apples in each bag.

   $4 + 3 = 7$
   $5 + 2 = 7$
   $6 + 1 = 7$

   Draw or write to explain.

2. Dax has 8 coins and two banks. Write three addition sentences to show how he could put the coins into each bank.

   $4 + 4 = 8$
   $5 + 3 = 8$
   $6 + 2 = 8$

3. Liza has 8 crayons and two boxes. Write three addition sentences to show how she could put crayons into the boxes.

   $7 + 1 = 8$
   $6 + 2 = 8$
   $5 + 3 = 8$

Use with text pages 47–48.

HOMEWORK 2.6

Name _____ Date _____ | Homework 2.6

Ways to Make 7 and 8

There are different ways to make 7. Here is one way.

$3 + 4 = 7$

Here is another way.

$2 + 5 = 7$

There are different ways to make 8. Here is one way.

$5 + 3 = 8$

Here is another way.

$1 + 7 = 8$

Use two colors to show a different way to make 7.

Answers will vary.

1.

Use two colors to show a different way to make 8.

Answers will vary.

2.

3.

Use with text pages 47–48.

Homework Workbook Page 13

ENGLISH LEARNERS 2.6

Name _____ Date _____ | English Learners 2.6

Ways to Make 7 and 8

Same   Different

Tell if the shapes are the same or different.

1.   same

2.   different

3.   same

4.   different

To the Teacher: Use the examples at the top of the page to demonstrate the meaning of the words different and same. Then have children label the shapes to tell if they are the same or different.

Use with text pages 47–48.

TEACHING LESSON 2.6

Objective Complete addition sentences with the sums of 7 and 8.

Resources Reteach, Practice, Enrichment, Problem Solving, Homework, English Learners, Transparencies, Math Center

Materials Cubes

Activity

Warm-Up Activity
Sums of 6

👥 Small Group	🕐 5 minutes	Auditory, Tactile

Materials: *cubes*

1. Provide each group with cubes of different colors, at least 6 of each color. Ask children to make as many 6-cube trains as they can, using all one color or a combination of two colors.

2. Have children write down the addition sentences that describe each train. **How many different ways did you find to make a sum of 6?** Invite volunteers from each group to read one of their addition sentences. Write each on the board until all seven addition sentences have been named.

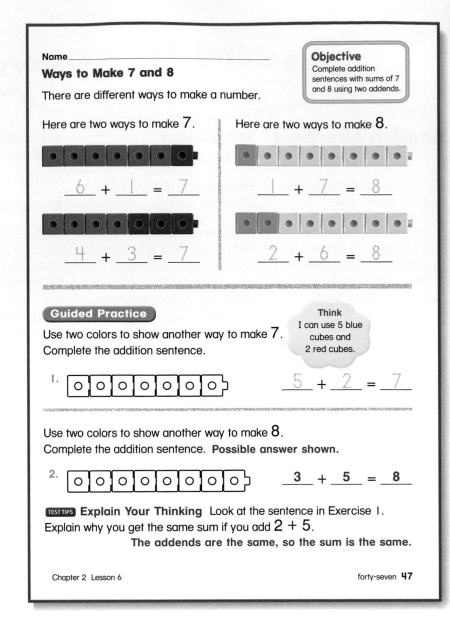

Name_____

Ways to Make 7 and 8

Objective Complete addition sentences with sums of 7 and 8 using two addends.

There are different ways to make a number.

Here are two ways to make 7.

$6 + 1 = 7$

$4 + 3 = 7$

Here are two ways to make 8.

$1 + 7 = 8$

$2 + 6 = 8$

Guided Practice

Use two colors to show another way to make 7. Complete the addition sentence.

Think I can use 5 blue cubes and 2 red cubes.

1. $5 + 2 = 7$

Use two colors to show another way to make 8. Complete the addition sentence. **Possible answer shown.**

2. $3 + 5 = 8$

TEST TIPS Explain Your Thinking Look at the sentence in Exercise 1. Explain why you get the same sum if you add $2 + 5$.

The addends are the same, so the sum is the same.

---

1 Introduce

Model Making Sums of 7 and 8

👥 Whole Group	🕐 5–10 minutes	Auditory, Kinesthetic

Materials: *cubes*

1. *Model facts for 7.* Use two colors of cubes to show sums of 7. First, show a train of 6 cubes of one color and 1 cube of another. **What addition sentence describes this cube train?** ($6 + 1 = 7$) Flip the cube train and ask, **What addition sentence does this train show?** ($1 + 6 = 7$)

2. **What other ways can we show 7?** (Possible responses: $5 + 2$, $4 + 3$, $7 + 0$.) Invite volunteers to make a cube train to show the sum of 7 and write the addition sentence.

3. Repeat the activity for sums of 8.

2 Develop

Guided Learning

Teaching Example Introduce the objective to the children. Guide them through the example to show that there are different ways to show the sum of 7 or 8 using two addends.

Guided Practice

Have children complete **Exercises 1–2** as you observe. Discuss children's responses to the Explain Your Thinking question.

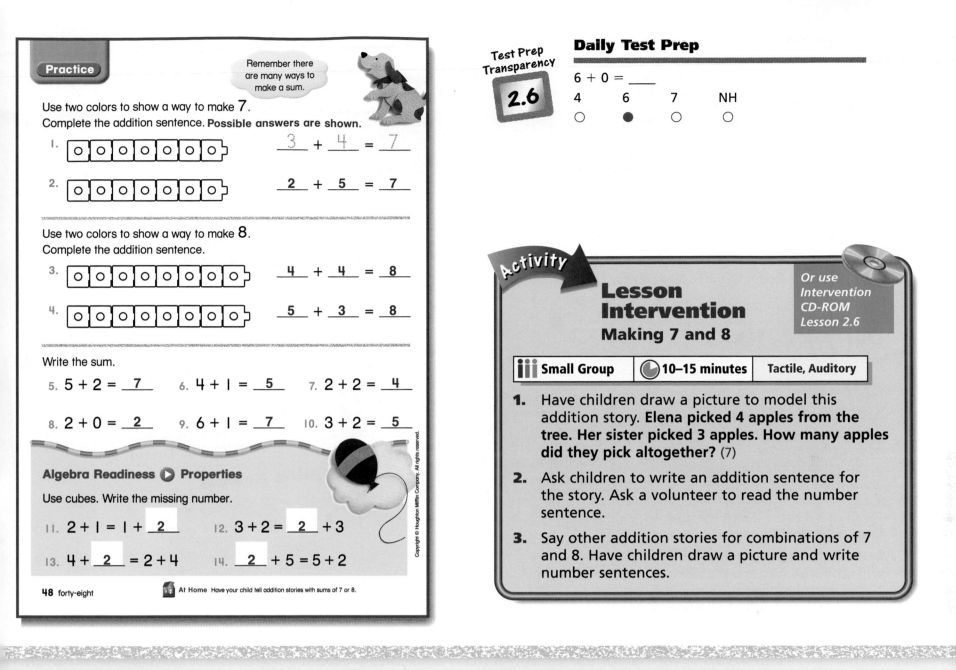

Daily Test Prep

6 + 0 = ___

4   6   7   NH
○   ●   ○   ○

Practice

Remember there are many ways to make a sum.

Use two colors to show a way to make 7.
Complete the addition sentence. **Possible answers are shown.**

1. $\underline{3} + \underline{4} = \underline{7}$

2. $\underline{2} + \underline{5} = \underline{7}$

Use two colors to show a way to make 8.
Complete the addition sentence.

3. $\underline{4} + \underline{4} = \underline{8}$

4. $\underline{5} + \underline{3} = \underline{8}$

Write the sum.

5. $5 + 2 = \underline{7}$ 6. $4 + 1 = \underline{5}$ 7. $2 + 2 = \underline{4}$

8. $2 + 0 = \underline{2}$ 9. $6 + 1 = \underline{7}$ 10. $3 + 2 = \underline{5}$

Algebra Readiness ▶ Properties

Use cubes. Write the missing number.

11. $2 + 1 = 1 + \underline{2}$ 12. $3 + 2 = \underline{2} + 3$

13. $4 + \underline{2} = 2 + 4$ 14. $\underline{2} + 5 = 5 + 2$

48 forty-eight   **At Home** Have your child tell addition stories with sums of 7 or 8.

Activity

Lesson Intervention
Making 7 and 8

Or use Intervention CD-ROM Lesson 2.6

| Small Group | 10–15 minutes | Tactile, Auditory |

1. Have children draw a picture to model this addition story. **Elena picked 4 apples from the tree. Her sister picked 3 apples. How many apples did they pick altogether?** (7)

2. Ask children to write an addition sentence for the story. Ask a volunteer to read the number sentence.

3. Say other addition stories for combinations of 7 and 8. Have children draw a picture and write number sentences.

---

3 Practice

Independent Practice

Children complete **Exercises 1–10** independently.

Algebra Readiness

After children complete **Exercises 11–14**, encourage them to discuss their responses and describe any patterns they see in their answers.

Common Error

Unable to Find Parts of a Number
Show children how to make a cube train of two colors for the sum, such as 8. Emphasize that each color is an addend. Then have the child write the addition as 1 + 7.

4 Assess and Close

What are 4 ways to make 7? (Possible responses: 7 + 0, 1 + 6, 2 + 5, 3 + 4)

Which sum is greater, 2 + 6 or 4 + 3? (2 + 6)

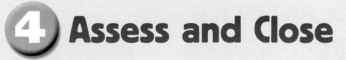

Keeping a Journal

Show four ways to make 7. Then show four ways to make 8. Write the addition sentences.

Lesson 2.7 — Add in Vertical Form

PLANNING THE LESSON

MATHEMATICS OBJECTIVE
Write addition sentences in vertical format.

Use Lesson Planner CD-ROM for Lesson 2.7.

Meeting North Carolina's Standards

1.03 Develop fluency with single-digit addition and corresponding differences using strategies such as modeling, composing and decomposing quantities, using doubles, and making tens.

Daily Routines

Calendar

Ask children to look at the calendar and name two numbers with a sum of 8. Continue until children have given all possible combinations in any order. $(0 + 8, 1 + 7, 2 + 6, 3 + 5, 4 + 4)$

Sunday	Monday	Tuesday	Wednesday	Thursday	Friday	Saturday
			1	2	3	4
5	6	7	8	9	10	11
12	13	14	15	16	17	18
19	20	21	22	23	24	25
26	27	28	29	30	31	

Vocabulary

Review the words **across** and **down** with children. Write each word across and then down on the board. Emphasize that either way, the meaning of the word does not change.

Vocabulary Cards

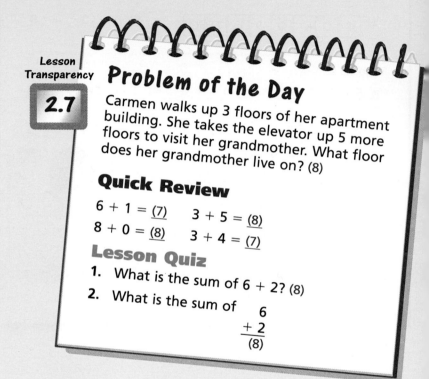

Lesson Transparency 2.7

Problem of the Day

Carmen walks up 3 floors of her apartment building. She takes the elevator up 5 more floors to visit her grandmother. What floor does her grandmother live on? (8)

Quick Review

$6 + 1 = \underline{(7)}$ $3 + 5 = \underline{(8)}$
$8 + 0 = \underline{(8)}$ $3 + 4 = \underline{(7)}$

Lesson Quiz

1. What is the sum of $6 + 2$? (8)
2. What is the sum of

$$\begin{array}{r} 6 \\ + 2 \\ \hline (8) \end{array}$$

LEVELED PRACTICE

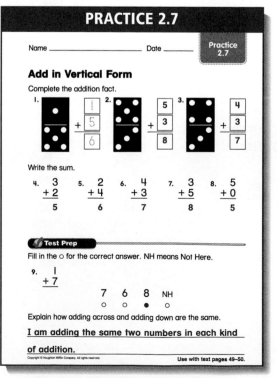

RETEACH 2.7

Name _____ Date _____   Reteach 2.7

Add in Vertical Form

You can add across to find the sum.

$3 + 2 = 5$

You can add down to find the sum.

$$\begin{array}{r} 3 \\ + 2 \\ \hline 5 \end{array}$$

Complete the addition fact.

1. $2 + 1 = 3$ $\begin{array}{r} 2 \\ + 1 \\ \hline 3 \end{array}$

2. $4 + 2 = 6$ $\begin{array}{r} 4 \\ + 2 \\ \hline 6 \end{array}$

Copyright © Houghton Mifflin Company. All rights reserved.   Use with text pages 49–50.

PRACTICE 2.7

Name _____ Date _____   Practice 2.7

Add in Vertical Form

Complete the addition fact.

1. $\begin{array}{r} 1 \\ + 5 \\ \hline 6 \end{array}$ 2. $\begin{array}{r} 5 \\ + 3 \\ \hline 8 \end{array}$ 3. $\begin{array}{r} 4 \\ + 3 \\ \hline 7 \end{array}$

Write the sum.

4. $\begin{array}{r} 3 \\ + 2 \\ \hline 5 \end{array}$ 5. $\begin{array}{r} 2 \\ + 4 \\ \hline 6 \end{array}$ 6. $\begin{array}{r} 4 \\ + 3 \\ \hline 7 \end{array}$ 7. $\begin{array}{r} 3 \\ + 5 \\ \hline 8 \end{array}$ 8. $\begin{array}{r} 5 \\ + 0 \\ \hline 5 \end{array}$

Test Prep

Fill in the ○ for the correct answer. NH means Not Here.

9. $\begin{array}{r} 1 \\ + 7 \end{array}$

○ 7   ○ 6   ● 8   ○ NH

Explain how adding across and adding down are the same.

<u>I am adding the same two numbers in each kind of addition.</u>

Copyright © Houghton Mifflin Company. All rights reserved.   Use with text pages 49–50.

ENRICHMENT 2.7

Name _____ Date _____   Enrichment 2.7

Across and Down

Add across and then down. Write the missing numbers.

Across		Down

1. $3 + 2 = \underline{5}$ $\begin{array}{r} 3 \\ + 2 \\ \hline 5 \end{array}$ $\begin{array}{r} 2 \\ + 3 \\ \hline 5 \end{array}$
   $\underline{2} + 3 = 5$

2. $6 + \underline{0} = 6$ $\begin{array}{r} 6 \\ + 0 \\ \hline 6 \end{array}$ $\begin{array}{r} 0 \\ + 6 \\ \hline 6 \end{array}$
   $\underline{6} + 0 = 6$

3. $4 + \underline{0} = 4$ $\begin{array}{r} 2 \\ + 6 \\ \hline 8 \end{array}$ $\begin{array}{r} 2 \\ + 6 \\ \hline 8 \end{array}$
   $0 + 4 = \underline{4}$

Write About It How can adding across and down give the same sum?

<u>The addends are the same.</u>

_____

Copyright © Houghton Mifflin Company. All rights reserved.   Use with text pages 49–50.

Practice Workbook Page 14

Reaching All Learners

Differentiated Instruction

English Learners

In order to write addition sentences in vertical form, children will need to understand the meaning of the terms *down* and *across*. Use Worksheet 2.7 to help English-language learners to understand these terms.

Special Needs

TACTILE, VISUAL

Materials: *beans*

Have pairs place 8 beans on the table. One child takes some of the beans and places them in a pile. The child counts the beans in each pile and the number in all. The partner records the addition sentence and checks the beans in each pile. Repeat several times, having partners switch roles.

Early Finishers

VISUAL, TACTILE

Materials: *index cards with facts for 8*

Give children two sets of addition fact cards for 8, without sums. One set shows horizontal facts and the other set shows vertical facts. Children work in pairs to match the cards with the same facts. Then have them write the facts on paper and solve.

TECHNOLOGY

Spiral Review

You can prepare students for standardized tests with **customized** spiral review on key skills using the *Ways to Assess* CD-ROM.

Lesson Planner

You can use the **Lesson Planner CD-ROM** to create a report of the lessons and standards you have taught.

Games

Students can practice their skills using the **Rock Hopper** math game, available on the *Ways to Success* CD-ROM.

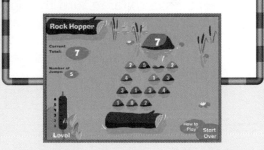

Art Connection

Show children a border design. Point out that the design goes *across* the top and bottom and *down* the sides. Have children create border designs and then draw an addition picture inside the border.

MATH CENTER

Real-Life Activity

Help children understand the usefulness of mathematics. This activity makes math come alive by connecting the lesson skills to a real-life situation.

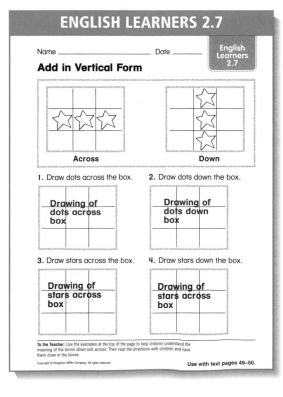

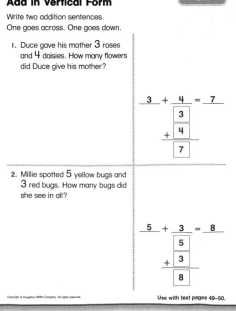

Homework Workbook Page 14

TEACHING LESSON 2.7

LESSON ORGANIZER

Objective Write addition sentences in vertical format.

Resources Reteach, Practice, Enrichment, Problem Solving, Homework, English Learners, Transparencies, Math Center

Materials number dot cards 1–4 (LT 17), blank transparency, connecting cubes

Activity

Warm-Up Activity
Modeling Addition Sentences

| 👤👤👤 Small Group | ⏱ 5 minutes | Visual, Tactile |

Materials: *number dot cards 1–4 (LT 17)*

1. Give each group several dot cards. Have a child place 2 dot cards on the table. **What addition fact do the dots show?** Have children draw a picture of the dot cards and write the addition sentence.

2. Next, have children turn the dot cards to change the order of the addends. **What addition fact do the dots now show?** Have children draw the dot cards on their papers and write the addition sentence.

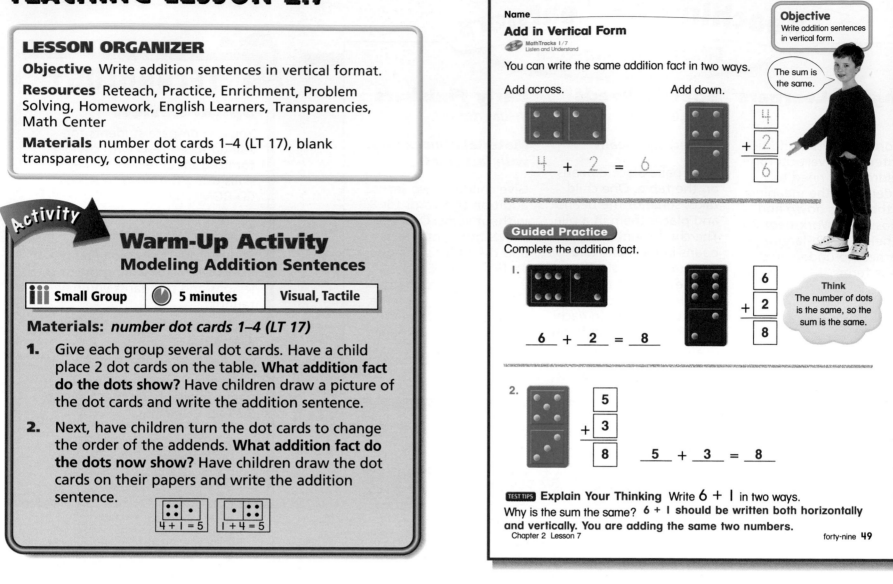

Name _____

Add in Vertical Form

🔵 MathTracks 1 / 7
Listen and Understand

Objective
Write addition sentences in vertical form.

The sum is the same.

You can write the same addition fact in two ways.

Add across.

_4_ + _2_ = _6_

Add down.

4
+ 2
6

Guided Practice
Complete the addition fact.

1.
_6_ + _2_ = _8_

6
+ 2
8

Think
The number of dots is the same, so the sum is the same.

2.
5
+ 3
8

_5_ + _3_ = _8_

TEST TIPS **Explain Your Thinking** Write 6 + 1 in two ways. Why is the sum the same? **6 + 1 should be written both horizontally and vertically. You are adding the same two numbers.**

Chapter 2 Lesson 7

forty-nine **49**

---

1 Introduce

Discuss Adding in Vertical Form

| 👤👤👤👤 Whole Group | ⏱ 5–10 minutes | Visual, Auditory |

Materials: *blank transparency*

1. *Add 2 + 5.* Draw a horizontal domino on the transparency with 2 dots on the left and 5 dots on the right. Below it write the addition sentence, 2 + 5 = 7. **The dots on the domino show 2 + 5 = 7.**

2. Draw the same domino in the vertical position, with the 2 dots on the top. **Are the addends the same as 2 + 5?** (yes) Write the vertical addition with the 2 on top.

3. Explain that when you write an addition fact this way, the line under the bottom addend is used in place of an equal sign. Also point out that the location of the plus sign is directly to the left of the bottom addend.

2 Develop

Guided Learning

Teaching Example Introduce the objective to the children. Guide them through the example to show that addition facts can be written in two ways, across and down.

Guided Practice

Have children complete **Exercises 1–2** as you observe. If children turn dominos and get 3 + 5 in **Exercise 2**, it is also a correct response. Discuss children's responses to the Explain Your Thinking question.

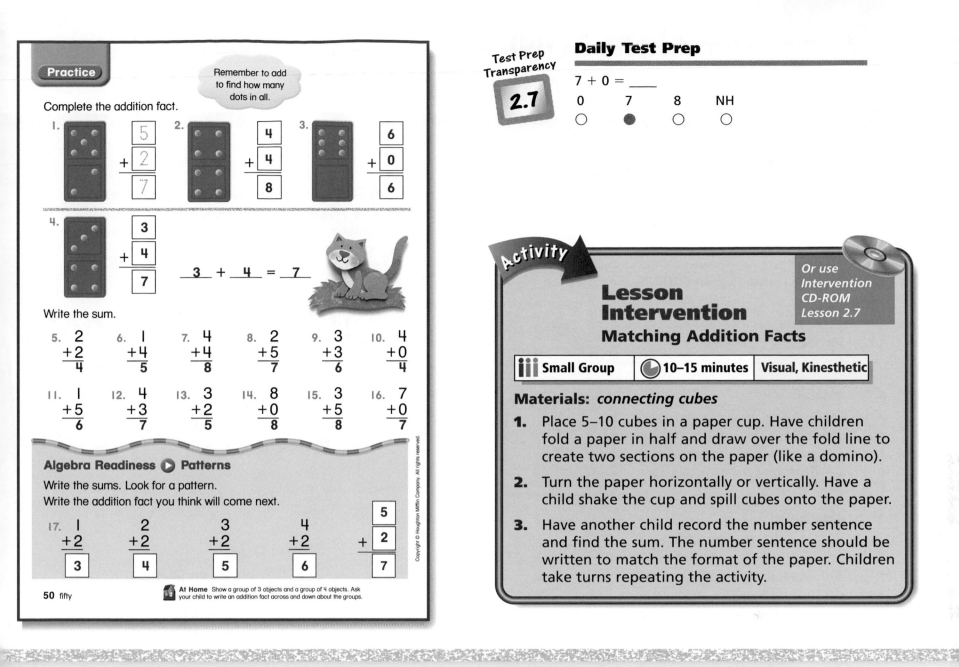

Practice

Complete the addition fact.

Remember to add to find how many dots in all.

1. 5 + 2 = 7
2. 4 + 4 = 8
3. 6 + 0 = 6
4. 3 + 4 = 7   3 + 4 = 7

Write the sum.

5. 2 + 2 = 4
6. 1 + 4 = 5
7. 4 + 4 = 8
8. 2 + 5 = 7
9. 3 + 3 = 6
10. 4 + 0 = 4

11. 1 + 5 = 6
12. 4 + 3 = 7
13. 3 + 2 = 5
14. 8 + 0 = 8
15. 3 + 5 = 8
16. 7 + 0 = 7

Algebra Readiness ▶ Patterns

Write the sums. Look for a pattern.
Write the addition fact you think will come next.

17. 1 + 2 = 3   2 + 2 = 4   3 + 2 = 5   4 + 2 = 6   5 + 2 = 7

At Home Show a group of 3 objects and a group of 4 objects. Ask your child to write an addition fact across and down about the groups.

50 fifty

Copyright © Houghton Mifflin Company. All rights reserved.

2.7

Daily Test Prep

7 + 0 = ____

0   ● 7   8   NH

Activity

Or use Intervention CD-ROM Lesson 2.7

Lesson Intervention
Matching Addition Facts

| 👥 Small Group | ⏱ 10–15 minutes | Visual, Kinesthetic |

Materials: *connecting cubes*

1. Place 5–10 cubes in a paper cup. Have children fold a paper in half and draw over the fold line to create two sections on the paper (like a domino).

2. Turn the paper horizontally or vertically. Have a child shake the cup and spill cubes onto the paper.

3. Have another child record the number sentence and find the sum. The number sentence should be written to match the format of the paper. Children take turns repeating the activity.

3 Practice

Independent Practice

Children complete **Exercises 1–16** independently.

Algebra Readiness

After children complete **Exercise 17**, call on volunteers to share their solutions. Have children share the different patterns they used to solve the problem.

Common Error

Recording the Sum in the Wrong Place
Remind children that the line in the vertical form means "equals." Reinforce this idea by suggesting they trace over the line before recording the sum.

4 Assess and Close

Is the sum the same if you write a number sentence across or if you write it down? (yes)

How would you write 7 plus 1 equals 8? (Children may write horizontally or vertically.)

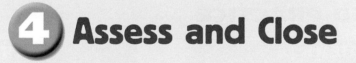

Keeping a Journal

Draw a picture about 3 + 5 and its sum. Show the addition fact for the story in two ways.

CHAPTER 2   Lesson 7   **50**

Problem Solving: Write a Number Sentence

Lesson 2.8

PLANNING THE LESSON

MATHEMATICS OBJECTIVE
Write addition sentences for problem situations.

Use Lesson Planner CD-ROM for Lesson 2.8.

Meeting North Carolina's Standards

1.04 Create, model, and solve problems that use addition, subtraction, and fair shares (between two or three).

Also 1.03

Daily Routines

Calendar

Ask children to look at the dates for the first week of the month. Have them use numbers of the two dates in an addition sentence and write the sum.

Sunday	Monday	Tuesday	Wednesday	Thursday	Friday	Saturday
			1	2	3	4
5	6	7	8	9	10	11
12	13	14	15	16	17	18
19	20	21	22	23	24	25
26	27	28	29	30	31	

Vocabulary

Draw a picture on the board and write an addition sentence for it. Review the terms **addend, sum,** and **addition sentence** as you point to them.

Vocabulary Cards

Lesson Transparency 2.8

Problem of the Day

What is the smallest sum you can get using the numbers 1, 2, or 3 in any order? (3, 1 + 2) What is the largest sum? (5, 2 + 3)

Quick Review

$$\begin{array}{c} 2 \\ + 0 \\ \hline (2) \end{array} \quad \begin{array}{c} 6 \\ + 1 \\ \hline (7) \end{array} \quad \begin{array}{c} 3 \\ + 5 \\ \hline (8) \end{array} \quad \begin{array}{c} 0 \\ + 7 \\ \hline (7) \end{array} \quad \begin{array}{c} 3 \\ + 3 \\ \hline (6) \end{array}$$

Lesson Quiz

There are 4 crayons on the desk. There are 3 crayons in the box. How many crayons in all? (7) Show how you solved the problem. (4 + 3 = 7)

LEVELED PRACTICE

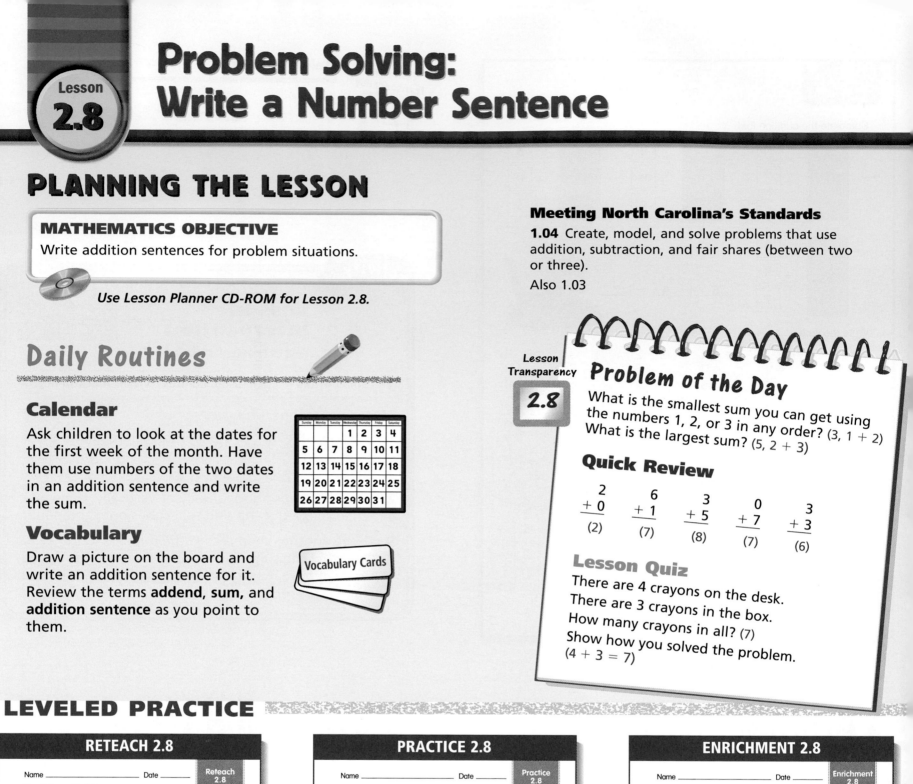

RETEACH 2.8

Name _____ Date _____ **Reteach 2.8**

Problem Solving
Write a Number Sentence

Read It Look for Information.
Melissa has 5 apples.
Her brother Michael has 3 apples.
How many apples do Melissa and Michael have?

Picture It

Melissa's apples	Michael's apples

Solve It Use the picture to solve the problem.

Melissa	Michael	How many apples in all?
_5_ apples	_3_ apples	_8_

Could you write a number sentence?

_5_ (+) _3_ (=) _8_

How many apples do Michael and Melissa have? _8_ apples

Copyright © Houghton Mifflin Company. All rights reserved.

Use with text pages 51–53.

PRACTICE 2.8

Name _____ Date _____ **Practice 2.8**

Problem Solving
Write a Number Sentence

Write the addition sentence.
Write the answer.

1. There are 4 rabbits eating. Then 2 more rabbits come. How many rabbits in all?
_4_ (+) _2_ (=) _6_
_6_ rabbits

2. There are 3 butterflies. Then 4 butterflies join them. How many butterflies in all?
_3_ (+) _4_ (=) _7_
_7_ butterflies

Test Prep

Fill in the ○ for the correct answer. NH means Not Here.

3. There are 4 bugs on a leaf. Then 4 bugs join them. How many bugs in all?
4 + 4 = ?
8   4   6   NH
●   ○   ○   ○

Copyright © Houghton Mifflin Company. All rights reserved.

Use with text pages 51–53.

ENRICHMENT 2.8

Name _____ Date _____ **Enrichment 2.8**

Add the Puppies

1. Read the problem.
There are 5 puppies in the basket. Lyn puts 3 more puppies in. How many puppies are there in all?

What do you know?
There are _5_ puppies in the basket. Lyn puts _3_ more puppies in the basket. Draw a picture to show what happened.

Write a number sentence to solve the problem.
_5_ + _3_ = _8_ puppies in all.

2. Write your own problem about puppies.

_____

Write a number sentence to solve.
___ + ___ = ___

Look back at your number sentence.
Does it show two sets?
Does the sum show how many in all?

Copyright © Houghton Mifflin Company. All rights reserved.

Use with text pages 51–53.

Practice Workbook Page 15

Reaching All Learners
Differentiated Instruction

English Learners

English-language learners may not be familiar with the subject-verb agreement necessary to understand and write word problems. Use Worksheet 2.8 to develop children's knowledge of subject-verb agreement for the verb *join*.

Inclusion
VISUAL, TACTILE

Materials: *index cards*

- Make domino index cards. Draw sets of dots in two colors on each card.
- Hold a card horizontally. Ask the child to count the dots in each set and tell how many.
- Turn the card vertically and repeat the activity. Reinforce that the sum is the same.

Gifted and Talented
TACTILE, VISUAL

- Have children make up addition sentences. Have them leave one number out. For example, 2 + ___ = 4.
- Ask children to exchange papers and find the missing numbers to complete the addition sentences.

2+___=4
___+3=5

TECHNOLOGY
Spiral Review

Create **customized** spiral review worksheets for individual students using the *Ways to Assess* CD-ROM.

Intervention

Use the *Ways to Success* CD-ROM intervention software to support students who need more help in understanding the concepts and skills taught in this chapter.

Lesson Planner

You can customize your teaching plan or meet your curriculum requirements with the **Lesson Planner CD-ROM**.

ScienceConnection

Discuss squirrels with children. Many children know that squirrels store nuts in the summer to eat in the winter. Have children draw 2 squirrel holes. Then draw 3 nuts in one hole and 4 nuts in the other. Have children write an addition sentence.

MATH CENTER

Number of the Week Activity

Display the Number of the Week to motivate children to use their problem-solving skills. The exercises cover topics across all math strands.

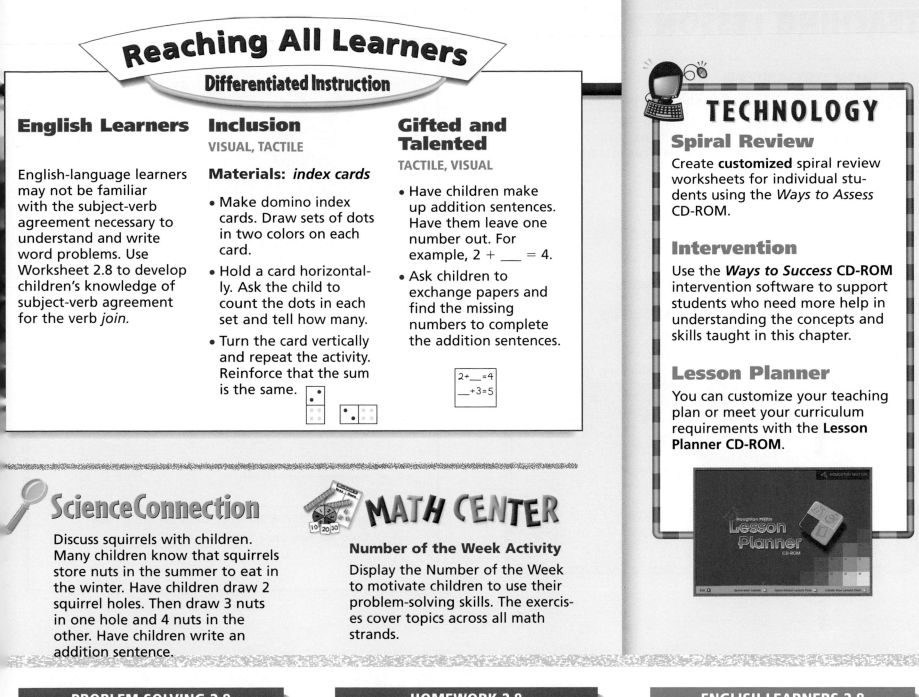

PROBLEM SOLVING 2.8

Name _____ Date _____

Problem Solving 2.8

Write a Number Sentence

There are 2 boys playing ball.
There are 5 girls jumping rope.
How many children are playing in all?

UNDERSTAND

What do I know? — **2 boys and 5 girls are playing.**

What do I need to find out? — **How many children are playing in all.**

PLAN

Can I write a number sentence to solve? — **Yes, I can write an addition sentence to solve.**

SOLVE

What addition sentence will I write? — **2 + 5 = 7**

How many children are playing? — **7** children

LOOK BACK

Is there another way I could have solved the problem? Explain. — **Yes. For example, I could have used counters and counted how many.**

Copyright © Houghton Mifflin Company. All rights reserved.

Use with text pages 51–53.

HOMEWORK 2.8

Name _____ Date _____

Homework 2.8

Problem Solving
Write a Number Sentence

One step in solving an addition problem is to write a number sentence.

Melissa has 3 trading cards.

Jeff has 5 trading cards.

3 + 5 = 8

Write a number sentence.

1. There are 5 kangaroos in the grass. 2 more kangaroos join them. How many kangaroos are there?

5 + 2 = 7

2. There are 6 koala bears. 2 more join them. How many koala bears are there?

6 + 2 = 8

Copyright © Houghton Mifflin Company. All rights reserved.

Use with text pages 51–53.

Homework Workbook Page 15

ENGLISH LEARNERS 2.8

Name _____ Date _____

English Learners 2.8

Write a Number Sentence

I clown **joins** the group. 2 clowns **join** the group.

Circle the correct word to complete each sentence.

1. 3 birds **joins** (**join**) the group.
2. I girl (**joins**) **join** the group.
3. 3 dogs **joins** (**join**) the group.
4. I boy (**joins**) **join** the group.

To the Teacher: Use the examples at the top of the page to demonstrate the correct usage of *joins* and *join*. Then read the sentences with children and have them circle the word to complete each sentence.

Copyright © Houghton Mifflin Company. All rights reserved.

Use with text pages 51–53.

TEACHING LESSON 2.8

LESSON ORGANIZER

Objective Write addition sentences for problem situations.

Resources Reteach, Practice, Enrichment, Problem Solving, Homework, English Learners, Transparencies, Math Center

Materials cubes in two colors

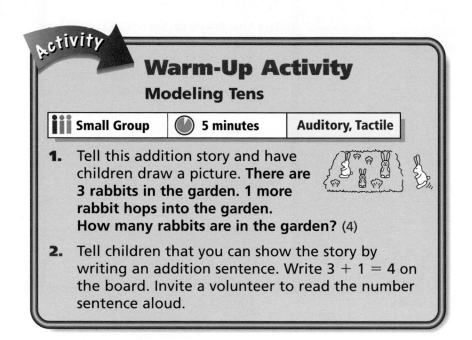

Warm-Up Activity
Modeling Tens

iii Small Group	⏱ 5 minutes	Auditory, Tactile

1. Tell this addition story and have children draw a picture. **There are 3 rabbits in the garden. 1 more rabbit hops into the garden. How many rabbits are in the garden?** (4)

2. Tell children that you can show the story by writing an addition sentence. Write 3 + 1 = 4 on the board. Invite a volunteer to read the number sentence aloud.

Name _____

Write a Number Sentence

Problem Solving

Objective Write addition sentences to solve story problems.

How many children in all?

UNDERSTAND
What do you know?
· There are 2 children in a group.
· 3 more children join them.

PLAN
Circle how you would solve the problem.   (add)   subtract

SOLVE
Write an addition sentence.

2 (+) 3 (=) 5

How many children in all?   5 children

LOOK BACK
Does the addition sentence show the two groups?
Does the sum show how many in all?

Chapter 2 Lesson 8   fifty-one 51

---

1 Introduce

Discuss Writing Addition Sentences

iiii Whole Group	⏱ 10–15 minutes	Visual, Auditory

1. **Solve an addition problem.** Present the problem: **There are 3 children in the swimming pool. 2 more children go into the pool.** Repeat each line as you write the addition sentence 3 + 2 = 5 on the board. Tell children that 3 + 2 = 5 is an addition sentence. It tells how many children are in the pool. Now, ask the question: **How many children are in the pool in all?** (5 children)

2. Present another addition problem. Then repeat each line as a volunteer writes the addition sentence on the board. Have children read the sentence and then answer the question to solve the problem.

2 Develop

Guided Learning

Teaching Example Introduce the objective to the children. Guide them through the problem-solving steps to help them understand how to write the addition sentence, 2 + 3 = 5, to help them solve the problem. Be sure children understand that the answer to the question is 5 children.

Guided Practice

Have children complete **Exercises 1–2** on page 52 as you observe. Remind children that they are joining two groups to find a sum.

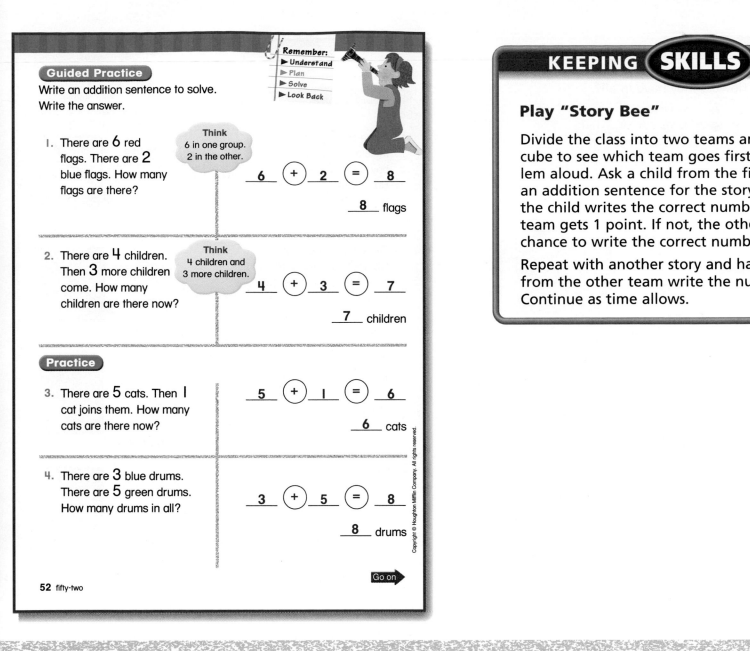

Guided Practice

Write an addition sentence to solve.
Write the answer.

Remember:
► Understand
► Plan
► Solve
► Look Back

1. There are 6 red flags. There are 2 blue flags. How many flags are there?

   Think
   6 in one group.
   2 in the other.

   __6__ ⊕ __2__ ⊜ __8__

   __8__ flags

2. There are 4 children. Then 3 more children come. How many children are there now?

   Think
   4 children and
   3 more children.

   __4__ ⊕ __3__ ⊜ __7__

   __7__ children

Practice

3. There are 5 cats. Then 1 cat joins them. How many cats are there now?

   __5__ ⊕ __1__ ⊜ __6__

   __6__ cats

4. There are 3 blue drums. There are 5 green drums. How many drums in all?

   __3__ ⊕ __5__ ⊜ __8__

   __8__ drums

Go on

52 fifty-two

KEEPING SKILLS SHARP

Play "Story Bee"

Divide the class into two teams and roll a number cube to see which team goes first. Say a story problem aloud. Ask a child from the first team to write an addition sentence for the story on the board. If the child writes the correct number sentence, the team gets 1 point. If not, the other team gets a chance to write the correct number sentence.

Repeat with another story and have a child from the other team write the number sentence. Continue as time allows.

---

3 Practice

Independent Practice

Children complete **Exercises 3–4** on page 52 independently.

Lesson continues

Test Prep Transparency 2.8

Daily Test Prep

Lili has 4 flowers. Sam has 3 flowers. Which shows how many flowers they have in all?

5   6   7   NH
○   ○   ●   ○

Activity

Lesson Intervention

Or use Intervention CD-ROM Lesson 2.8

Model Addition Stories

| 👤👤👤 Small Group | 🕐 5 minutes | Tactile, Visual |

Materials: *cubes in two colors*

1. Have children share cubes.
   There are 4 bagels on the table. There are two bagels in the bag. How many bagels are there in all?

    4 + 2 = 6

2. Ask children to use the cubes to model the story. Then have them write an addition sentence using the numbers.

3. Have children compare and check their addition sentences.

Name _____

Choose a Strategy

Strategies
Write a Number Sentence
Draw a Picture
Act It Out With Models

Solve.

1. There are 2 girls playing the clarinet. There are 5 boys playing the clarinet. How many children are playing the clarinet?

   Draw or write to explain. **Allow children to use any strategy or method they want.**

   __7__ children

2. There are 5 oboes on the top shelf. There is 1 more oboe on the bottom shelf than on the top shelf. How many oboes are on the bottom shelf?

   __6__ oboes

3. There are 6 flute players. 2 more flute players join them. Now how many flute players are there?

   __8__ flute players

4. **Multistep** There are 5 trumpet players. 1 more trumpet player joins them. Then, 1 trumpet player leaves. How many trumpet players are there now?

   __5__ trumpet players

Chapter 2

At Home Read problems 1 through 4 using different numbers or objects and have your child tell how to solve the problems.

fifty-three **53**

---

3 Practice

Mixed Strategy Practice

Read the problem-solving strategies with children. Make sure children can read and comprehend the problems in **Exercises 1–4** on page 53. If necessary, pair more proficient readers with less proficient readers. Encourage children to discuss the problems before solving.

Common Error

Writing the Wrong Numbers

Have children circle the numbers they will use to help them remember to check that they write the correct numbers in the addition sentences.

---

4 Assess and Close

There are 5 ducks swimming in a pond. 2 more ducks get into the pond. How many ducks are in the pond? (7)

How will you solve this problem? (add)

What numbers will you add? (5 and 2)

Write an addition sentence. (5 + 2 = 7)

Keeping a Journal

Write an addition story problem about children in a playground. Then write an addition sentence for your problem.

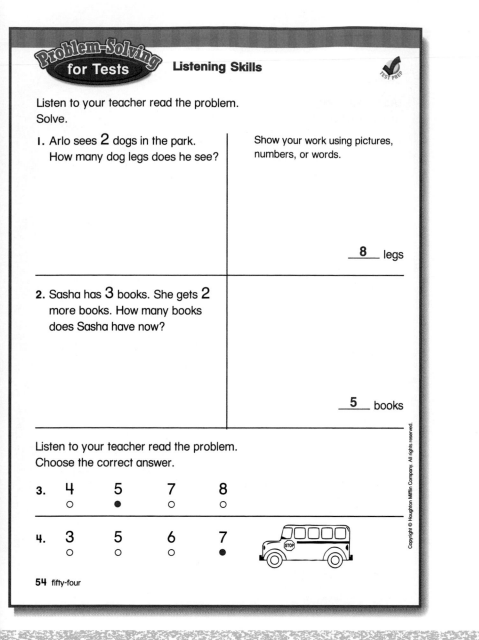

Listen to your teacher read the problem. Solve.

1. Arlo sees 2 dogs in the park. How many dog legs does he see?

Show your work using pictures, numbers, or words.

___8___ legs

2. Sasha has 3 books. She gets 2 more books. How many books does Sasha have now?

___5___ books

Listen to your teacher read the problem. Choose the correct answer.

3. 4 5 7 8
       ○ ● ○ ○

4. 3 5 6 7
       ○ ○ ○ ●

54 fifty-four

Problem-Solving for Tests

Listening Skills

This page provides children practice with the oral problem-solving format used in some standardized test items.

You may want to read each item only once to mimic the style of oral tests.

Use with Items 1 and 2

Listening Strategy: Read the problem silently while the teacher reads it aloud.

- **This problem is on the page. Read it to yourself while I read it aloud.**
- **Listen to the whole problem. Wait until I finish to start writing.**

Use with Item 3

Listening Strategy: Listen to the problem. Then draw a picture to help you find the answer.

- **This problem is not on the page. Look at me and listen as I read the problem.**

  Luanne drops some counters onto her workmat. Four of the counters land yellow side up. One counter lands red side up. How many counters does Luanne drop?

- **You can draw a picture now. Then mark your answer.**

Use with Item 4

Listening Strategy: Listen for important facts and numbers.

- **Listen for the question the problem asks.**

  Five children are riding on the school bus. The bus stops and two more children get on. How many children are riding on the school bus in all?

- **Use the numbers to find the answer to the question. Then mark your answer.**

Quick Check

Have children complete the Quick Check exercises independently to assess their understanding of concepts and skills taught in **Lessons 5–8**.

Item	Lesson	Error Analysis	Intervention
1–2	2.5	Children may not reverse the order of addends.	Reteach Resource 2.5 *Ways to Success* 2.5
3–8	2.6	Children may be unable to find more than one fact for a sum.	Reteach Resource 2.6 *Ways to Success* 2.6
9-14	2.7	Children may record sums in the wrong position.	Reteach Resource 2.7 *Ways to Success* 2.7
15	2.8	Children may record numbers from a problem incorrectly.	Reteach Resource 2.8 *Ways to Success* 2.8

Name_____

Quick Check

Add. Then change the order and complete a new addition sentence.

1. $3 + 2 = \underline{5}$
    $\underline{2} + \underline{3} = \underline{5}$

2. $1 + 5 = \underline{6}$
    $\underline{5} + \underline{1} = \underline{6}$

Write the sum.

3. $4 + 4 = \underline{8}$
4. $5 + 2 = \underline{7}$
5. $7 + 1 = \underline{8}$

6. $0 + 7 = \underline{7}$
7. $3 + 4 = \underline{7}$
8. $8 + 0 = \underline{8}$

9. $\begin{array}{r} 3 \\ +1 \\ \hline 4 \end{array}$
10. $\begin{array}{r} 0 \\ +5 \\ \hline 5 \end{array}$
11. $\begin{array}{r} 6 \\ +2 \\ \hline 8 \end{array}$
12. $\begin{array}{r} 1 \\ +6 \\ \hline 7 \end{array}$
13. $\begin{array}{r} 3 \\ +3 \\ \hline 6 \end{array}$
14. $\begin{array}{r} 2 \\ +4 \\ \hline 6 \end{array}$

Write an addition sentence to solve.

15. There are 2 red balloons. There are 5 yellow balloons. How many balloons are there?

$\underline{2} \; (+) \; \underline{5} \; (=) \; \underline{7}$

$\underline{7}$ balloons

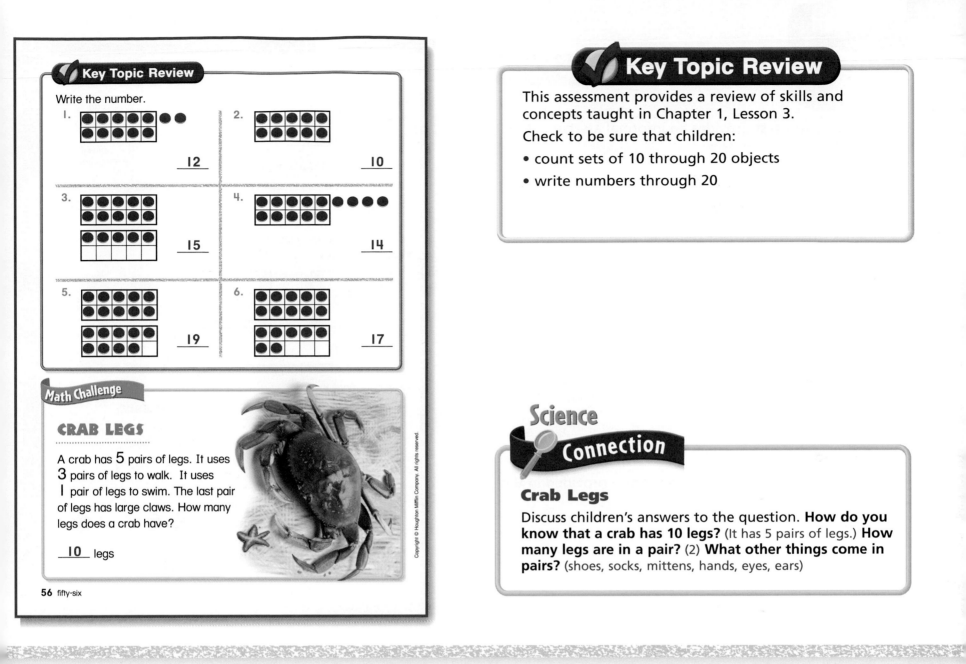

Write the number.

1. 12

2. 10

3. 15

4. 14

5. 19

6. 17

Math Challenge

CRAB LEGS

A crab has 5 pairs of legs. It uses 3 pairs of legs to walk. It uses 1 pair of legs to swim. The last pair of legs has large claws. How many legs does a crab have?

10 legs

56 fifty-six

Key Topic Review

This assessment provides a review of skills and concepts taught in Chapter 1, Lesson 3.

Check to be sure that children:

• count sets of 10 through 20 objects

• write numbers through 20

Science Connection

Crab Legs

Discuss children's answers to the question. **How do you know that a crab has 10 legs?** (It has 5 pairs of legs.) **How many legs are in a pair?** (2) **What other things come in pairs?** (shoes, socks, mittens, hands, eyes, ears)

Chapter Review/Test

Purpose: This test provides an informal assessment of the Chapter 2 objectives.

Chapter Test Items 1–25

To assign a numerical grade for this Chapter Test, use 4 points for each test item.

Item 3 story: There are 2 red balls. There are 3 yellow balls. How many balls are there in all? (5 balls)

Check Understanding

Use children's work on word problems to informally assess progress on chapter content.

Customizing Your Instruction

For children who have not yet mastered these objectives, you can use the reteaching resources listed in the chart below.

Assessment Options

A summary test for this chapter is also provided in the Unit Resource Folder.

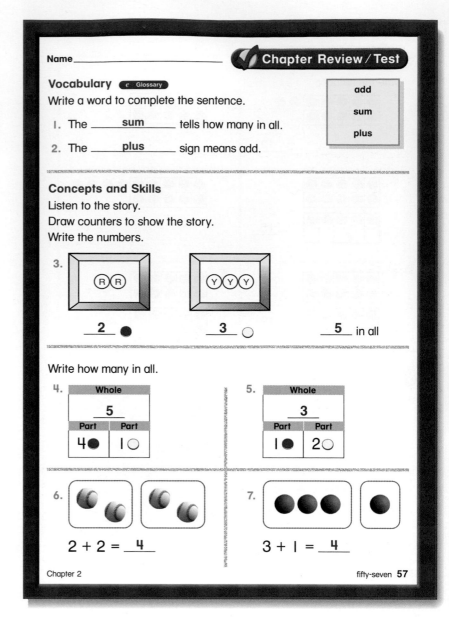

Reteaching Support

Chapter Test Items	Summary Test Items	Chapter Objectives Tested	TE Pages	Use These Reteaching Resources
1–2	1–2	**2A** Develop and use math vocabulary relating to addition concepts.	39A–40	Reteach Resource and *Ways to Success* CD: 2.3 Skillsheet 10
3–10, 13–24	3–8, 5–20	**2B** Solve addition problems horizontally and vertically through 8 using + and =, including problems with 0 as an addend.	35A–42, 47A–50	Reteach Resources and *Ways to Success* CD: 2.1–2.4, 2.6, 2.7 Skillsheets 11–12
11–12	11–14	**2C** Understand the order property of addition.	45A–46	Reteach Resource and *Ways to Success* CD: 2.5 Skillsheet 13
25	9–10	**2D** Write number sentences to solve story problems.	51A–54	Reteach Resource and *Ways to Success* CD: 2.8 Skillsheet 4

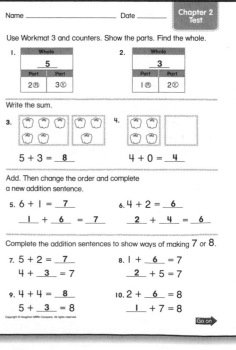

Write the sum.

8. $2 + 0 = \underline{2}$ 9. $0 + 0 = \underline{0}$ 10. $0 + 5 = \underline{5}$

Add. Then change the order and complete
a new addition sentence.

11. $4 + 1 = \underline{5}$ 12. $2 + 4 = \underline{6}$

    $\underline{1} + \underline{4} = \underline{5}$ $\underline{4} + \underline{2} = \underline{6}$

Write the sum.

13. $3 + 3 = \underline{6}$ 14. $5 + 3 = \underline{8}$ 15. $2 + 5 = \underline{7}$

16. $0 + 6 = \underline{6}$ 17. $4 + 3 = \underline{7}$ 18. $2 + 6 = \underline{8}$

19.	20.	21.	22.	23.	24.
$\begin{array}{r} 1 \\ +3 \\ \hline 4 \end{array}$	$\begin{array}{r} 6 \\ +0 \\ \hline 6 \end{array}$	$\begin{array}{r} 2 \\ +2 \\ \hline 4 \end{array}$	$\begin{array}{r} 6 \\ +1 \\ \hline 7 \end{array}$	$\begin{array}{r} 4 \\ +4 \\ \hline 8 \end{array}$	$\begin{array}{r} 0 \\ +8 \\ \hline 8 \end{array}$

Problem Solving

Write an addition sentence to solve.
Write the answer.

25. There are 3 red balloons.
    There are 4 yellow balloons.
    How many balloons in all?

$\underline{3}$ (+) $\underline{4}$ (=) $\underline{7}$

$\underline{7}$ balloons

Use the End of Grade Test Prep Assessment Guide
to help familiarize your children with the format
of standardized tests.

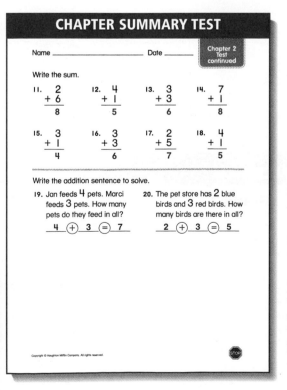

CHAPTER SUMMARY TEST

Name _____ Date _____   Chapter 2 Test continued

Write the sum.

11.	12.	13.	14.
$\begin{array}{r} 2 \\ +6 \\ \hline 8 \end{array}$	$\begin{array}{r} 4 \\ +1 \\ \hline 5 \end{array}$	$\begin{array}{r} 3 \\ +3 \\ \hline 6 \end{array}$	$\begin{array}{r} 7 \\ +1 \\ \hline 8 \end{array}$

15.	16.	17.	18.
$\begin{array}{r} 3 \\ +1 \\ \hline 4 \end{array}$	$\begin{array}{r} 3 \\ +3 \\ \hline 6 \end{array}$	$\begin{array}{r} 2 \\ +5 \\ \hline 7 \end{array}$	$\begin{array}{r} 4 \\ +1 \\ \hline 5 \end{array}$

Write the addition sentence to solve.

19. Jan feeds 4 pets. Marci
    feeds 3 pets. How many
    pets do they feed in all?
    $\underline{4}$ (+) $\underline{3}$ (=) $\underline{7}$

20. The pet store has 2 blue
    birds and 3 red birds. How
    many birds are there in all?
    $\underline{2}$ (+) $\underline{3}$ (=) $\underline{5}$

STOP

Addition Concepts   58

CHAPTER 3

Lesson by Lesson Overview
Subtraction Concepts

Lesson 1
- Children are introduced to the concept of subtraction through oral problems, which they act out.
- Learning subtraction in a context helps children understand the concept.
- The initial introduction to subtraction uses take away, which most children can understand.

Lesson 2
- Using a part-part-whole workmat and counters provides children with a physical representation of that aspect of subtraction.
- This model is used to illustrate subtraction situations where the whole and one part is known.

Lesson 3
- Children are introduced to subtraction sentences.
- Pictorial representations provide a visual for finding differences.
- The use of symbols − and = takes children to the symbolic level of subtraction.

Lesson 4
- Writing a subtraction sentence for a pictured model requires children to interpret the symbolic representation of taking away.
- Circling and drawing an X through the objects that are subtracted provides a clear model.
- Children create and solve their own problems as they interpret a picture problem.

Lesson 5
- Subtracting with zero can be difficult for some children.
- Pictures help children visualize the ideas of taking none away and taking all away.

Lesson 6
- Children use models and write subtraction sentences to find different ways to subtract from 7 and 8.
- The algebra readiness activity has children write a subtraction sentence to solve a problem.

Lesson 7
- The vertical form is presented with the horizontal form to show children that subtraction can be written two ways.
- The use of a single model reinforces the sameness of the two forms.

Lesson 8
- Children use models to act out subtraction problems.
- Acting out a problem is a strategy that helps children solve problems directly without the use of number sentences.
- Subtraction is practiced throughout the lesson.

SKILLS TRACE: SUBTRACTION CONCEPTS

Grade K	Grade 1	Grade 2
• model subtraction (ch. 14)	• model subtraction as take away	• use the addition properties to find the difference (ch. 3)
• complete subtraction sentences (ch. 14)	• model subtraction as part-part-whole	
• subtract 1 from 1 through 10 (ch. 14)	• find the difference of a subtraction sentence	
• subtract 2 from 2 through 10 (ch. 14)	• subtract all or none	
	• write subtraction sentences	
	• subtract in vertical form	

Chapter Planner

Lesson	Objective	Vocabulary	Materials	✓ NCTM Standards
3.1 (Hands-On) Subtraction Stories p. 61A	Model subtraction stories.		two-color counters, crayons	Model situations that involve the addition and subtraction of whole numbers, using objects, pictures, and symbols.
3.2 (Hands-On) Model Subtraction p. 63A	Show the meaning of subtraction as parts and wholes.	whole part subtract	two-color counters, overhead two-color counters, part-part-whole transparency, Workmat 3, green and red crayons	Develop and use strategies for whole-number computations, with a focus on addition and subtraction.
3.3 Use Symbols to Subtract p. 65A	Solve subtraction sentences using symbols.	minus sign equal sign	index cards, counters, blank transparency	Develop and use strategies for whole-number computations, with a focus on addition and subtraction.
3.4 Write Subtraction Sentences p. 67A	Write subtraction sentences to show the difference.	subtraction sentence difference	counters, cubes, number and symbol cards (Learning Tool (LT) 14 and 15), blank transparency	Model situations that involve the addition and subtraction of whole numbers, using objects, pictures and symbols.
3.5 Zero in Subtraction p. 71A	Subtract 0 or find a difference of 0.	zero	counters	Connect number words and numerals to the quantities they represent, using various physical models and representations.
3.6 (Hands-On) Subtract from 8 or Less p. 73A	Model subtraction from 8 or less; write subtraction sentences to find the difference.		cubes, counters, index cards	Develop and use strategies for whole number ... addition and subtraction.
3.7 Subtract in Vertical Form p. 75A	Subtract in vertical form.		blank transparency, number cards (LT14), symbol cards 1–6 (LT15)	Develop and use strategies for whole number... addition and subtraction.
3.8 Problem Solving: Act It Out With Models p. 77A	Use models to act out subtraction problems.		counters, real or play coins, tagboard	Solve problems that arise in mathematics and in other contexts

Resources For Reaching All Learners

LESSON RESOURCES: Reteach, Practice, Enrichment, Problem Solving, Homework, English Learners, Daily Routines, Transparencies, Math Center.

ADDITIONAL RESOURCES FROM HOUGHTON MIFFLIN: Chapter Challenges, Combination Classroom Planning Guide, Every Day Counts, Math to Learn (Student Handbook)

Every Day Counts
The Daily Depositor, Number Stories, Daily Domino, and Counting Tape activities in Every Day Counts support the math in this chapter.

Assessing Prior Knowledge

Before beginning the chapter, you can assess student understandings in order to assist you in differentiating instruction.

Complete Chapter Pretest in Unit Resource Folder

Use this test to assess both prerequisite skills (**Are You Ready?** — one page) and chapter content (**Check What You Know** — two pages).

Chapter 3 Prerequisite Skills Pretest

Chapter 3 New Content Pretest

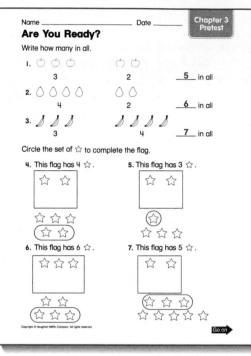

Customizing Instruction

For Students Having Difficulty

Items	Prerequisites	Ways to Success
1–3	Understands how to count and add numbers through 10.	CD: 2.5 Skillsheet 15
4–7	Understands how to count and add sets of numbers through 10.	CD: 2.5 Skillsheet 16

Ways to Success: Intervention for every concept and skill (CD-ROM or Chapter Intervention Skillsheets).

For Students Having Success

Items	Objectives	Resources
1–2	3A Use vocabulary relating to subtraction concepts.	Enrichment 3.2–3.4
3–4	3B Model and write subtraction sentences.	Enrichment 3.2–3.4
5–8	3C Solve subtraction problems from 8 or less.	Enrichment 3.5–3.7
9–10	3D Use models to act out subtraction problems.	Enrichment 3.8

Consider using **Chapter Challenges** with any students who have success with all new chapter content.

Other Pretest Options

Informal Pretest

The pretest assesses vocabulary and prerequisite skills needed for success in this chapter.

***Ways to Success* CD-ROM**

The *Ways to Success* chapter pretest has automatic assignment of appropriate review lessons.

Chapter Resources

Assessing Prior Knowledge

Calendar Countdown (count backward)

- Have one partner pick a number between 5 and 20. Both partners count backward to 0 from that number.
- Then have the second partner choose a different number and repeat the countdown.

Ongoing Skill Activity

Zeroes for Breakfast? (subtracting 0, 1, 2 and 3)

- Prepare a simple game board that looks like a bowl of cereal. Include a start/finish space. Write subtraction facts in game spaces around the rim of the bowl.
- Players take turns rolling a number cube with the numbers 1, 2, and 3 on it, then advance the number of spaces shown on the cube.
- Players use counters to find the difference of the exercise they land on. Have other players check the subtraction. If correct, the player stays on the space. If the answer is incorrect, they return to the previous space.
- When a player lands on a space in which the difference is 0, he or she gets an extra turn.

Connecting to the Unit Project

- Tell children the following subtraction story. Encourage them to model the story with counters.
- **Mrs. Garcia had 8 tomatoes. She used 3 of them to make tacos. How many tomatoes does she have left?** (5 tomatoes)

Teacher Support

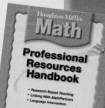

Professional Resources Handbook

Research, Mathematics Content, and Language Intervention

Research-Based Teaching

According to Ginsburg (1989), the way number facts should be taught is via a "thinking approach." This teaching process proposes to begin encouraging children to utilize their informal counting principles to explore and solve number facts. Teaching children that problems make sense and can be solved in a familiar way is much more important than getting children to produce quick, memorized solutions. Knowledge of patterns and principles lead to effective thinking strategies. See *Professional Resources Handbook, Grade 1,* Unit 1.

For more ideas relating to Unit 1, see the Teacher Support Handbook at the back of this Teacher's Edition.

Language Intervention

In China, the basic subtraction facts are also taught using an approach that reinforces the importance of 10 as a special organizer of our number system. As in the case for addition facts, children's ability to compose and decompose numbers less than or equal to 10 is essential. For further explanation, see "Mathematical Language and Subtraction Facts" in the *Professional Resources Handbook Grade 1.*

 Technology

Time-Saving Technology Support
Ways to Assess Customized Spiral Review
  Test Generator CD
Lesson Planner CD-ROM
Ways to Success Intervention CD-ROM
MathTracks CD-ROM
Education Place: www.eduplace.com/math/mw
Houghton Mifflin Math eBook CD-ROM
eManipulatives
eGames

Starting Chapter 3
Subtraction Concepts

CHAPTER OBJECTIVES

3A Develop and use math vocabulary relating to subtraction concepts.

3B Model subtraction, with parts and wholes, in stories and write subtraction sentences.

3C Solve subtraction problems from 8 or less horizontally and vertically using − and =, including problems with 0.

3D Use models to act out subtraction problems.

Math Background

Subtraction Concepts

Addition and subtraction are said to be inverse operations because if the addition of a number (b) to a quantity (a) is followed by the subtraction of the same number (b), the result is the original quantity (a).

There are three types of subtraction.

1) If you want to take away or remove one quantity from another, you use subtraction.

2) If you know one part and the whole amount and you need to know the other part, you use subtraction.

3) If you want to compare one quantity to another, you can use subtraction.

The take-away type of subtraction is studied in this chapter. Children progress from using manipulatives to using pictures to subtract. Vertical subtraction here serves as a readiness activity for future subtraction of multi-digit numbers.

As is found in addition, there is an Identity Property of subtraction. This property states that zero subtracted from any number is equal to that number. Another property of subtraction states that any number subtracted from itself equals zero. However, there is no Commutative Property of subtraction.

Subtraction Concepts

INVESTIGATION

When the pig takes the pumpkin, how many pumpkins will be left?

CHAPTER 3

Chapter 3

fifty-nine **59**

Using The Investigation

- Hold up 4 crayons. **How many crayons do you see?** (4 crayons) Take 2 crayons away. **How many crayons are left?** (2 crayons) **This is the *difference*.**

- Have children find a group of 4 or fewer items from the classroom. Then ask them to take away 1–3 items from that group and tell how many are left.

- Read the question to children. **Look at the pumpkins. When the pig takes the pumpkin, how many pumpkins will be left?** (2)

 For more information about projects and investigations, visit Education Place. **eduplace.com/math/mw/**

Harvest Time
....
Listen to your teacher.

For Mathematically Promising Students

The *Chapter Challenges* resource book provides blackline masters for activities that explore, extend, and connect the mathematics in every chapter. To support this independent work, see the Teacher Notes for each activity.

Explore: Circus Ring Stories, page 13, after Lesson 1
Extend: Function Tables, page 15, after Lesson 3
Connect: Counter Facts, page 17, after Lesson 5

Using This Page

- Read these stories to the children.
- Have children model each story using counters and the workmat on this page.

José has 3 apples in his bag. He gives 1 apple to Sammy. How many apples does José have left?

- Have each child put 3 counters on the workmat and then remove 1. Count how many are left. (2)

Lexi has 2 pumpkins in her garden. She gives 1 to her grandmother. How many pumpkins does Lexi have left in her garden? (1)

- Have the children explain how they solved the problem using counters.
- Create other subtraction stories and have children explain how they solved the problems.

NSF Children's Math Worlds

Children's Math Worlds focuses on the use of models to represent mathematical situations. Thus, using a *Children's Math Worlds* lesson helps students develop a general facility with drawing models to support their thinking that will transfer to all their mathematical work.

Hands-On: Subtraction Stories

Lesson 3.1

PLANNING THE LESSON

MATHEMATICS OBJECTIVE

Model subtraction stories.

Use Lesson Planner CD-ROM for Lesson 3.1.

Daily Routines

Calendar

Have a volunteer find today's date on the calendar. Ask what the date was two days ago. Have a volunteer count back to find the date.

Sunday	Monday	Tuesday	Wednesday	Thursday	Friday	Saturday
			1	2	3	4
5	6	7	8	9	10	11
12	13	14	15	16	17	18
19	20	21	22	23	24	25
26	27	28	29	30	31	

Vocabulary

Show children a group of 5 books. Tell them that you are going to *take away,* or *subtract,* 1 book; then remove a book from the group. Ask a child to come and *remove* various numbers of books.

Vocabulary Cards

Meeting North Carolina's Standards

1.03 Develop fluency with single-digit addition and corresponding differences using strategies such as modeling, composing and decomposing quantities, using doubles, and making tens. Also **1.04**

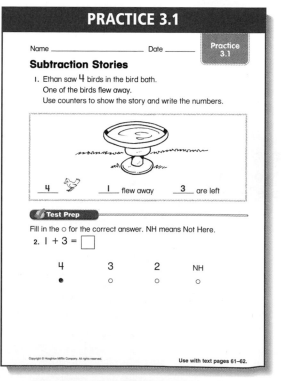

Lesson Transparency 3.1

Problem of the Day

Elsa had 5 fish. Her brother gave her 2 more fish. How many fish does Elsa have in all? (7 fish)

Quick Review

$$\begin{array}{r} 5 \\ + 3 \\ \hline (8) \end{array} \qquad \begin{array}{r} 2 \\ + 6 \\ \hline (8) \end{array} \qquad \begin{array}{r} 4 \\ + 3 \\ \hline (7) \end{array} \qquad \begin{array}{r} 5 \\ + 2 \\ \hline (7) \end{array} \qquad \begin{array}{r} 1 \\ + 7 \\ \hline (8) \end{array}$$

Lesson Quiz

There were 6 frogs on a log. Two frogs hopped off. How many frogs are left? (4 frogs)

LEVELED PRACTICE

RETEACH 3.1

Name _____ Date _____ **Reteach 3.1**

Activity: Subtraction Stories

You can use counters to show the numbers in a story.
Noah saw 3 rabbits. 2 rabbits ran away.
How many rabbits were left?

rabbits   ran away   left

You can write the numbers in a story.
You can count to tell how many are left.

Show the story with counters. Write the numbers.

The rabbit found 4 carrots. It ate 2 carrots.
Use counters to show the story.

Write the numbers to tell how many carrots are left.

__4__ carrots __2__ eaten __2__ left

Copyright © Houghton Mifflin Company. All rights reserved.   Use with text pages 61–62.

PRACTICE 3.1

Name _____ Date _____ **Practice 3.1**

Subtraction Stories

1. Ethan saw 4 birds in the bird bath.
   One of the birds flew away.
   Use counters to show the story and write the numbers.

__4__ _____ __1__ flew away __3__ are left

Test Prep

Fill in the ○ for the correct answer. NH means Not Here.

2. 1 + 3 = ☐

   4 ●   3 ○   2 ○   NH ○

Copyright © Houghton Mifflin Company. All rights reserved.   Use with text pages 61–62.

ENRICHMENT 3.1

Name _____ Date _____ **Enrichment 3.1**

Story Time

1. Make up a story for the problem.
   Show the story with ⊖ and ⬭.
   Write the numbers.

   __3__   __1__ picked up __2__ left

2. Tell a subtraction story.
   Show the story with ⊖ and ⬭.
   Write the numbers.

   ___ ___ ___ left

Copyright © Houghton Mifflin Company. All rights reserved.   Use with text pages 61–62.

Practice Workbook Page 16

Reaching All Learners
Differentiated Instruction

English Learners

- The word *left* has several meanings in English. Worksheet 3.1 introduces the meaning of the word *left* in the context of subtraction. English-language learners will need to understand this meaning as they learn to subtract.

Inclusion
AUDITORY, TACTILE

Materials: *counters*

- Give the child 6 counters. Tell him or her to pretend that each counter is a mouse.
- Tell a story about 2 mice running away from the group. Ask how many counters should be taken away to show the story.
- Have the child count the remaining counters and ask how many mice are left.

Gifted and Talented
AUDITORY, KINESTHETIC

Materials: *toy cars*

- Give children several toy cars. Let them work with a partner to create "take-away stories" about the cars.
- Allow time for partners to share their stories with the class.

Literature Connection

Read *Ten Little Mice* by Joyce Dunbar. Retell the passage that describes when 7 mice were in a tunnel and 1 mouse ran home when he saw a badger's snout. Have children use counters to model that passage and tell how many little mice are left.

MATH CENTER

Cross-Curricular Activity

As you use this activity to relate the mathematics of this lesson to another curriculum area, children will see how math can help them with other subjects.

PROBLEM SOLVING 3.1

Name _____ Date _____ | Problem Solving 3.1

Subtraction Stories

Draw or show the story with counters.
Write the numbers. Then solve.

The man had 5 balloons.
2 balloons blew away.
How many balloons were left?

_5_ balloons _2_ blew away _3_ balloons left

1. Del had 2 bags of popcorn. He gave 1 bag to his friend. How many bags were left?

Draw or write to explain.

_2_ bags _1_ given away
_1_ bag left

2. Kace had 4 carrots. She ate 2 carrots. How many carrots were left?

_4_ carrots _2_ eaten
_2_ carrots left

3. There were 3 eggs in the nest. 1 egg hatched. How many eggs were left?

_3_ eggs _1_ hatched
_2_ eggs left

Copyright © Houghton Mifflin Company. All rights reserved.

Use with text pages 61–62.

HOMEWORK 3.1

Name _____ Date _____ | Homework 3.1

Subtraction Stories

Paul had 4 balloons.
He gave 2 balloons to Brad.
How many balloons did Paul have left?

Use 4 counters to show the problem.
Take 2 counters away.
Count how many are left. Write the number.

_4_ – _2_ = _2_ left

Draw the story. Write the numbers.

1. Emily had 5 balls. She left one in the park. How many balls does she have left?

_5_ – _1_ = _4_ left

Draw here.

2. You have 5 books and take 2 to school. How many books do you have left?

_5_ – _2_ = _3_ left

Draw here.

Copyright © Houghton Mifflin Company. All rights reserved.

Use with text pages 61–62.

Homework Workbook Page 16

ENGLISH LEARNERS 3.1

Name _____ Date _____ | English Learners 3.1

Subtraction Stories

5 mice play.   2 mice run away.
        3 mice are **left**.

How many are left?

1.

6 foxes play.   4 run away.
        There are _2_ **left**.

2.

8 rabbits play.   3 run away.
        There are _5_ **left**.

To the Teacher: Use the example at the top of the page to demonstrate the meaning of the word *left*. Then have children count the animals and write the numbers. Have them write the number of animals left in each group.

Copyright © Houghton Mifflin Company. All rights reserved.

Use with text pages 61–62.

TEACHING LESSON 3.1

LESSON ORGANIZER

Objective Model subtraction stories.

Resources Reteach, Practice, Enrichment, Problem Solving, Homework, English Learners, Transparencies, Math Center

Materials two-color counters, crayons

Warm-Up Activity
Take-Away Subtraction

iii Small Group	⏱ 5 minutes	Visual, Auditory

Materials: counters

1. Give each child 6 counters. Tell a story involving take-away subtraction that can be modeled with counters.

2. Ask volunteers to tell stories for the children to model.

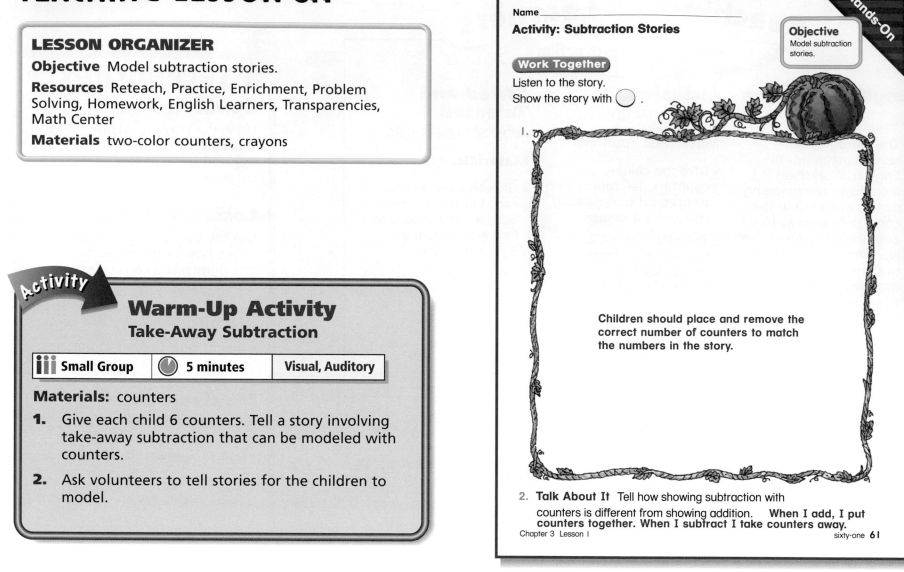

Name_____

Activity: Subtraction Stories

Objective Model subtraction stories.

Work Together

Listen to the story.
Show the story with ◯ .

1.

Children should place and remove the correct number of counters to match the numbers in the story.

2. **Talk About It** Tell how showing subtraction with counters is different from showing addition. When I add, I put counters together. When I subtract I take counters away.

Chapter 3 Lesson 1

sixty-one **61**

① Introduce
Discuss Modeling Subtraction

iiii Whole Group	⏱ 5–10 minutes	Auditory, Tactile

Materials: *two-color counters*

1. *Subtract 1 from 5.* Tell a story. **There are 5 children in the lunch line.** Ask children to place 5 counters in a line. **One child leaves the line and sits down.** Have children remove 1 counter. **How many children are in line now?** Have children count to find how many are left. (4 children)

2. **What happens when we take 1 or more away from a group? Do we have more or fewer in the group?** (fewer) Explain that one meaning of subtraction is to take away from a group.

② Develop

Work Together

Give counters to children and say: **There are 5 carrots in the garden.** Have children place 5 counters on the page to show how many in all. Explain that the counters stand for the carrots. **Mama rabbit takes away 2 carrots.** Have children remove 2 counters. **How many carrots are left?** (3 carrots) Have them draw the counters that show the difference.

Encourage children to create other stories about carrots and a rabbit taking some of the carrots. Allow time for volunteers to tell their stories as the children place and remove counters on the page.

Use the **Talk About It** to discuss how showing subtraction with counters is different from showing addition.

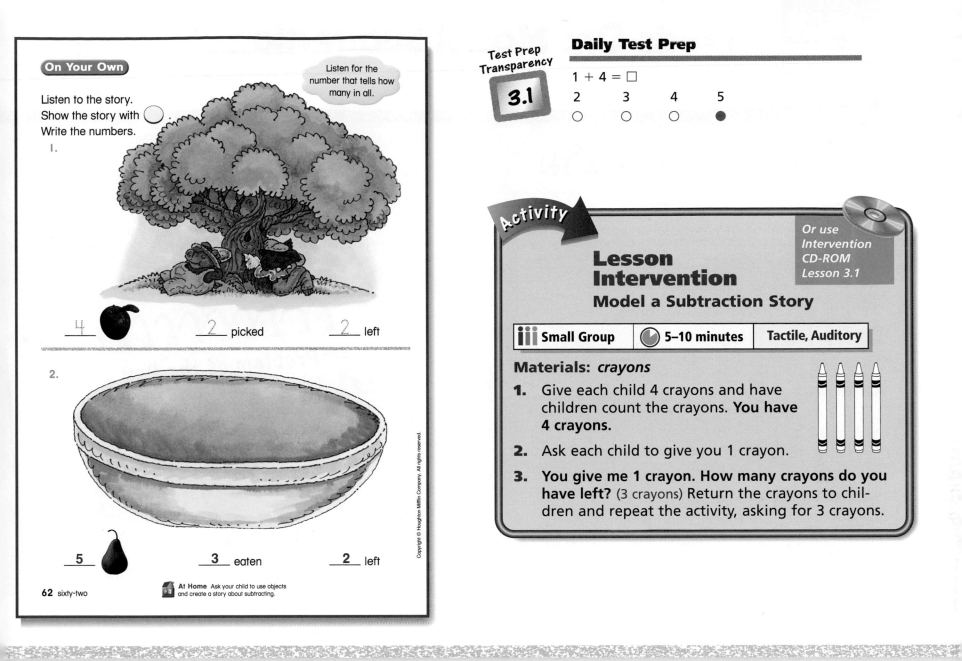

On Your Own

Listen to the story.
Show the story with ◯.
Write the numbers.

Listen for the number that tells how many in all.

1.

___4___ ___2___ picked ___2___ left

2.

___5___ ___3___ eaten ___2___ left

62 sixty-two

At Home Ask your child to use objects and create a story about subtracting.

Daily Test Prep

$1 + 4 = \square$

2 ◯ 3 ◯ 4 ◯ 5 ●

Activity

Or use Intervention CD-ROM Lesson 3.1

Lesson Intervention
Model a Subtraction Story

| 👤👤👤 Small Group | 🕐 5–10 minutes | Tactile, Auditory |

Materials: *crayons*

1. Give each child 4 crayons and have children count the crayons. **You have 4 crayons.**

2. Ask each child to give you 1 crayon.

3. **You give me 1 crayon. How many crayons do you have left?** (3 crayons) Return the crayons to children and repeat the activity, asking for 3 crayons.

③ Practice

On Your Own

Have children look at the apple tree as you tell this story: **There are 4 apples on the tree.** Ask children to place 4 counters on the tree. Explain that the counters stand for the number of apples in all. **Two of the apples are picked.** Let children remove 2 counters. **How many apples are left?** (2 apples) Have children write the numbers on the lines to show how many in all, how many were picked, and how many are left.

Continue with the next picture. **Five pears are in the bowl. Someone eats 3 of the pears. How many pears are left?** (2 pears) Have children model the problem and write the numbers.

Common Error

Removing the Wrong Number of Counters

Children may lose track of the number of counters they need to remove. Have children count aloud as they remove each counter.

④ Assess and Close

When you subtract in this activity, what are you doing? (taking away, or removing, part of a whole group; telling how many are left)

If you had 4 oranges in a bag, could you take away 5 oranges? (no) **Why not?** (You cannot take away more than you start with.)

Keeping a Journal

Think about a group of things you have, like socks or books. Write a story about taking away some of them. Use counters to find out how many are left. Write the number that tells how many are left.

Hands-On: Model Subtraction

Lesson 3.2

PLANNING THE LESSON

MATHEMATICS OBJECTIVE
Show the meaning of subtraction as parts and wholes.

Use Lesson Planner CD-ROM for Lesson 3.2.

Meeting North Carolina's Standards
1.03 Develop fluency with single-digit addition and corresponding differences using strategies such as modeling, composing and decomposing quantities, using doubles, and making tens.

Daily Routines

Calendar
Count the number of days in a whole week. Place stickers on the 2 days that begin with S. Have children tell how many days do not begin with S.

Sunday	Monday	Tuesday	Wednesday	Thursday	Friday	Saturday
			1	2	3	4
5	6	7	8	9	10	11
12	13	14	15	16	17	18
19	20	21	22	23	24	25
26	27	28	29	30	31	

Vocabulary
Introduce the word **subtract** and demonstrate its meaning in part-part-whole. Tell children that when you know how many in all, or the **whole** such as 5, and you know one **part**, such as 3, you subtract to find the other part, 2.

Vocabulary Cards

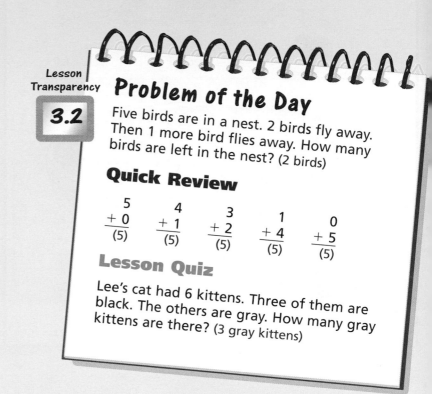

Lesson Transparency 3.2

Problem of the Day
Five birds are in a nest. 2 birds fly away. Then 1 more bird flies away. How many birds are left in the nest? (2 birds)

Quick Review

$$\begin{array}{ccccc} 5 & 4 & 3 & 1 & 0 \\ +0 & +1 & +2 & +4 & +5 \\ \hline (5) & (5) & (5) & (5) & (5) \end{array}$$

Lesson Quiz
Lee's cat had 6 kittens. Three of them are black. The others are gray. How many gray kittens are there? (3 gray kittens)

LEVELED PRACTICE

RETEACH 3.2

Name _____ Date _____ **Reteach 3.2**

Model Subtraction

If you know the whole and one of the parts, you can subtract one part to find the other part.

There are 3 counters in all.	2 counters are red.	1 counter is yellow.
Whole **3** / Part __ Part __	Whole **3** / Part 2 (R) Part __	Whole **3** / Part 2 (R) Part 1 (Y)

Use Workmat 3 and counters.
Show the red part. Find the yellow part.
Write how many are yellow.

1. Whole **5** / Part 3 (R) Part 2 (Y)
2. Whole **4** / Part 3 (R) Part 1 (Y)
3. Whole **2** / Part 1 (R) Part 1 (Y)
4. Whole **5** / Part 2 (R) Part 3 (Y)

Copyright © Houghton Mifflin Company. All rights reserved.   Use with text pages 63–64.

PRACTICE 3.2

Name _____ Date _____ **Practice 3.2**

Model Subtraction
Use Workmat 3 and counters.
Show the red part. Find the yellow part.
Write how many yellow.

1. Whole **4** / Part 3 (R) Part 1 (Y)
2. Whole **5** / Part 1 (R) Part 4 (Y)
3. Whole **3** / Part 1 (R) Part 2 (Y)
4. Whole **4** / Part 2 (R) Part 2 (Y)

Test Prep

Fill in the ○ for the correct answer. NH means Not Here.

5. There are 5 birds in all. Then 3 birds fly away. How many birds are left?

  2 ● 3 ○ 4 ○ NH ○

Copyright © Houghton Mifflin Company. All rights reserved.   Use with text pages 63–64.

ENRICHMENT 3.2

Name _____ Date _____ **Enrichment 3.2**

Pet Math

Write the missing number.

1. 4 🐟 in all / 3 🐟   1 🐟
2. 5 🦭 in all / 3 🦭   2 🦭
3. 6 🐢 in all / 2 🐢   4 🐢

Write About It How are you able to know the missing numbers? I know that 2 parts equal the whole. The number that is there added to the missing number makes the whole.

Copyright © Houghton Mifflin Company. All rights reserved.   Use with text pages 63–64.

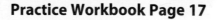

Practice Workbook Page 17

Reaching All Learners
Differentiated Instruction

English Learners

- Children will need to understand the term *more than* in order to explain the process behind their thinking. Use Worksheet 3.2 to develop an understanding of this term.

Special Needs
VISUAL, TACTILE

Materials: *beads, string*

- Show 3 red and 4 blue beads on a string. Ask: How many beads in all? (7 beads)

- Ask how many beads are in the blue part. (4) How many beads are in the red part? (3)
- Repeat with different problems.

Early Finishers
TACTILE, VISUAL

Materials: *counters*

- Have one child pick up from 3 to 8 counters and put some in one hand and hide the rest in the other hand.
- Have the child tell a partner how many counters there are in all, then show the contents of one hand.
- Have the partner decide how many counters are in the other hand, then count to check.

Art Connection

Have children use craft sticks to make simple people puppets. Then have them use the puppets to act out subtraction stories about people.

MATH CENTER

Basic Skills Activity

Motivate children to build basic skills. Use this activity to address multiple learning styles using hands-on activities related to the skills of this lesson.

TECHNOLOGY

Spiral Review

To reinforce skills on lessons taught earlier, create **customized** spiral review worksheets using the *Ways to Assess* CD-ROM.

Lesson Planner

You can use the **Lesson Planner CD-ROM** to create a report of the lessons and standards you have taught.

Education Place

Encourage students to visit **Education Place** at **eduplace.com/kids/mw/** for more student activities.

Manipulatives

Interactive Counters with several workmats are available on the *Ways to Success* CD-ROM.

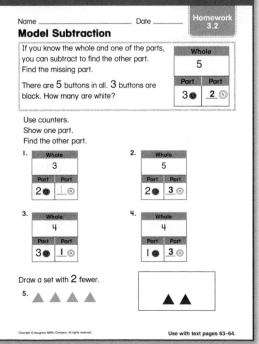

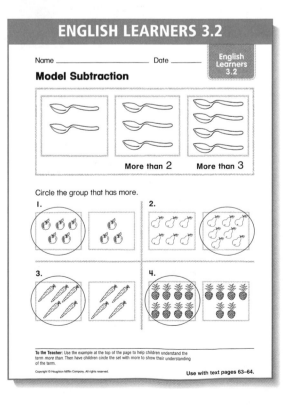

Homework Workbook Page 17

TEACHING LESSON 3.2

LESSON ORGANIZER

Objective Show the meaning of subtraction as parts and wholes.

Resources Reteach, Practice, Enrichment, Problem Solving, Homework, English Learners, Transparencies, Math Center

Materials Two-color counters, overhead two-color counters, part-part-whole transparency, Workmat 3, green and red crayons.

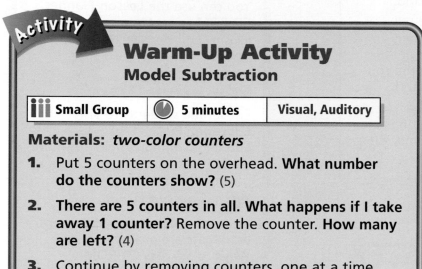

Warm-Up Activity
Model Subtraction

👥 Small Group	🕐 5 minutes	Visual, Auditory

Materials: *two-color counters*

1. Put 5 counters on the overhead. **What number do the counters show?** (5)

2. There are 5 counters in all. **What happens if I take away 1 counter?** Remove the counter. **How many are left?** (4)

3. Continue by removing counters, one at a time. Ask: **How many in all?** (4) **How many are being taken away?** (1) **How many are left?** (3)

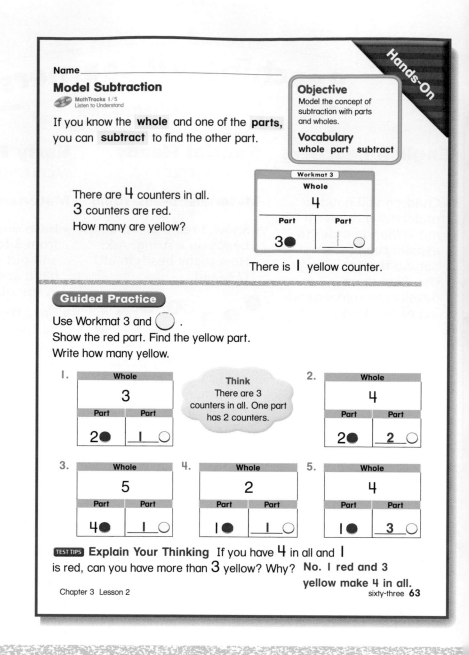

Name _____

Model Subtraction

MathTracks 1/5
Listen to Understand

If you know the **whole** and one of the **parts**, you can **subtract** to find the other part.

Objective
Model the concept of subtraction with parts and wholes.

Vocabulary
whole part subtract

There are 4 counters in all.
3 counters are red.
How many are yellow?

Workmat 3
Whole
4

Part	Part
3●	___ ○

There is 1 yellow counter.

Guided Practice

Use Workmat 3 and ○.
Show the red part. Find the yellow part.
Write how many yellow.

1.

Whole
3

Part	Part
2●	1 ○

Think
There are 3 counters in all. One part has 2 counters.

2.

Whole
4

Part	Part
2●	2 ○

3.

Whole
5

Part	Part
4●	1 ○

4.

Whole
2

Part	Part
1●	1 ○

5.

Whole
4

Part	Part
1●	3 ○

TEST TIPS **Explain Your Thinking** If you have 4 in all and 1 is red, can you have more than 3 yellow? Why? **No. 1 red and 3 yellow make 4 in all.**

Chapter 3 Lesson 2

sixty-three **63**

1 Introduce
Model Part-Part-Whole Subtraction

👥 Whole Group	🕐 10–15 minutes	Visual, Auditory

Materials: *overhead two-color counters, part-part-whole transparency, Workmat 3, counters*

1. *Subtract 2 from 5.* Write 5 in the whole portion of the workmat. **I have a *whole* group of counters. In this group there are 5 in all.**

2. **Two of the counters are red. The rest are yellow.** Place 2 red counters in the left part of the mat. **There are 5 in all and 2 are red. How many counters are yellow?** (3)

3. **How can we make a whole group again?** (Add the parts together.)

4. Repeat the process with several more examples having children model them with Workmat 3 and counters.

2 Develop

Guided Learning

Teaching Example Introduce the objective and vocabulary to the children. Guide them through the example. Show them if they know there are 4 counters in all and 3 are red, then they can find out how many counters are yellow. Have children model the problem on Workmat 3 using two-color counters.

Guided Practice

Have children complete **Exercises 1–5** as you observe. Give several children the opportunity to answer the Explain Your Thinking question. Then discuss the responses with the class.

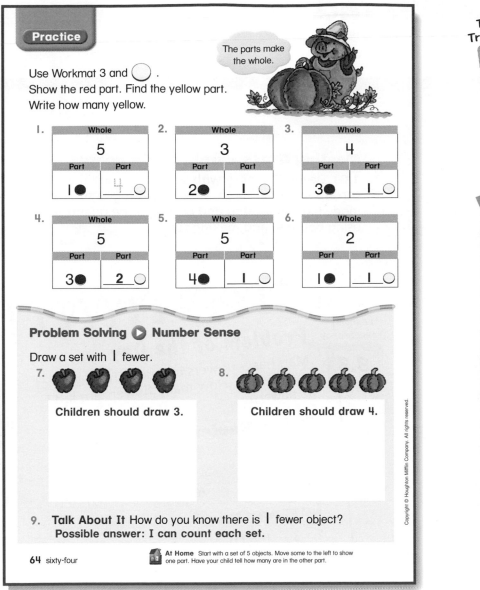

Practice

The parts make the whole.

Use Workmat 3 and ◯ .
Show the red part. Find the yellow part.
Write how many yellow.

1. Whole		2. Whole		3. Whole	
5		3		4	
Part	Part	Part	Part	Part	Part
1 ●	4 ◯	2 ●	1 ◯	3 ●	1 ◯

4. Whole		5. Whole		6. Whole	
5		5		2	
Part	Part	Part	Part	Part	Part
3 ●	2 ◯	4 ●	1 ◯	1 ●	1 ◯

Problem Solving ▶ Number Sense

Draw a set with 1 fewer.

7.

Children should draw 3.

8.

Children should draw 4.

9. **Talk About It** How do you know there is 1 fewer object?
Possible answer: I can count each set.

64 sixty-four

At Home Start with a set of 5 objects. Move some to the left to show one part. Have your child tell how many are in the other part.

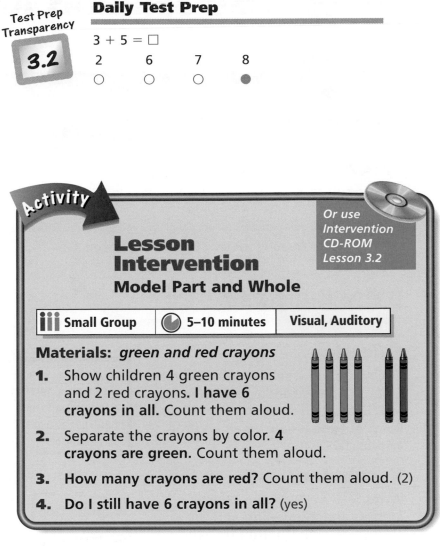

Daily Test Prep

3 + 5 = ☐

2	6	7	8
◯	◯	◯	●

Activity

Or use Intervention CD-ROM Lesson 3.2

Lesson Intervention
Model Part and Whole

👤👤👤 Small Group	🕐 5–10 minutes	Visual, Auditory

Materials: *green and red crayons*

1. Show children 4 green crayons and 2 red crayons. **I have 6 crayons in all.** Count them aloud.

2. Separate the crayons by color. **4 crayons are green.** Count them aloud.

3. **How many crayons are red?** Count them aloud. (2)

4. **Do I still have 6 crayons in all?** (yes)

---

③ Practice

Independent Practice

Children complete **Exercises 1–6** independently.

Problem Solving

After children complete **Exercises 7–8**, call on volunteers to share their solutions. Use the **Talk About It** in Exercise 9 to discuss how children can verify that there is one fewer object.

Common Error

Using the Wrong Operation

Children may add the two given numbers instead of subtracting. Provide exercises in which the children model the whole, move counters to show the known part, and then move counters to show the unknown part.

④ Assess and Close

There are 4 children at the reading table. Three of the children are boys. How many are girls? (1 girl)

There are 5 counters in all. 1 is yellow. How many are red? (4)

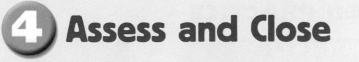

Keeping a Journal

Write a problem about a group of items that has 5 in all. How many are there in one part? How many are in the other part?

Use Symbols to Subtract

PLANNING THE LESSON

MATHEMATICS OBJECTIVE
Solve subtraction sentences using symbols.

Use Lesson Planner CD-ROM for Lesson 3.3.

Meeting North Carolina's Standards
1.03 Develop fluency with single-digit addition and corresponding differences using strategies such as modeling, composing and decomposing quantities, using doubles, and making tens.

Daily Routines

Calendar
Circle one full week on the calendar. Color Sunday, Monday, and Tuesday red. Color the remaining days blue. Point out the whole week and the two parts. Discuss $7 - 3 = 4$.

Sunday	Monday	Tuesday	Wednesday	Thursday	Friday	Saturday
			1	2	3	4
5	6	7	8	9	10	11
12	13	14	15	16	17	18
19	20	21	22	23	24	25
26	27	28	29	30	31	

Vocabulary
Write $5 - 3 = 2$ on the board and identify the **minus sign** and the **equal sign**. Tell children that the number sentence shows subtraction.

Vocabulary Cards

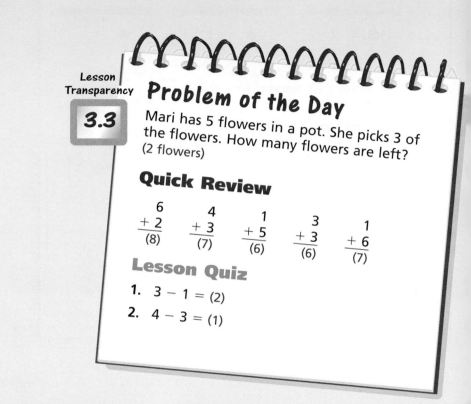

Lesson Transparency 3.3

Problem of the Day
Mari has 5 flowers in a pot. She picks 3 of the flowers. How many flowers are left? (2 flowers)

Quick Review

$$\begin{array}{ccccc} 6 & 4 & 1 & 3 & 1 \\ +2 & +3 & +5 & +3 & +6 \\ \hline (8) & (7) & (6) & (6) & (7) \end{array}$$

Lesson Quiz
1. $3 - 1 = (2)$
2. $4 - 3 = (1)$

LEVELED PRACTICE

RETEACH 3.3
Name _____ Date _____ Reteach 3.3

Use Symbols to Subtract

You can use a minus sign and an equal sign to write about subtraction.

$$4 \quad - \quad 3 \quad = \quad 1$$
minus sign   equal sign

You can circle and cross out to show subtraction.

Circle and cross out to subtract.
Write how many are left.

1. $3 - 1 = 2$
2. $6 - 4 = 2$
3. $4 - 2 = 2$
4. $5 - 3 = 2$
5. $2 - 1 = 1$
6. $6 - 5 = 1$

Use with text pages 65–66.

PRACTICE 3.3
Name _____ Date _____ Practice 3.3

Use Symbols to Subtract
Circle and cross out to subtract.
Write how many are left.

1. $5 - 1 = 4$
2. $6 - 2 = 4$
3. $4 - 3 = 1$
4. $6 - 3 = 3$

Test Prep

Fill in the ○ for the correct answer. NH means Not Here.

5. Allen has 4 ❋. He gives 2 away. How many does he have left?

   4 ○   3 ○   2 ●   NH ○

Explain how you got the answer.

I drew 4 circles, then I crossed out 2 of them.
There were 2 left.

Use with text pages 65–66.

ENRICHMENT 3.3
Name _____ Date _____ Enrichment 3.3

Quick Draw

Draw a picture to show the subtraction. Circle and cross out to subtract. Write how many are left.

1. $5 - 2 = 3$
2. $4 - 3 = 1$
3. $3 - 1 = 2$
4. $6 - 4 = 2$

Use with text pages 65–66.

Practice Workbook Page 18

Reaching All Learners
Differentiated Instruction

English Learners

- To provide children with a visual tool they can use to subtract, they will need to understand the term *cross out*. Use Worksheet 3.3 to help English-language learners understand this term.

Inclusion
AUDITORY, VISUAL

- Draw 4 balls as shown. Write the subtraction sentence 4 − 1 = 3.
- Help the child relate the 4 balls to the 4 in the sentence and the 1 ball to the 1 in the sentence.
- Point to the 3 balls that are not crossed out and to the 3 in the sentence. Identify the 3 as the difference.

Early Finishers
TACTILE, VISUAL

Materials: *index cards*

- Prepare two sets of 10 index cards: subtraction facts to 6 on one set and dot pictures for differences on the other.
- Mix up each set. Have small groups of children work together to match the subtraction on one card and the pictured difference on the other.

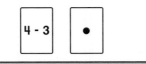

TECHNOLOGY

Spiral Review

Help students remember skills they learned earlier by creating **customized** spiral review worksheets using the *Ways to Assess* CD-ROM.

Education Place

You can visit **Education Place** at eduplace.com/math/mw/ for teacher support materials.

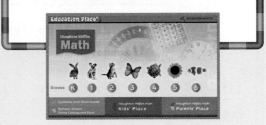

Art Connection

Have children use paint and sponge or potato stamps to make a row of 6 shapes. After the paint dries, have children cross out some of the shapes to subtract. Have them write how many are left.

MATH CENTER

Basic Skills Activity

Motivate children to build basic skills. Use this activity to address multiple learning styles using hands-on activities related to the skills of this lesson.

PROBLEM SOLVING 3.3

Name _____ Date _____
Problem Solving 3.3

Use Symbols to Subtract

Write how many are left.

Draw or write to explain.

1. There are 5 birds in a tree.
   Then 3 birds fly away.
   How many birds are left?
   5 − 3 = __2__ birds left

2. 6 frogs sit on a log.
   2 frogs hop away.
   How many frogs are left?
   6 − 2 = __4__ frogs left

3. 4 candles light the room.
   1 candle burns out.
   How many candles are left burning?
   4 − 1 = __3__ candles left

4. 3 cows graze in the field.
   2 cows return to the barn.
   How many cows are left in the field?
   3 − 2 = __1__ cow left

Copyright © Houghton Mifflin Company. All rights reserved.

Use with text pages 65–66.

HOMEWORK 3.3

Name _____ Date _____
Homework 3.3

Use Symbols to Subtract

You can use a minus sign and an equal sign to write about subtraction.

5 − 2 = 3

minus sign   equal sign

You can circle and cross out to show subtraction.

Circle and cross out to subtract.
Write how many are left.

1. 4 − 2 = __2__   2. 3 − 2 = __1__

3. 6 − 4 = __2__   4. 5 − 2 = __3__

5. Circle the picture that shows 4 − 3.

Copyright © Houghton Mifflin Company. All rights reserved.

Use with text pages 65–66.

ENGLISH LEARNERS 3.3

Name _____ Date _____
English Learners 3.3

Use Symbols to Subtract

The truck is **crossed out**.

1. Cross out the bike.

2. Cross out the boat.

3. Cross out the van.

To the Teacher: Use the example at the top of the page to demonstrate the meaning of the term *cross out*. Then read the sentences with children and have them cross out the objects.

Copyright © Houghton Mifflin Company. All rights reserved.

Use with text pages 65–66.

Homework Workbook Page 18

TEACHING LESSON 3.3

LESSON ORGANIZER

Objective Solve subtraction sentences using symbols.

Resources Reteach, Practice, Enrichment, Problem Solving, Homework, English Learners, Transparencies, Math Center

Materials counters, blank transparency, index cards

Activity
Warm-Up Activity
Model *Take Away* Problems

Small Group	**5 minutes**	**Auditory, Visual**

Materials: *counters*

1. Place 6 counters on the overhead. **How many counters?** (6) Remove 4 counters from the group of 6. **I have 6 and I take away 4. How many are left?** (2)

2. **What is 6 minus 4?** (2)

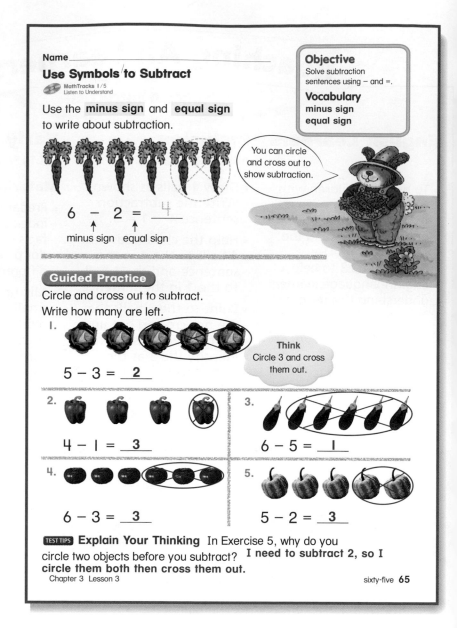

<image name="worksheet">
Name_____

Use Symbols to Subtract
MathTracks 1/5
Listen to Understand

Objective
Solve subtraction sentences using − and =.

Vocabulary
minus sign
equal sign

Use the **minus sign** and **equal sign** to write about subtraction.

You can circle and cross out to show subtraction.

$$6 - 2 = 4$$
↑ minus sign   ↑ equal sign

Guided Practice

Circle and cross out to subtract.
Write how many are left.

1. $5 - 3 = \underline{2}$ **Think** Circle 3 and cross them out.

2. $4 - 1 = \underline{3}$

3. $6 - 5 = \underline{1}$

4. $6 - 3 = \underline{3}$

5. $5 - 2 = \underline{3}$

TEST TIPS **Explain Your Thinking** In Exercise 5, why do you circle two objects before you subtract? **I need to subtract 2, so I circle them both then cross them out.**

Chapter 3 Lesson 3   sixty-five **65**

1 Introduce
Model Symbols for Subtraction

Whole Group	**5–10 minutes**	**Auditory, Visual**

Materials: *blank transparency*

1. *Subtract 5 − 2.* Draw a row of five eggs. Tell this story: **Felipa had 5 eggs. She dropped 2 on the floor.** Draw a circle around 2 eggs to show the eggs that she dropped. Then cross out that group to show they are gone.

2. **How many eggs are left?** Count the eggs aloud. (3 eggs)

2. Retell the story as you write the subtraction sentence $5 - 2 = 3$ under the row of eggs.

3. Point to the minus sign. **This is a minus sign. It means subtract.** Read the sentence aloud as you point to each number and symbol. Have children repeat. **5 minus 2 equals 3.**

2 Develop

Guided Learning

Teaching Example Introduce the objective and vocabulary to the children. Guide them through the example, reading the subtraction sentence aloud. Explain that the circled carrots are the ones that are being taken away, or subtracted.

Guided Practice

Have children complete **Exercises 1–5** as you observe. Give several children the opportunity to answer the Explain Your Thinking question. Then discuss the responses with the class.

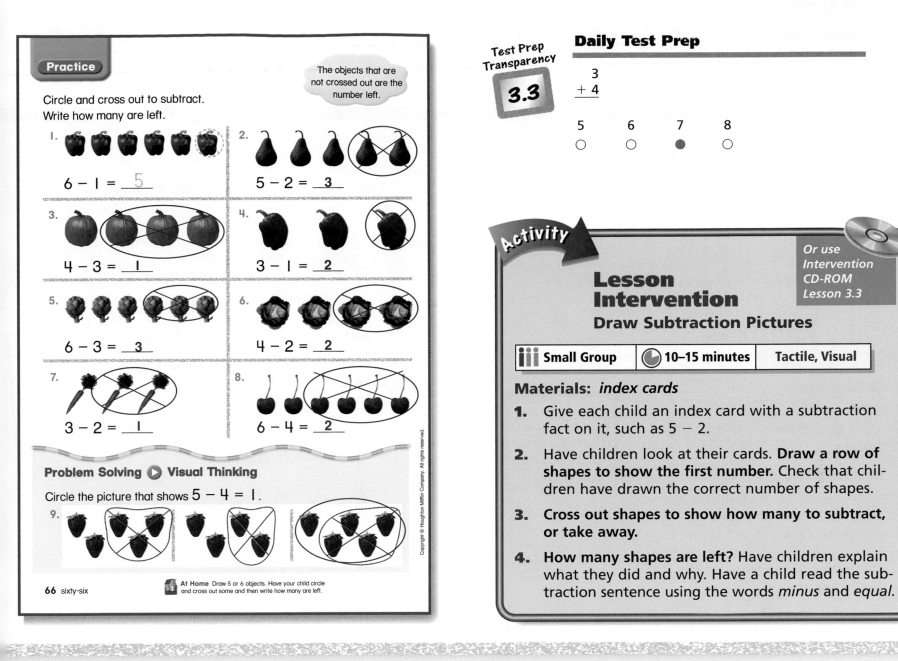

Practice

Circle and cross out to subtract.
Write how many are left.

> The objects that are not crossed out are the number left.

1. $6 - 1 = \underline{5}$

2. $5 - 2 = \underline{3}$

3. $4 - 3 = \underline{1}$

4. $3 - 1 = \underline{2}$

5. $6 - 3 = \underline{3}$

6. $4 - 2 = \underline{2}$

7. $3 - 2 = \underline{1}$

8. $6 - 4 = \underline{2}$

Problem Solving ▷ Visual Thinking

Circle the picture that shows $5 - 4 = 1$.

9.

66 sixty-six

At Home Draw 5 or 6 objects. Have your child circle and cross out some and then write how many are left.

Daily Test Prep

$$\begin{array}{r} 3 \\ + 4 \\ \hline \end{array}$$

5 ○   6 ○   7 ●   8 ○

Activity

Lesson Intervention
Draw Subtraction Pictures

Or use Intervention CD-ROM Lesson 3.3

iii Small Group	⏱ 10–15 minutes	Tactile, Visual

Materials: *index cards*

1. Give each child an index card with a subtraction fact on it, such as $5 - 2$.

2. Have children look at their cards. **Draw a row of shapes to show the first number.** Check that children have drawn the correct number of shapes.

3. **Cross out shapes to show how many to subtract, or take away.**

4. **How many shapes are left?** Have children explain what they did and why. Have a child read the subtraction sentence using the words *minus* and *equal*.

---

3 Practice

Independent Practice

Children complete **Exercises 1–8** independently.

Problem Solving

After children complete **Exercise 9**, call on volunteers to share their responses and explain their reasoning. Ask what the other pictures show.

Common Error

Crossing Out the Wrong Number of Objects

Children may lose track of the number of pictured objects they are subtracting. Have children place a small counter on each object being subtracted, circle the counters on the pictures, remove the counters, and cross out the circled pictures.

---

4 Assess and Close

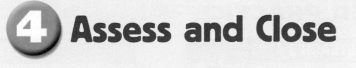

If you draw a picture to show that you subtract 2 apples from a group of 6 apples, how many apples would you circle and cross out? (2 apples)

What is the name of the sign used to write about subtraction? (minus sign)

 **Keeping a Journal**

Draw a subtraction picture about your favorite fruit. Write how many are left.

Write Subtraction Sentences

Lesson
3.4

PLANNING THE LESSON

MATHEMATICS OBJECTIVE
Write subtraction sentences to show the difference.

Use Lesson Planner CD-ROM for Lesson 3.4.

Meeting North Carolina's Standards
1.03 Develop fluency with single-digit addition and corresponding differences using strategies such as modeling, composing and decomposing quantities, using doubles, and making tens.

Daily Routines

Calendar
Choose a date. Ask children to count back 2 days at a time from that day.

Sunday	Monday	Tuesday	Wednesday	Thursday	Friday	Saturday
				1	2	3	4
5	6	7	8	9	10	11
12	13	14	15	16	17	18
19	20	21	22	23	24	25
26	27	28	29	30	31	

Vocabulary
Draw 4 stars on the board. Circle a group of 3 stars and cross out the group. Write 4 − 3 = 1 under the drawing. Explain that it is called a **subtraction sentence**. Identify 1 as the **difference**.

Vocabulary Cards

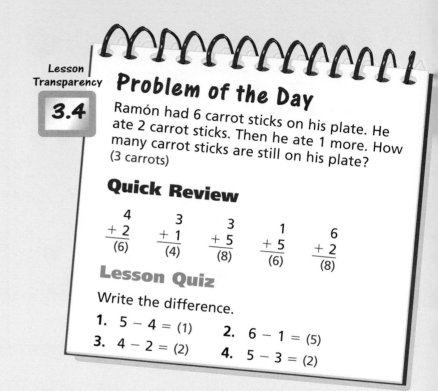

Lesson Transparency
3.4

Problem of the Day
Ramón had 6 carrot sticks on his plate. He ate 2 carrot sticks. Then he ate 1 more. How many carrot sticks are still on his plate? (3 carrots)

Quick Review
$$\begin{array}{ccccc} 4 & 3 & 3 & 1 & 6 \\ +2 & +1 & +5 & +5 & +2 \\ \hline (6) & (4) & (8) & (6) & (8) \end{array}$$

Lesson Quiz
Write the difference.
1. 5 − 4 = (1)   2. 6 − 1 = (5)
3. 4 − 2 = (2)   4. 5 − 3 = (2)

LEVELED PRACTICE

RETEACH 3.4
Reteach 3.4

Write Subtraction Sentences
Write a subtraction sentence to find how many are left.

There are **3** sandwiches. The boys ate **2** for lunch. **I** sandwich is left.

subtraction sentence
3 − 2 = 1
↑ difference

Tell a story.
Write the subtraction sentence.
1. 5 − 2 = 3
2. 6 − 3 = 3
3. 4 − 1 = 3
4. 6 − 1 = 5

Use with text pages 67–68.

PRACTICE 3.4
Practice 3.4

Write Subtraction Sentences
Write the subtraction sentence.
1. 6 − 3 = 3
2. 4 − 1 = 3
3. 5 − 2 = 3
4. 6 − 4 = 2

Write the difference.
5. 5 − 4 = 1   6. 5 − 3 = 2   7. 3 − 2 = 1
8. 6 − 2 = 4   9. 2 − 1 = 1   10. 4 − 3 = 1

Test Prep
Fill in the ○ for the correct answer. NH means Not Here.
11. There are 6 on the team. Then 1 goes home. How many are still playing?
2   7   4   NH
Explain how you arrived at your answer.
I wrote the subtraction sentence: 6 − 1 = 5.

Use with text pages 67–68.

ENRICHMENT 3.4
Enrichment 3.4

What's the Difference?
Circle and cross out some objects in each row. Write the subtraction sentence.
1. 6 − 2 = 4
2. ___ − ___ = ___
3. ___ − ___ = ___
4. ___ − ___ = ___

Write About It If you subtract 4 from 5, will your answer be more or less than 5? Why? **Less than 5. If you are taking away from 5, your answer cannot be more than 5.**

Use with text pages 67–68.

Practice Workbook Page 19

67A   CHAPTER 3   Lesson 4

Reaching All Learners
Differentiated Instruction

English Learners

- The word *difference* has several meanings in English. Children will need to understand the word as part of the language used in subtraction. Worksheet 3.4 will introduce English-language learners to the word in the context of subtraction sentences.

Inclusion
VISUAL, TACTILE

Materials: *two-color counters*

- Tell the child to show 6 counters and explain that you want to subtract 4 from 6.
- Help the child write $6 - 4 =$ ____.
- Guide him or her through the subtraction to find the difference of 2.
- Repeat by subtracting other numbers from 6.

Early Finishers
KINESTHETIC, VISUAL

Materials: *two-color counters, paper cup*

- Give pairs of children 6 two-color counters in a paper cup. Have children gently shake and toss the counters.
- Children write subtraction sentences by counting the total number of counters and subtracting the number of yellow counters.

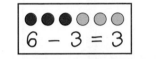
$6 - 3 = 3$

TECHNOLOGY

Spiral Review

You can prepare students for standardized tests with **customized** spiral review on key skills using the *Ways to Assess* CD-ROM.

eBook

eMathBook allows students to review lessons and do homework without carrying their textbooks home.

Lesson Planner

You can customize your teaching plan or meet your curriculum requirements with the **Lesson Planner CD-ROM**.

Music Connection

Sing the song "Bingo" with children. Have children count the number of times they clap as they spell B-i-n-g-o. Then ask them to write 3 subtraction sentences that begin with the number 5.

MATH CENTER

Basic Skills Activity

Motivate children to build basic skills. Use this activity to address multiple learning styles using hands-on activities related to the skills of this lesson.

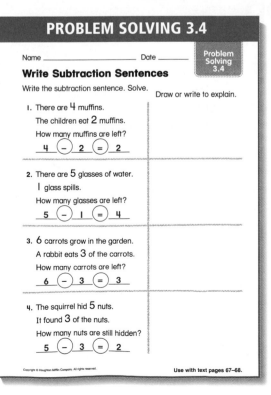

PROBLEM SOLVING 3.4

Name _____ Date _____

Problem Solving 3.4

Write Subtraction Sentences

Write the subtraction sentence. Solve.

Draw or write to explain.

1. There are 4 muffins.
   The children eat 2 muffins.
   How many muffins are left?
   $4 - 2 = 2$

2. There are 5 glasses of water.
   1 glass spills.
   How many glasses are left?
   $5 - 1 = 4$

3. 6 carrots grow in the garden.
   A rabbit eats 3 of the carrots.
   How many carrots are left?
   $6 - 3 = 3$

4. The squirrel hid 5 nuts.
   It found 3 of the nuts.
   How many nuts are still hidden?
   $5 - 3 = 2$

HOMEWORK 3.4

Name _____ Date _____

Homework 3.4

Write Subtraction Sentences

You can write a subtraction sentence to show the difference.

$6 - 4 = 2$ ← difference

The difference tells how many are left.

Write the subtraction sentence.

1. $4 - 2 = 2$

2. $3 - 2 = 1$

Write the difference.

3. $4 - 1 = 3$

4. $5 - 2 = 3$

5. $6 - 4 = 2$

6. $2 - 1 = 1$

7. Solve the problem.
   I am less than 4.
   I am greater than 1.
   I am not 2.
   What number am I?

   3

   Draw or write to explain.

ENGLISH LEARNERS 3.4

Name _____ Date _____

English Learners 3.4

Write Subtraction Sentences

A boy has 6 pencils. He loses 2 pencils. He has 4 pencils left.

$6 - 2 = 4$

The answer to a subtraction sentence is the **difference**.
4 is the **difference**.

Circle the difference.

1. $4 - 1 = $ ③

2. $5 - 3 = $ ②

3. $3 - 2 = $ ①

4. $2 - 1 = $ ①

To the Teacher: Use the example at the top of the page to demonstrate how to write a subtraction sentence and determine the difference. Then have children circle the difference in each of the subtraction sentences.

Use with text pages 67–68.

Use with text pages 67–68.

Use with text pages 67–69.

Copyright © Houghton Mifflin Company. All rights reserved.

Homework Workbook Page 19

CHAPTER 3 **Lesson 4** **67B**

TEACHING LESSON 3.4

LESSON ORGANIZER

Objective Write subtraction sentences to show the difference.

Resources Reteach, Practice, Enrichment, Problem Solving, Homework, English Learners, Transparencies, Math Center

Materials counters, blank transparency, cubes, number and symbol cards (Learning Tools (LT) 14 and 15)

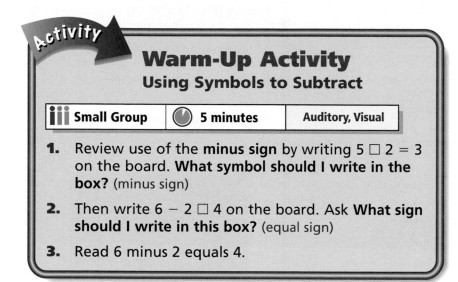

Warm-Up Activity
Using Symbols to Subtract

👤 Small Group	🕐 5 minutes	Auditory, Visual

1. Review use of the **minus sign** by writing 5 □ 2 = 3 on the board. **What symbol should I write in the box?** (minus sign)

2. Then write 6 − 2 □ 4 on the board. Ask **What sign should I write in this box?** (equal sign)

3. Read 6 minus 2 equals 4.

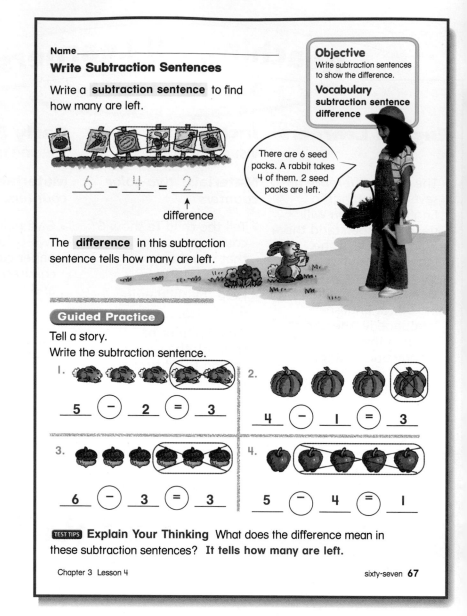

Name_____

Write Subtraction Sentences

Write a **subtraction sentence** to find how many are left.

$6 - 4 = 2$

↑
difference

Objective
Write subtraction sentences to show the difference.

Vocabulary
subtraction sentence
difference

There are 6 seed packs. A rabbit takes 4 of them. 2 seed packs are left.

The **difference** in this subtraction sentence tells how many are left.

Guided Practice

Tell a story.
Write the subtraction sentence.

1. $\underline{5} - \underline{2} = \underline{3}$

2. $\underline{4} - \underline{1} = \underline{3}$

3. $\underline{6} - \underline{3} = \underline{3}$

4. $\underline{5} - \underline{4} = \underline{1}$

TEST TIPS **Explain Your Thinking** What does the difference mean in these subtraction sentences? **It tells how many are left.**

Chapter 3 Lesson 4   sixty-seven **67**

---

1 Introduce

Model Writing Subtraction Sentences

👥 Whole Group	🕐 5–10 minutes	Auditory, Tactile

Materials: *blank transparency, counters*

1. Model taking 2 counters away from a group of 6 counters. **How many counters did we start with?** (6) **How many counters were taken away?** (2) **How many counters are left?** (4)

2. Write the subtraction sentence, 6 − 2 = 4, on the board. Circle the 4. **The number you get when you subtract is called a** *difference*. **The difference is 4. It tells how many are left.**

3. Repeat with similar exercises.

2 Develop

Guided Learning

Teaching Example Introduce the objective and vocabulary to the children. Guide them through the example and show them how the picture correlates to the numbers in the subtraction sentence. Emphasize the *difference*.

Guided Practice

Have children complete **Exercises 1–4** as you observe. Give children the opportunity to answer the Explain Your Thinking question. Then discuss the responses with the class.

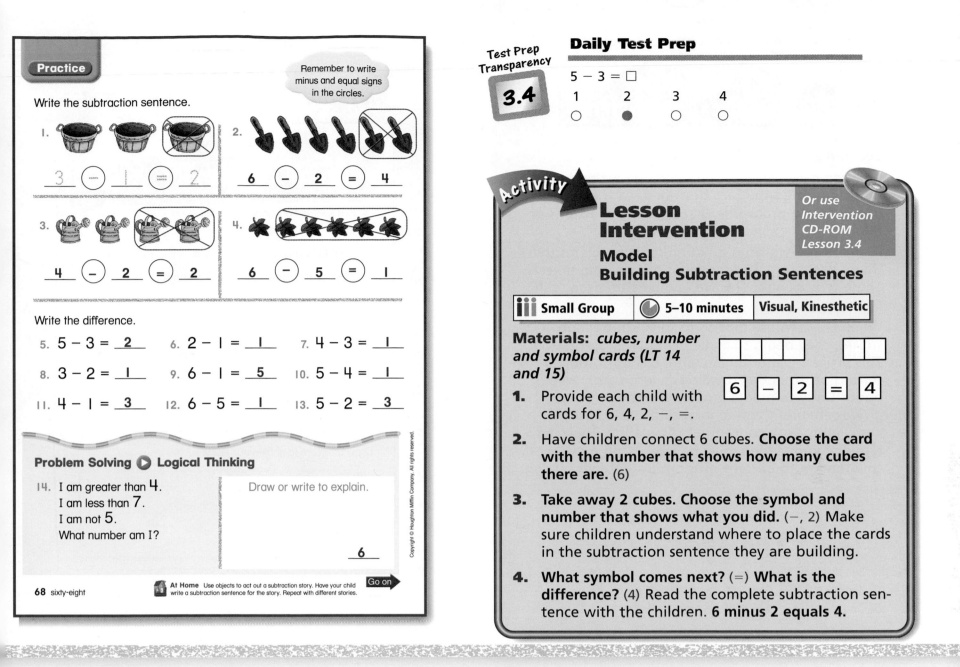

Practice

Remember to write minus and equal signs in the circles.

Write the subtraction sentence.

1. 3 ⊖ 1 ⊜ 2

2. 6 ⊖ 2 ⊜ 4

3. 4 ⊖ 2 ⊜ 2

4. 6 ⊖ 5 ⊜ 1

Write the difference.

5. $5 - 3 = \underline{2}$ 6. $2 - 1 = \underline{1}$ 7. $4 - 3 = \underline{1}$

8. $3 - 2 = \underline{1}$ 9. $6 - 1 = \underline{5}$ 10. $5 - 4 = \underline{1}$

11. $4 - 1 = \underline{3}$ 12. $6 - 5 = \underline{1}$ 13. $5 - 2 = \underline{3}$

Problem Solving ▶ Logical Thinking

14. I am greater than 4.
I am less than 7.
I am not 5.
What number am I?

Draw or write to explain.

$\underline{6}$

At Home Use objects to act out a subtraction story. Have your child write a subtraction sentence for the story. Repeat with different stories.

Go on ▶

68 sixty-eight

Test Prep Transparency **3.4**

Daily Test Prep

$5 - 3 = \square$

1   2   3   4
○   ●   ○   ○

Activity

Lesson Intervention

Or use Intervention CD-ROM Lesson 3.4

Model
Building Subtraction Sentences

👥 Small Group | ⏲ 5–10 minutes | Visual, Kinesthetic

Materials: cubes, number and symbol cards (LT 14 and 15)

6 ⊖ 2 ⊜ 4

1. Provide each child with cards for 6, 4, 2, −, =.

2. Have children connect 6 cubes. **Choose the card with the number that shows how many cubes there are.** (6)

3. **Take away 2 cubes. Choose the symbol and number that shows what you did.** (−, 2) Make sure children understand where to place the cards in the subtraction sentence they are building.

4. **What symbol comes next?** (=) **What is the difference?** (4) Read the complete subtraction sentence with the children. **6 minus 2 equals 4.**

3 Practice

Independent Practice

Children complete **Exercises 1–13** independently.

Problem Solving

After children complete **Exercise 14**, call on volunteers to explain how they figured out the riddle.

Common Error

Finding a Sum Instead of a Difference
Review several examples and have children model the subtraction. Compare adding the same numbers that were subtracted. Discuss how the differences and sums are very different results.

4 Assess and Close

What is 6 − 4? (2) **What is 6 − 2?** (4)

If you wrote a subtraction sentence about taking 3 counters away from 7 counters, what would the first number in the subtraction sentence be? (7) **What would the difference be?** (4)

✏ Keeping a Journal

Draw a picture of 6 ants on a leaf. Cross out some ants. Write a subtraction sentence that goes with your picture.

Lesson continues ▶

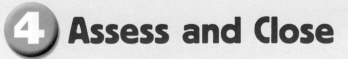

ACHIEVING
Mathematical Proficiency

Learning to Solve Problems

Children can solve word problems by acting out, or modeling, the situations described. As they do so, **they create a procedure that mimics the actions or relationships explained in the problem.**

In the primary grades, children solve problems that they can represent or model using concrete objects. These typically also involve numbers that they can easily count.

When children use models to solve subtraction stories, they begin to make mental representations. This process is the fundamental basis of problem-solving proficiency. Providing children with ample opportunity to model problems in the primary grades enables them to integrate procedural knowledge with conceptual knowledge. **These two types of knowledge must be integrated together if children are to become efficient at problem solving.**

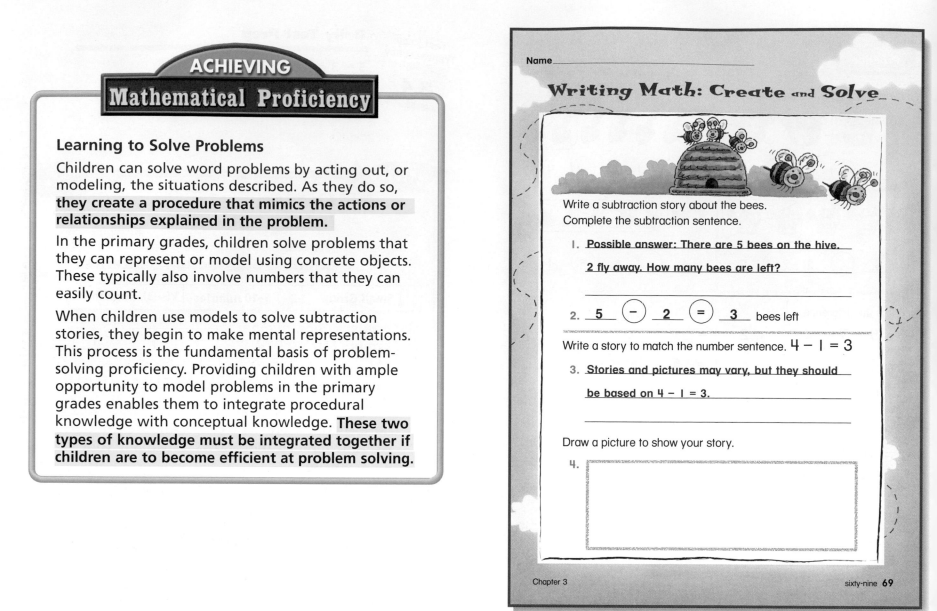

Writing Math: Create and Solve

Write a subtraction story about the bees.
Complete the subtraction sentence.

1. <u>Possible answer: There are 5 bees on the hive.</u>
   <u>2 fly away. How many bees are left?</u>
   _____

2. __5__ $-$ __2__ $=$ __3__ bees left

Write a story to match the number sentence. $4 - 1 = 3$

3. <u>Stories and pictures may vary, but they should</u>
   <u>be based on $4 - 1 = 3$.</u>
   _____

Draw a picture to show your story.

4. [blank box]

Writing Math: Create and Solve

Discuss the picture for **Exercise 1** to be sure children understand that it shows a group of bees and some of them are flying away. After children write their story, they write a subtraction sentence for **Exercise 2**. Have several children relate their subtraction story verbally to the class.

Explain that for **Exercises 3 and 4**, children will write a subtraction story to match the number sentence. Then they draw a picture to show the story. Let them share their stories.

Quick Check

Listen to the story.
Draw counters to show the story.
Write the numbers.

1.

___4___ 🌑   ___1___ eaten   ___3___ left

Use Workmat 3 and ◯.
Show the red part. Find the yellow part.
Write how many yellow.

2.

Whole
5

Part	Part
1 ●	_4_ ◯

3.

Whole
6

Part	Part
4 ●	_2_ ◯

Circle and cross out to subtract.
Write how many are left.

4. ● ● ● ⬮⬮ $6 - 3 = \underline{3}$

5. ● ● ● ⬮⬮ $5 - 2 = \underline{3}$

Write the difference.

6. $4 - 3 = \underline{1}$ 7. $3 - 2 = \underline{1}$ 8. $5 - 3 = \underline{2}$

9. $6 - 1 = \underline{5}$ 10. $2 - 1 = \underline{1}$ 11. $4 - 2 = \underline{2}$

70 seventy

Quick Check

Have children complete the Quick Check exercises independently to assess their understanding of concepts and skills taught in **Lessons 1–4.**

Read the following story for Item 1:

There are 4 peaches on the tray. Children draw 4 counters on the tray on the page. Remind them that the counters represent the peaches. **A boy eats 1 peach**. Children cross out 1 counter on the tray. **How many peaches are left?** (3 peaches) Have children write the numbers on the lines to show how many peaches in all, how many were eaten, and how many are left.

Item	Lesson	Error Analysis	Intervention
1	3.1	Children may lose track of the number of counters they are removing.	Reteach Resource 3.1 *Ways to Success* 3.1
2–3	3.2	Children may add the given numbers.	Reteach Resource 3.2 *Ways to Success* 3.2
4–5	3.3	Children may lose count when circling pictured objects.	Reteach Resource 3.3 *Ways to Success* 3.3
6–11	3.4	Children may add instead of subtracting.	Reteach Resource 3.4 *Ways to Success* 3.4

Zero in Subtraction

Lesson 3.5

PLANNING THE LESSON

MATHEMATICS OBJECTIVE
Subtract 0 or find a difference of 0.

Use Lesson Planner CD-ROM for Lesson 3.5.

Daily Routines

Calendar

Have a volunteer find today's date on the calendar. Ask: **If you leave on a vacation today and come home in 4 days, what day will you return?** Count on pointing to the calendar days.

Sunday	Monday	Tuesday	Wednesday	Thursday	Friday	Saturday
			1	2	3	4
5	6	7	8	9	10	11
12	13	14	15	16	17	18
19	20	21	22	23	24	25
26	27	28	29	30	31	

Vocabulary

Review the concept of **zero** by showing children containers with various numbers of counters interspersed with empty containers. Have children tell how many counters in each container.

Vocabulary Cards

Meeting North Carolina's Standards

1.03 Develop fluency with single-digit addition and corresponding differences using strategies such as modeling, composing and decomposing quantities, using doubles, and making tens.

Lesson Transparency **3.5**

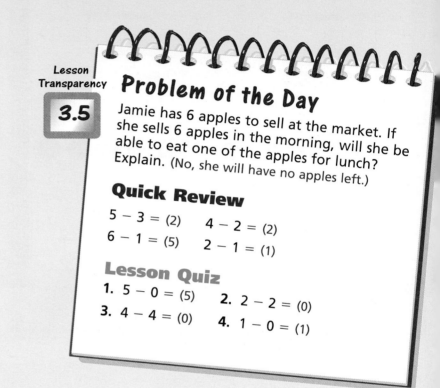

Problem of the Day

Jamie has 6 apples to sell at the market. If she sells 6 apples in the morning, will she be able to eat one of the apples for lunch? Explain. (No, she will have no apples left.)

Quick Review

$5 - 3 = (2)$ $4 - 2 = (2)$
$6 - 1 = (5)$ $2 - 1 = (1)$

Lesson Quiz

1. $5 - 0 = (5)$ 2. $2 - 2 = (0)$
3. $4 - 4 = (0)$ 4. $1 - 0 = (1)$

LEVELED PRACTICE

RETEACH 3.5

Name _____ Date _____   Reteach 3.5

Zero in Subtraction

When you subtract zero from a number, you get the number.	When you subtract a number from itself, you get zero.
$4 - 0 = \underline{4}$	$4 - 4 = \underline{0}$

Write the difference.

1. $5 - 5 = \underline{0}$ 2. $3 - 0 = \underline{3}$

3. $2 - 0 = \underline{2}$ 4. $6 - 6 = \underline{0}$

5. $1 - 1 = \underline{0}$ 6. $5 - 0 = \underline{5}$

Use with text pages 71–72.

PRACTICE 3.5

Name _____ Date _____   Practice 3.5

Zero in Subtraction

Write the difference.

1. $2 - 2 = \underline{0}$ 2. $4 - 4 = \underline{0}$

3. $6 - 0 = \underline{6}$ 4. $3 - 3 = \underline{0}$

5. $1 - 1 = \underline{0}$ 6. $3 - 0 = \underline{3}$ 7. $5 - 5 = \underline{0}$

8. $2 - 0 = \underline{2}$ 9. $6 - 6 = \underline{0}$ 10. $1 - 0 = \underline{1}$

Test Prep

Fill in the ○ for the correct answer. NH means Not Here.

11. Martin has 5 🖍. He doesn't lose any of them. How many does he have left?

○ 0   ○ 1   ● 5   ○ NH

Explain what happens when you subtract zero from a number.
You get the same number because you take away nothing.

Use with text pages 71–72.

ENRICHMENT 3.5

Name _____ Date _____   Enrichment 3.5

How Many Are Left?

Draw a picture.
Complete the subtraction sentence.

1. There are 4 apples. Matt eats 0. How many are left?

   $4 - 0 = \underline{4}$ Draw here.

2. There are 4 plums. The children eat 4. How many are left?

   $4 - 4 = \underline{0}$

3. Lea has 6 bananas. She does not eat any. How many are left?

   $6 - 0 = \underline{6}$

Write About It What happens when you subtract 0 objects from a group? Why? **When you subtract 0 objects from a group, you get the same number because you are taking away nothing from the group.**

Use with text pages 71–72.

Practice Workbook Page 20

Reaching All Learners

Differentiated Instruction

English Learners

- Children will need to understand the relationship among the words *no, none,* and *zero* in order to understand what happens when they subtract 0 or find a difference of 0. Use Worksheet 3.5 to help English-language learners understand this relationship.

Special Needs
AUDITORY, TACTILE

Materials: *counters*

- Tell the child to show 6 counters in his or her hand. Explain that you want to subtract 6 from 6 and take away the counters. Ask how many are left. (0)
- Then have the child show 6 counters and say that you will subtract 0 counters. Ask how many are left. (6)
- Repeat with other numbers.

Early Finishers
VISUAL, TACTILE

Materials: *index cards*

Make these cards:

Have pairs of children use the cards to play a concentration game. They place the cards face down in an array and turn over two cards at a time. The goal is to match an exercise to its difference.

TECHNOLOGY

Spiral Review

Create **customized** spiral review worksheets for individual students using the *Ways to Assess* CD-ROM.

eBook

An electronic version of this lesson can be found in **eMathBook**.

Education Place

Recommend that parents visit **Education Place** at eduplace.com/parents/mw/ for parent support activities.

Social Studies Connection

The fire department has different kinds of trucks for different jobs. Discuss the different kinds of fire trucks, such as hook and ladder, pumper, and ambulance. There are five fire trucks. Two leave for the fire. How many trucks are left?

MATH CENTER

Basic Skills Activity

Motivate children to build basic skills. Use this activity to address multiple learning styles using hands-on activities related to the skills of this lesson.

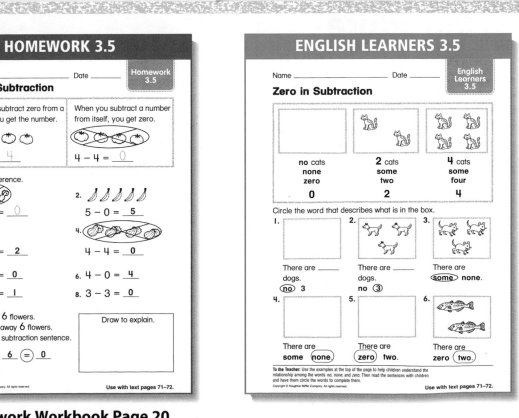

Homework Workbook Page 20

TEACHING LESSON 3.5

LESSON ORGANIZER

Objective Subtract 0 or find a difference of 0.

Resources Reteach, Practice, Enrichment, Problem Solving, Homework, English Learners, Transparencies, Math Center

Materials counters

Activity

Warm-Up Activity
Adding with 0

| iii Small Group | ⏰ 5 minutes | Auditory, Kinesthetic |

1. Review adding with 0 by having volunteers act out this story. **Two friends are playing. One more friend comes to play. How many children are playing now?** Write 2 + 1 = 3 to show the story.

2. Continue the story. **The three children are playing. No other friends come. How many children are playing now? What addition sentence tells this story?** Write 3 + 0 = 3.

3. **What happens when you add zero to a number?** (The sum is the number you started with.)

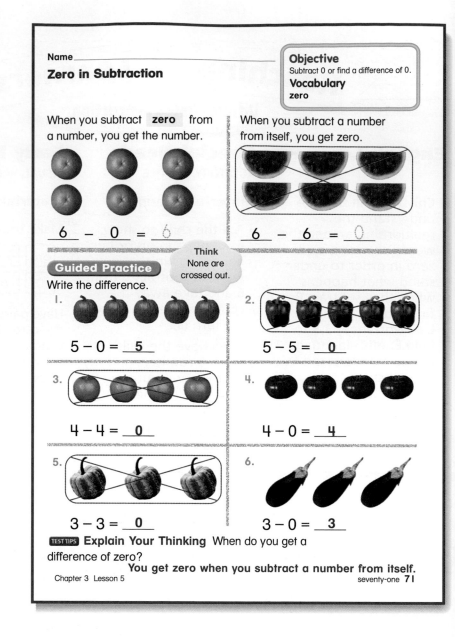

Name_____

Zero in Subtraction

Objective Subtract 0 or find a difference of 0.
Vocabulary zero

When you subtract **zero** from a number, you get the number.

When you subtract a number from itself, you get zero.

$$\underline{6} - \underline{0} = \underline{6}$$

$$\underline{6} - \underline{6} = \underline{0}$$

Think None are crossed out.

Guided Practice
Write the difference.

1. $5 - 0 = \underline{5}$

2. $5 - 5 = \underline{0}$

3. $4 - 4 = \underline{0}$

4. $4 - 0 = \underline{4}$

5. $3 - 3 = \underline{0}$

6. $3 - 0 = \underline{3}$

TEST TIPS Explain Your Thinking When do you get a difference of zero?

You get zero when you subtract a number from itself.

Chapter 3 Lesson 5   seventy-one **71**

---

① Introduce

Model Zero in Subtraction

| iiii Whole Group | ⏰ 5–10 minutes | Auditory, Visual |

1. Draw 3 stars on the board. **I am going to subtract zero stars. I will not circle and cross out any stars because I am subtracting zero. How many stars are left after I subtract 0?** (3)
   Explain: **This is the subtraction sentence that shows this story.** Write 3 − 0 = 3.

2. **Now I am going to subtract 3 stars, so I will circle and cross out 3 stars. How many stars are left after I subtract 3 stars?** (zero)
   Explain: **This is the subtraction sentence that shows this story.** Write 3 − 3 = 0.

② Develop

Guided Learning

Teaching Example Introduce the objective and vocabulary to the children. Guide them through the example. Make sure that children understand the difference in the two problems—subtracting zero from a number, and subtracting a number from itself to get zero.

Guided Practice

Have children complete **Exercises 1–6** as you observe. Give children the opportunity to answer the Explain Your Thinking question. Then discuss their responses with the class.

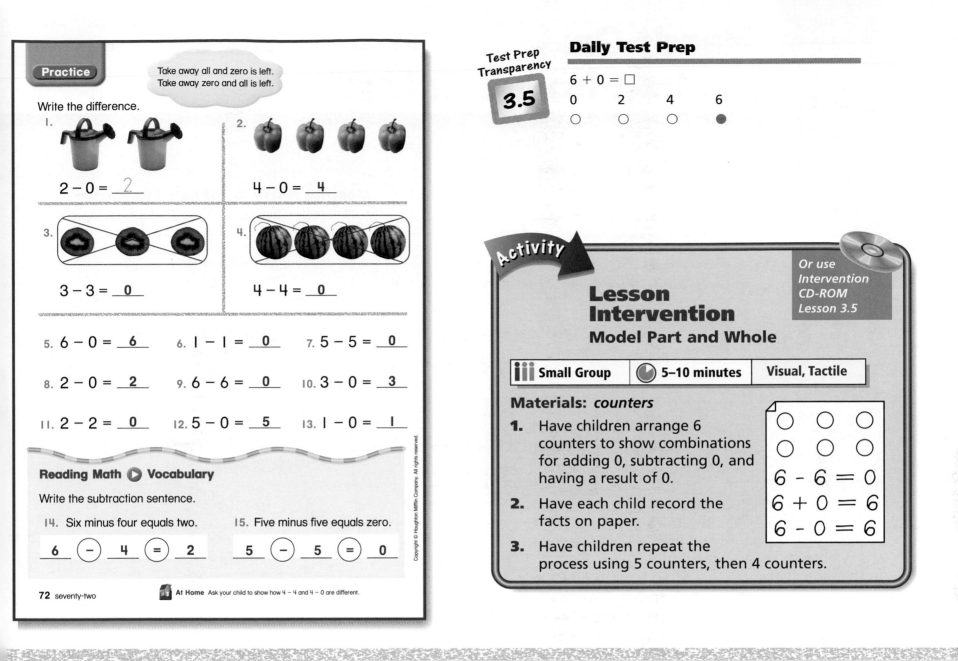

Practice

Take away all and zero is left.
Take away zero and all is left.

Write the difference.

1. $2 - 0 = \underline{2}$

2. $4 - 0 = \underline{4}$

3. $3 - 3 = \underline{0}$

4. $4 - 4 = \underline{0}$

5. $6 - 0 = \underline{6}$
6. $1 - 1 = \underline{0}$
7. $5 - 5 = \underline{0}$

8. $2 - 0 = \underline{2}$
9. $6 - 6 = \underline{0}$
10. $3 - 0 = \underline{3}$

11. $2 - 2 = \underline{0}$
12. $5 - 0 = \underline{5}$
13. $1 - 0 = \underline{1}$

Reading Math ▶ Vocabulary

Write the subtraction sentence.

14. Six minus four equals two.

$\underline{6}\; (-)\; \underline{4}\; (=)\; \underline{2}$

15. Five minus five equals zero.

$\underline{5}\; (-)\; \underline{5}\; (=)\; \underline{0}$

72 seventy-two

🏠 **At Home** Ask your child to show how 4 – 4 and 4 – 0 are different.

Test Prep Transparency **3.5**

Daily Test Prep

$6 + 0 = \square$

0　　2　　4　　6
○　　○　　○　　●

Activity

Or use Intervention CD-ROM Lesson 3.5

Lesson Intervention
Model Part and Whole

👤👤👤 Small Group　|　⏱ 5–10 minutes　|　Visual, Tactile

Materials: *counters*

1. Have children arrange 6 counters to show combinations for adding 0, subtracting 0, and having a result of 0.

2. Have each child record the facts on paper.

3. Have children repeat the process using 5 counters, then 4 counters.

$6 - 6 = 0$
$6 + 0 = 6$
$6 - 0 = 6$

---

③ Practice

Independent Practice

Children complete **Exercises 1–13** independently.

Reading Math

After children complete **Exercises 14–15**, call on volunteers to share the subtraction sentences they have written.

Common Error

Confusing Subtracting 0 and Subtracting All
Provide extra work with counters, helping children read each number sentence aloud. Have children model each exercise before writing the difference.

④ Assess and Close

Which subtraction sentence has a difference of 0: 4 − 0 or 4 − 4? (4 − 4)

If you draw a picture to show subtracting 0 apples from 3 apples, how many apples would you circle and cross out? (none)

✏️ **Keeping a Journal**

Write a rule about subtracting zero from a number.

Hands-On: Subtract from 8 or Less

PLANNING THE LESSON

MATHEMATICS OBJECTIVE
Model subtraction from 8 or less; write subtraction sentences to find the difference.

Use Lesson Planner CD-ROM for Lesson 3.6.

Meeting North Carolina's Standards
1.03 Develop fluency with single-digit addition and corresponding differences using strategies such as modeling, composing and decomposing quantities, using doubles, and making tens.

Daily Routines

Calendar
Point to the number 8. Ask children to subtract 3. Point to each number as you count back to find the difference.

Vocabulary
Review the terms **minus sign** and **equal sign**. Write several subtraction sentences on the board and point to the symbols as children identify them in the sentences.

Vocabulary Cards

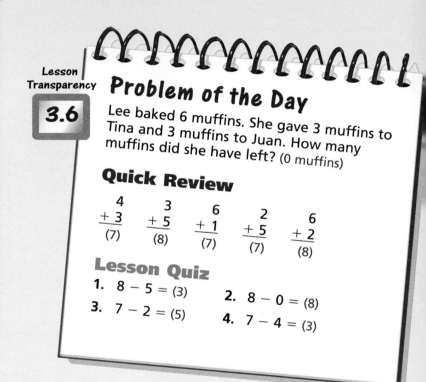

Lesson
Transparency
3.6

Problem of the Day
Lee baked 6 muffins. She gave 3 muffins to Tina and 3 muffins to Juan. How many muffins did she have left? (0 muffins)

Quick Review

$$\begin{array}{ccccc} 4 & 3 & 6 & 2 & 6 \\ +3 & +5 & +1 & +5 & +2 \\ \hline (7) & (8) & (7) & (7) & (8) \end{array}$$

Lesson Quiz
1. $8 - 5 = (3)$ 2. $8 - 0 = (8)$
3. $7 - 2 = (5)$ 4. $7 - 4 = (3)$

LEVELED PRACTICE

RETEACH 3.6

Name _____ Date _____   Reteach 3.6

Subtract From 8 or Less

You can use cubes to subtract from 7 or 8.
You can write a subtraction sentence to show what you did.

$7 \;(-)\; 3 \;(=)\; 4$

$8 \;(-)\; 2 \;(=)\; 6$

Use cubes. Snap off some.
Circle and cross out. Write the subtraction sentence.
Answers may vary. Possible answers are shown.

Use 7 cubes.

1. $7 \;(-)\; 6 \;(=)\; 1$

2. $7 \;(-)\; 2 \;(=)\; 5$

Use 8 cubes.

3. $8 \;(-)\; 4 \;(=)\; 4$

4. $8 \;(-)\; 7 \;(=)\; 1$

Use with text pages 73–74.

PRACTICE 3.6

Name _____ Date _____   Practice 3.6

Subtract from 8 or Less

Use 8 cubes. Snap off some.
Circle and cross out the ones you snapped off.
Write the subtraction sentence.

1. $8 - 3 = 5$

Answers may vary. Possible answers are shown.

2. $8 - 2 = 6$

3. $8 - 5 = 3$

Test Prep

Fill in the ○ for the correct answer. NH means Not Here.

4. Ed makes a tower with 8 blocks.
Then 3 fall off.
How many blocks are left?

8   4   3   NH
○   ○   ○   ●

Use with text pages 73–74.

ENRICHMENT 3.6

Name _____ Date _____   Enrichment 3.6

Life on the Pond

Look at the picture.
Complete the subtraction sentence.
Use cubes to help.

1. $8 - 2 = 6$

2. $7 - 3 = 4$

3. $7 - 2 = 5$

4. $8 - 1 = 7$

Write About It How can you use ▢
to show subtraction? I can use cubes to show the animals. Then I can remove cubes to show how many to take away.

Use with text pages 73–74.

Practice Workbook Page 21

Reaching All Learners
Differentiated Instruction

English Learners

- Children will need to understand the term *stands for* when they write subtraction sentences based on word problems. Use Worksheet 3.6 to help English-language learners understand this term.

Special Needs
TACTILE, AUDITORY

Materials: *cubes*

- Have the child connect 8 cubes. **How many cubes do you have?** (8)
- **Break off two cubes. How many cubes are you taking away?** (2)
- **How many cubes are left?** (6)
- Write the subtraction sentence 8 − 2 = 6 and discuss how it relates to the modeling.
- Repeat with other facts for 8.

Early Finishers
KINESTHETIC, VISUAL

Materials: *pennies*

- Have pairs of children place 8 pennies in a row.

- Have one child close his or her eyes while the other child removes some or none of the pennies. The other child opens his or her eyes and tells how many pennies were removed. Players switch roles and continue the game.

TECHNOLOGY

Spiral Review

Using the *Ways to Assess* CD-ROM, you can create **customized** spiral review worksheets covering any lessons you choose.

Lesson Planner

Use the **Lesson Planner CD-ROM** to see how lesson objectives for this chapter are correlated to standards.

Manipulatives

Interactive Connecting Cubes with several workmats are available on the *Ways to Success* CD-ROM.

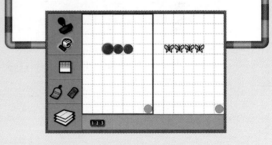

ScienceConnection

Show a collection of 8 leaves; 5 with the same number of points. Discuss the different shapes of the leaves. Create subtraction sentences using the leaves.

MATH CENTER
Basic Skills Activity

Motivate children to build basic skills. Use this activity to address multiple learning styles using hands-on activities related to the skills of this lesson.

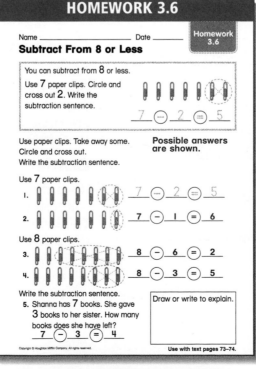

Homework Workbook Page 21

TEACHING LESSON 3.6

LESSON ORGANIZER

Objective Model subtraction from 8 or less; write subtraction sentences to find the difference.

Resources Reteach, Practice, Enrichment, Problem Solving, Homework, English Learners, Transparencies, Math Center

Materials Counters, cubes, index cards

Activity

Warm-Up Activity
Model Subtraction Concepts

👤👤👤 Small Group	⏱ 5 minutes	Auditory, Visual

Materials: *counters*

1. Use counters to model this story. **Roberto grows 6 pumpkins. He picks 2 of the pumpkins. How many pumpkins are left?**

$$\underline{6} - \underline{2} = \underline{4}$$

2. Write _____ – _____ = _____ on the board. **What numbers should I write to show the subtraction story?**

3. Help the child correlate the numbers to the subtraction story.

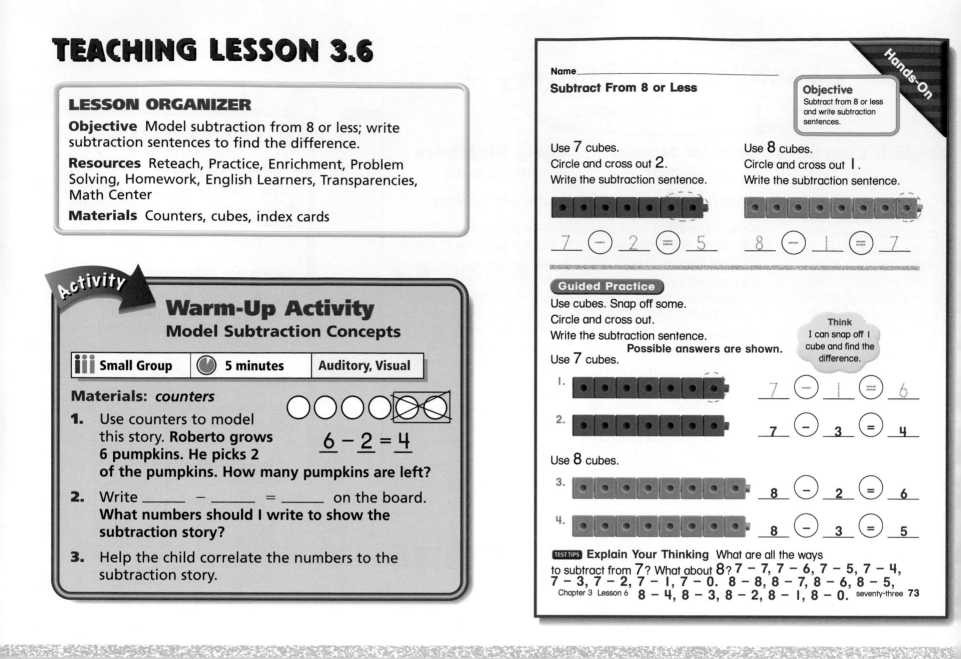

Name _____

Subtract From 8 or Less

Objective Subtract from 8 or less and write subtraction sentences.

Use 7 cubes.
Circle and cross out 2.
Write the subtraction sentence.

7 ◯ 2 ◯ 5

Use 8 cubes.
Circle and cross out 1.
Write the subtraction sentence.

8 ◯ 1 ◯ 7

Guided Practice

Use cubes. Snap off some.
Circle and cross out.
Write the subtraction sentence. **Possible answers are shown.**

> **Think** I can snap off 1 cube and find the difference.

Use 7 cubes.

1. 7 ◯ 1 ◯ 6

2. 7 ◯ 3 ◯ 4

Use 8 cubes.

3. 8 ◯ 2 ◯ 6

4. 8 ◯ 3 ◯ 5

TEST TIPS Explain Your Thinking What are all the ways to subtract from 7? What about 8? 7 − 7, 7 − 6, 7 − 5, 7 − 4, 7 − 3, 7 − 2, 7 − 1, 7 − 0. 8 − 8, 8 − 7, 8 − 6, 8 − 5, 8 − 4, 8 − 3, 8 − 2, 8 − 1, 8 − 0.

Chapter 3 Lesson 6   seventy-three **73**

---

① Introduce

Activity

Model Subtraction

👤👤👤 Whole Group	⏱ 5–10 minutes	Auditory, Visual

Materials: *cubes*

1. **Subtract 3 from 8.** Show children a train of 8 cubes. **How many cubes do I have?** (8)

2. Snap off 3 cubes. **I had 8 cubes. I took away 3 cubes.** Write 8 − 3 on the board.

3. **How many cubes are left?** (5) Finish writing the subtraction sentence, 8 − 3 = 5.

4. Repeat with similar exercises having children model them with cubes.

② Develop

Guided Learning

Teaching Example Introduce the objective to the children. Guide them through the examples, while you have them count how many cubes there are in all and how many cubes are circled and crossed out. Then read the subtraction sentences together.

Guided Practice

Have children complete **Exercises 1–4** as you observe. Give children the opportunity to answer the Explain Your Thinking question as you list the facts for 7 and for 8 on the board.

Practice

Use cubes. Snap off some.
Circle and cross out.
Write the subtraction sentence.

> The number you subtract is the number of cubes you snap off.

Possible answers are shown.

Use **7** cubes.

1. $7 - 4 = 3$

2. $7 - 5 = 2$

Use **8** cubes.

3. $8 - 4 = 4$

4. $8 - 5 = 3$

Write the difference.

5. $7 - 0 = \underline{7}$ 6. $8 - 1 = \underline{7}$ 7. $7 - 6 = \underline{1}$

8. $8 - 6 = \underline{2}$ 9. $7 - 7 = \underline{0}$ 10. $8 - 0 = \underline{8}$

Algebra Readiness ▶ Number Sentences

Write the subtraction sentence.

11. Pat has **7** apples.
He eats **2** of them.
How many apples are left?

$7 - 2 = 5$

12. **Talk About It** What do the numbers in the subtraction sentence stand for? **7 is the number of apples, 2 is the number taken away, 5 is the number left.**

74 seventy-four

At Home Show 8 or fewer objects. Take some away. Ask your child to write the subtraction sentence.

$6 - 1 = \square$

3   4   5   6
○   ○   ●   ○

Activity

Lesson Intervention
Model Subtraction

| 👥 Small Group | ⏱ 5–10 minutes | Visual, Tactile |

Or use Intervention CD-ROM Lesson 3.6

Materials: *two-color counters, index cards*

○○○○○ ○○

[8 – 2]

1. Write these expressions on index cards: $8 - 6$, $8 - 4$, $8 - 2$, $7 - 2$, $7 - 1$, and $7 - 5$.

2. Have a child choose a card and count out the number of counters to show the number in all.

3. Have another child remove the counters to be subtracted.

4. Point out that the remaining counters show the difference. Have a child write the complete subtraction sentence on a piece of paper.

---

❸ Practice

Independent Practice

Children complete **Exercises 1–10** independently.

Algebra Readiness

After children complete **Exercise 11**, call on volunteers to explain how they arrived at their answer. Use the **Talk About It** in Exercise 12 to have children identify what the numbers in the subtraction sentence represent.

Common Error

Writing the Wrong Difference
Have children use cubes to model all exercises when they do not remember a fact.

❹ Assess and Close

Your friend has a pizza that is cut into 8 pieces. You eat 2 pieces and your friend eats 2 pieces. How many pieces are left? (4 pieces)

If there are 7 birds on a branch and 5 birds fly away, how many birds are left? (2 birds)

Keeping a Journal

Write a subtraction story about 8 people. Write the subtraction sentence that goes with your story.

Subtract in Vertical Form

Lesson
3.7

PLANNING THE LESSON

MATHEMATICS OBJECTIVE
Subtract in vertical form.

Use Lesson Planner CD-ROM for Lesson 3.7.

Meeting North Carolina's Standards

1.03 Develop fluency with single-digit addition and corresponding differences using strategies such as modeling, composing and decomposing quantities, using doubles, and making tens.

Daily Routines

Calendar
Ask children to find the date that is 5 days before the 15th. Have volunteers tell the date and explain how they found it.

Sunday	Monday	Tuesday	Wednesday	Thursday	Friday	Saturday
				1	2	3	4
5	6	7	8	9	10	11
12	13	14	15	16	17	18
19	20	21	22	23	24	25
26	27	28	29	30	31	

Vocabulary
Write the words *across* and *down* on the board. Remind children how addition can be written across or down by writing examples below each word.

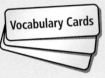
Vocabulary Cards

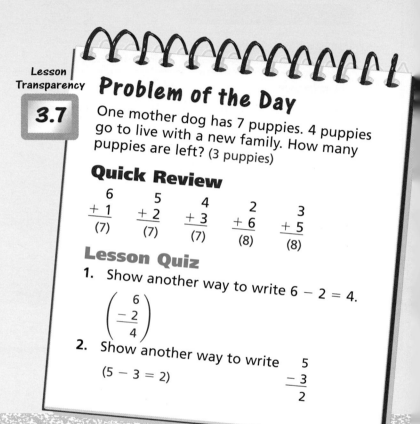

Lesson Transparency **3.7**

Problem of the Day
One mother dog has 7 puppies. 4 puppies go to live with a new family. How many puppies are left? (3 puppies)

Quick Review

$$\begin{array}{r} 6 \\ + 1 \\ \hline (7) \end{array} \quad \begin{array}{r} 5 \\ + 2 \\ \hline (7) \end{array} \quad \begin{array}{r} 4 \\ + 3 \\ \hline (7) \end{array} \quad \begin{array}{r} 2 \\ + 6 \\ \hline (8) \end{array} \quad \begin{array}{r} 3 \\ + 5 \\ \hline (8) \end{array}$$

Lesson Quiz
1. Show another way to write $6 - 2 = 4$.

$$\begin{array}{r} 6 \\ - 2 \\ \hline 4 \end{array}$$

2. Show another way to write

$(5 - 3 = 2)$
$$\begin{array}{r} 5 \\ - 3 \\ \hline 2 \end{array}$$

LEVELED PRACTICE

RETEACH 3.7

Reteach 3.7

Name _____ Date _____

Subtract in Vertical Form

You can write the same subtraction fact in two ways.

Subtract across.

$8 - 2 = 6$
↑
difference

Subtract down.
$$\begin{array}{r} 8 \\ - 2 \\ \hline 6 \end{array}$$ ← difference

The difference is the same.

Complete the subtraction fact.

1.
$$\begin{array}{r} 7 \\ - 5 \\ \hline 2 \end{array}$$
$7 - 5 = 2$

2.
$$\begin{array}{r} 8 \\ - 1 \\ \hline 7 \end{array}$$
$8 - 1 = 7$

3.
$$\begin{array}{r} 6 \\ - 3 \\ \hline 3 \end{array}$$
$6 - 3 = 3$

4.
$$\begin{array}{r} 5 \\ - 1 \\ \hline 4 \end{array}$$
$5 - 1 = 4$

Use with text pages 75–76.

PRACTICE 3.7

Practice 3.7

Name _____ Date _____

Subtract in Vertical Form

Complete the subtraction fact.

1.
$$\begin{array}{r} 6 \\ - 4 \\ \hline 2 \end{array}$$

2.
$$\begin{array}{r} 8 \\ - 3 \\ \hline 5 \end{array}$$

Write the difference.

3.	4.	5.	6.	7.	8.
$\begin{array}{r}7\\-7\\\hline 0\end{array}$	$\begin{array}{r}3\\-0\\\hline 3\end{array}$	$\begin{array}{r}4\\-2\\\hline 2\end{array}$	$\begin{array}{r}3\\-2\\\hline 1\end{array}$	$\begin{array}{r}5\\-5\\\hline 0\end{array}$	$\begin{array}{r}2\\-2\\\hline 0\end{array}$

Test Prep

Fill in the ○ for the correct answer. NH means Not Here.

9. Jody has 7 🖼. She mails 6 🖼.

How many does she have left?

7   1   5   NH
○   ●   ○   ○

Complete the subtraction fact you used to solve the problem.

$$\begin{array}{r} 7 \\ - 6 \\ \hline 1 \end{array}$$

Use with text pages 75–76.

ENRICHMENT 3.7

Enrichment 3.7

Name _____ Date _____

What's Missing?

Write the missing number.

1.
$$\begin{array}{r} 7 \\ - 3 \\ \hline 4 \end{array}$$

2.
$$\begin{array}{r} 6 \\ - 3 \\ \hline 3 \end{array}$$

3.
$$\begin{array}{r} 8 \\ - 1 \\ \hline 7 \end{array}$$

4.
$$\begin{array}{r} 5 \\ - 3 \\ \hline 2 \end{array}$$

5.
$$\begin{array}{r} 5 \\ - 1 \\ \hline 4 \end{array}$$

6.
$$\begin{array}{r} 6 \\ - 5 \\ \hline 1 \end{array}$$

7.
$$\begin{array}{r} 8 \\ - 6 \\ \hline 2 \end{array}$$

8.
$$\begin{array}{r} 4 \\ - 4 \\ \hline 0 \end{array}$$

Write About It How are subtraction sentences and vertical subtraction the same? **They have the same numbers and the same answers.**

Use with text pages 75–76.

Practice Workbook Page 22

Reaching All Learners

Differentiated Instruction

English Learners

- English-language learners may not have the language skills to explain the process behind their thinking. Use Worksheet 3.7 to provide children with sentence frames they can use to complete the Explain Your Thinking activity.

Special Needs
VISUAL, TACTILE

Materials: *cubes*

- Give the child a cube train with 8 cubes. Write 8 − 1 = _____ .
- Have the child snap off 1 cube to find the difference.
- Write the subtraction in vertical form and repeat the process.

Gifted and Talented
TACTILE, VISUAL

- Display part of a subtraction story, such as *Jamaal had 8 tadpoles. Now Jamaal has 5 tadpoles.*
- Have children create the middle part of the story that leads to the last sentence. For example, a child could write *3 tadpoles swam away.*
- Then have children write the number sentence that matches the story.

TECHNOLOGY

Spiral Review

To reinforce skills on lessons taught earlier, create **customized** spiral review worksheets using the *Ways to Assess* CD-ROM.

eBook

eMathBook allows students to review lessons and do homework without carrying their textbooks home.

Games

Students can practice their skills using the **Rock Hopper** math game, available on the *Ways to Success* CD-ROM.

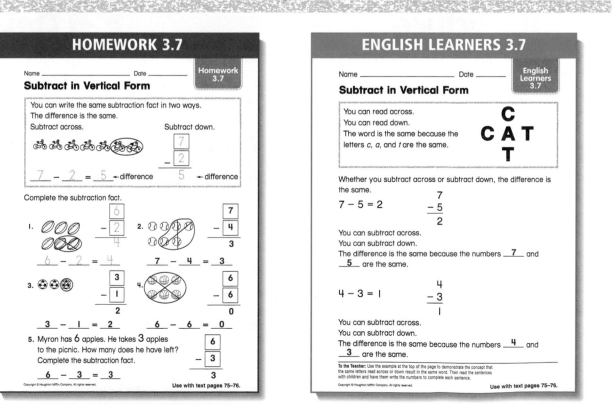

Literature Connection

In the story, *Ten Little Mice* by Joyce Dunbar, 10 little mice clean, dig, climb, frolic, and explore. One by one they go home to their nest. Children can use 10 cubes to subtract the mice in the story.

MATH CENTER

Basic Skills Activity

Motivate children to build basic skills. Use this activity to address multiple learning styles using hands-on activities related to the skills of this lesson.

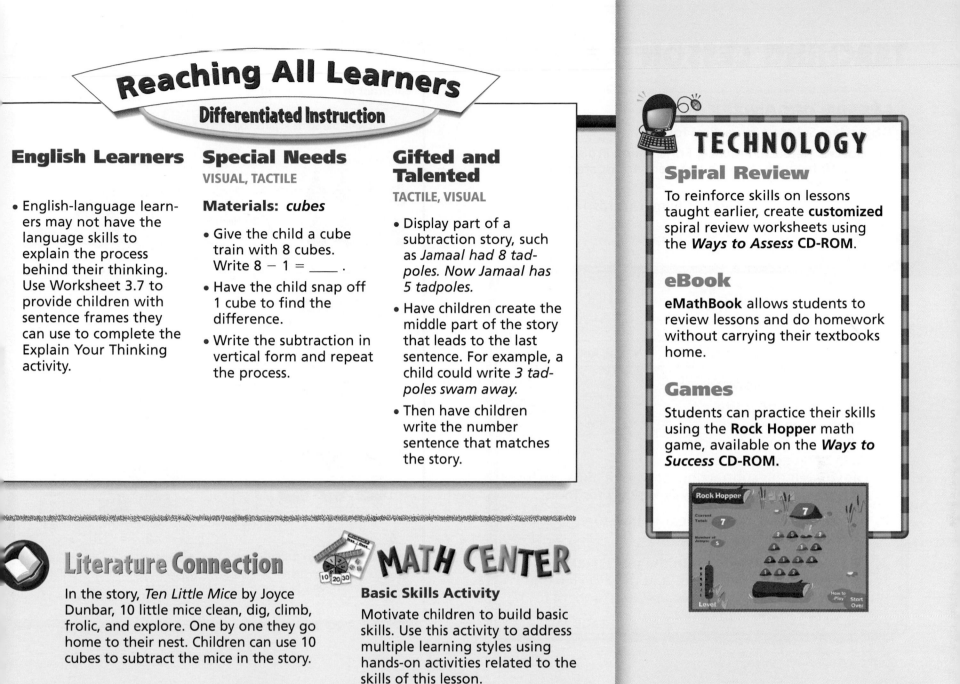

Homework Workbook Page 22

TEACHING LESSON 3.7

LESSON ORGANIZER

Objective Subtract in vertical form.

Resources Reteach, Practice, Enrichment, Problem Solving, Homework, English Learners, Transparencies, Math Center

Materials Blank transparency, number cards 1–6 (LT 14), symbol cards (LT 15)

Activity

Warm-Up Activity
Writing a Subtraction Sentence

| 👤👤👤👤 Whole Group | ⏱ 5 minutes | Visual, Auditory |

Materials: *blank transparency*

1. Review how to write a subtraction sentence. Draw a picture of 5 birds and circle and cross out 2 as you tell this subtraction story. **Five birds are in the tree. Two birds fly away looking for food.**

   5 − 2 = 3

2. **What numbers did you hear in the story?** (5 and 2) Write 5 − 2 below the picture.

3. **How many birds are left in the tree?** (3) Discuss the meaning of the 3 birds and the 2 circled and crossed out birds in the picture. Relate them to the numerals in the subtraction sentence.

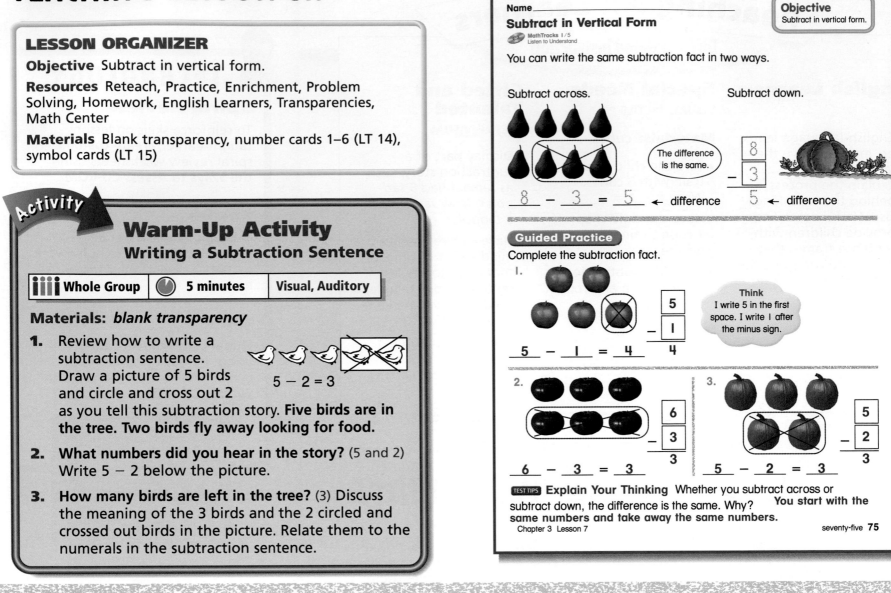

Name_____

Subtract in Vertical Form

MathTracks 1 / 5
Listen to Understand

Objective
Subtract in vertical form.

You can write the same subtraction fact in two ways.

Subtract across.

Subtract down.

The difference is the same.

8
− 3
5

8 − 3 = 5 ← difference   5 ← difference

Guided Practice

Complete the subtraction fact.

1.

5
− 1
4

Think
I write 5 in the first space. I write 1 after the minus sign.

5 − 1 = 4

2.

6
− 3
3

6 − 3 = 3

3.

5
− 2
3

5 − 2 = 3

TEST TIPS Explain Your Thinking Whether you subtract across or subtract down, the difference is the same. Why? **You start with the same numbers and take away the same numbers.**

Chapter 3 Lesson 7

seventy-five **75**

① Introduce
Discuss Subtracting in Vertical Form

| 👤👤👤👤 Whole Group | ⏱ 10–15 minutes | Visual, Auditory |

Materials: *blank transparency*

1. *Subtract 7 − 3.* Draw a picture of 7 frogs and cross out 3 as you tell this subtraction story. **7 frogs are in the pond. 3 frogs hop away into the grass. 4 frogs are left in the pond.** Write 7 − 3 = 4.

2. Explain that there is another way to write 7 − 3 = 4.

   Write the vertical form below the picture.

   $$\begin{array}{r} 7 \\ -\ 3 \\ \hline 4 \end{array}$$

   Relate the numerals in the vertical subtraction to the picture and to the horizontal equation.

② Develop

Guided Learning

Teaching Example Introduce the objective to the children. Guide them through the example to show how you can write 8 − 3 across and down.

Guided Practice

Have children complete **Exercises 1–3** as you observe. Give several children the opportunity to answer the Explain Your Thinking question. Then discuss the responses with the class.

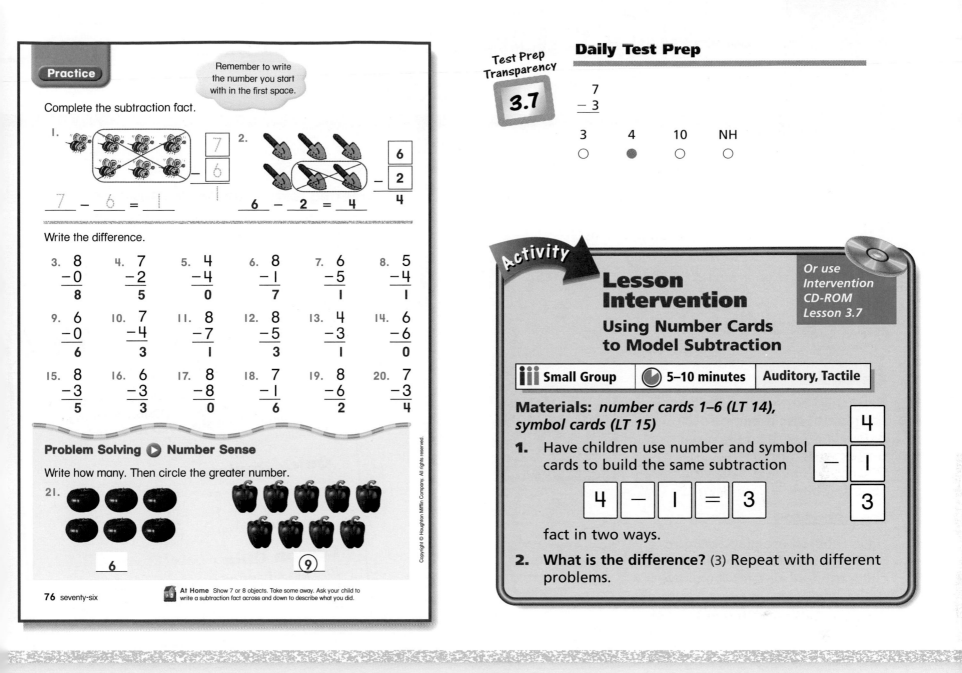

Remember to write the number you start with in the first space.

Complete the subtraction fact.

1.

$$\boxed{7} \\ -\boxed{6}$$

7 − 6 = 1

2.

$$\boxed{6} \\ -\boxed{2} \\ \hline 4$$

6 − 2 = 4

Write the difference.

3.	4.	5.	6.	7.	8.
8 −0 8	7 −2 5	4 −4 0	8 −1 7	6 −5 1	5 −4 1

9.	10.	11.	12.	13.	14.
6 −0 6	7 −4 3	8 −7 1	8 −5 3	4 −3 1	6 −6 0

15.	16.	17.	18.	19.	20.
8 −3 5	6 −3 3	8 −8 0	7 −1 6	8 −6 2	7 −3 4

Problem Solving ▶ Number Sense

Write how many. Then circle the greater number.

21.

6   ⑨

76 seventy-six

At Home Show 7 or 8 objects. Take some away. Ask your child to write a subtraction fact across and down to describe what you did.

Daily Test Prep

3.7

$$\begin{array}{r} 7 \\ -\,3 \\ \hline \end{array}$$

3 ○   4 ●   10 ○   NH ○

Activity

Lesson Intervention

Or use Intervention CD-ROM Lesson 3.7

Using Number Cards to Model Subtraction

👥 Small Group	🕐 5–10 minutes	Auditory, Tactile

Materials: *number cards 1–6 (LT 14), symbol cards (LT 15)*

1. Have children use number and symbol cards to build the same subtraction

   4 − 1 = 3

   $$\boxed{4} \\ -\boxed{1} \\ \boxed{3}$$

   fact in two ways.

2. **What is the difference?** (3) Repeat with different problems.

3 Practice

Independent Practice

Children complete **Exercises 1–20** independently.

Problem Solving

After children complete **Exercise 21**, call on volunteers to explain how they arrived at their answer.

Common Error

Vertical Subtraction Errors

Children may interpret vertical subtraction as unrelated to horizontal. Provide numerous exercises in both forms and have children find the differences.

6 − 1 = 5

$$\begin{array}{r} 6 \\ -\,1 \\ \hline 5 \end{array}$$

4 Assess and Close

How can you write 7 − 3 = 4 in another way? (Write 7 on top, then write − 3 below the 7. Draw a line under the − 3, and write the difference.)

✏️ Keeping a Journal

Show how to write 7 minus 2 equals 5 two different ways. Write the difference for both problems.

Problem Solving: Act It Out With Models

PLANNING THE LESSON

MATHEMATICS OBJECTIVE
Use models to act out subtraction problems.

Use Lesson Planner CD-ROM for Lesson 3.8.

Meeting North Carolina's Standards
1.04 Create, model, and solve problems that use addition, subtraction, and fair shares (between two or three).

Also 1.03

Daily Routines

Calendar
Have children find the 7th day of the month. Ask them to count back 2 days and say the date. Have a volunteer write the subtraction sentence. Continue with other dates counting back 1, 2, or 3.

Sunday	Monday	Tuesday	Wednesday	Thursday	Friday	Saturday
				1	2	3	4
5	6	7	8	9	10	11
12	13	14	15	16	17	18
19	20	21	22	23	24	25
26	27	28	29	30	31	

Vocabulary
Have children use play-acting to **act out** subtraction problems. Have 6 children sit at a table. Then have 2 get up and leave. Have children tell you how many children are still at the table.

Vocabulary Cards

Lesson Transparency 3.8

Problem of the Day
Sandy is writing a story that will be 4 pages long. She has written 2 pages. How many more pages does she need to write? (2 pages)

Quick Review
$$\begin{array}{r} 8 \\ -4 \\ \hline (4) \end{array} \quad \begin{array}{r} 7 \\ -3 \\ \hline (4) \end{array} \quad \begin{array}{r} 5 \\ -1 \\ \hline (4) \end{array} \quad \begin{array}{r} 6 \\ -2 \\ \hline (4) \end{array} \quad \begin{array}{r} 4 \\ -0 \\ \hline (4) \end{array}$$

Lesson Quiz
Jose has 4 bags of popcorn. He gives 3 away. How many bags of popcorn does he have left? (1 bag)

LEVELED PRACTICE

RETEACH 3.8

Name _____ Date _____ **Reteach 3.8**

Problem Solving
Act It Out With Models

Read It
There are 7 children jumping rope. 2 children get tired and stop. How many children are left?

Picture It

7 children jump rope.	2 stop.	How many are left?
●●●●● ●●	●●● ●●(⊗)	?

Solve It
You know that when someone leaves, there are fewer than before. That means you have to subtract. Act out the problem with counters.
Write the answer. __5__

1. 5 children swing. 4 children leave. How many children are still swinging? __1__

2. 8 children play tag. 5 children get caught. How many children are left to play tag? __3__

Copyright © Houghton Mifflin Company. All rights reserved.   Use with text pages 77–79.

PRACTICE 3.8

Name _____ Date _____ **Practice 3.8**

Problem Solving
Act It Out With Models

Act out the problem with counters.
Write the answer.

1. Joanne has 7 party balloons. Then 3 balloons pop. How many balloons are left?

   __4__ balloons

   Draw or write to explain.

2. Beth has 8 party hats and 2 hats are blue. How many hats are not blue?

   __6__ hats

Test Prep

Fill in the ○ for the correct answer. NH means Not Here.

3. James gets 6 presents. He opens 3 of them. How many presents are unopened?

   9 ○   5 ○   3 ●   NH ○

Copyright © Houghton Mifflin Company. All rights reserved.   Use with text pages 77–80.

ENRICHMENT 3.8

Name _____ Date _____ **Enrichment 3.8**

A Sandwich Solution

1. Read the problem.
   Act it out. Model the problem in the box.
   Use counters.
   Mom makes 7 sandwiches. The family eats 4 sandwiches. How many sandwiches are left?

   [ ]

   __3__ sandwiches are left

2. Write your own problem about sandwiches.
   Act it out.
   Use counters.

   Answers will vary.

   _____ sandwiches are left.

Copyright © Houghton Mifflin Company. All rights reserved.   Use with text pages 77–80.

Practice Workbook Page 23

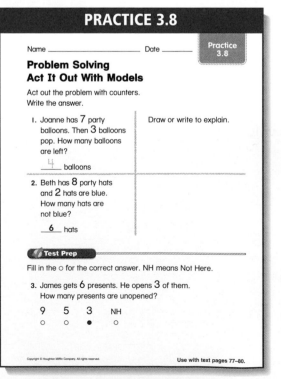

Reaching All Learners
Differentiated Instruction

English Learners

- Children will need to understand the term *take away* to understand some subtraction problems. Use Worksheet 3.8 to introduce the term to English-language learners.

Special Needs
TACTILE, AUDITORY

Materials: *counters*

- Give the child several counters.
- Present a subtraction story for 5 − 1 = 4.
- Have the child model the story with counters.
- Guide the child to count and write how many counters in all. (5) How many are taken away? (1) How many are left? (4)

Gifted and Talented
TACTILE, VISUAL

Materials: *pennies*

- Display a story problem. *Mark had 4 pennies. His brother gave him some pennies. Now he has 7 pennies. How many pennies did his brother give him?* (3 pennies)
- Have children draw pictures or use coins to act out the problem.
- Then have children write and solve similar problems.

TECHNOLOGY

Spiral Review

Help students remember skills they learned earlier by creating **customized** spiral review worksheets using the *Ways to Assess* **CD-ROM**.

Lesson Planner

You can use the **Lesson Planner CD-ROM** to create a report of the lessons and standards you have taught.

Intervention

Use the *Ways to Success* **CD-ROM** intervention software to support students who need more help in understanding the concepts and skills taught in this chapter.

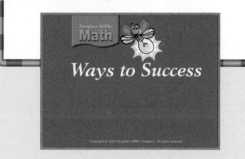

Art Connection

Invite children to make up subtraction stories that involve animals. Have them use old socks, buttons, and scraps of felt or other fabric to create animal puppets. Invite children to act out their subtraction stories.

MATH CENTER

Number of the Week Activity

Display the Number of the Week to motivate children to use their problem-solving skills. The exercises cover topics across all math strands.

PROBLEM SOLVING 3.8

Name _____ Date _____   Problem Solving 3.8

Act It Out With Models

There are 8 🐝 on a 🌻. Then 3 🐝 fly away.
How many 🐝 are on the 🌻?

UNDERSTAND	
What do I know? What do I need to find out?	I know there are 8 bees and 3 fly away. How many bees are left?

PLAN	
I can act out the problem or I can draw a picture.	I will act out the problem.

SOLVE	
How can I show 8 🐝? How can I show 3 🐝 flying away?	I can use counters to show 8. I can take away 3 counters. 5 counters are left.

LOOK BACK	
How can I check my answer?	I can start with 5 counters and add 3 to get 8.

Copyright © Houghton Mifflin Company. All rights reserved.   Use with text pages 77–79.

HOMEWORK 3.8

Name _____ Date _____   Homework 3.8

Problem Solving
Act It Out With Models

Use models to act out subtraction problems.
There are 5 birds.
3 birds fly away.
How many birds are left?
To model the problem,
show 5 ⬤ for birds.
Now take away 3.
Count how many are left.
There are __2__ birds left.

Draw the problem. Write the answer. | Draw or write to explain.

1. David has 2 hot dogs. He eats 1 hot dog. How many hot dogs does he have left?
____ hot dog

2. Orlee has 6 dolls. She gives 3 dolls away. How many dolls does she have left?
__3__ dolls

3. Jenny has 8 flowers. She gives 5 away. How many flowers does she have left?
__3__ flowers

Copyright © Houghton Mifflin Company. All rights reserved.   Use with text pages 77–79.

Homework Workbook Page 23

ENGLISH LEARNERS 3.8

Name _____ Date _____   English Learners 3.8

Act It Out With Models

He will **take away** the car.

Circle the correct words.

1.
She will (**take away**) wash off the dirt.

2.
He will sweep up (**take away**) the rocks.

3.
She will (**brush off**) take away the trash.

To the Teacher: Use the example at the top of the page to help children understand the term *take away*. Then read the sentences with children and have them circle the words to complete them.

Copyright © Houghton Mifflin Company. All rights reserved.   Use with text pages 77–79.

TEACHING LESSON 3.8

LESSON ORGANIZER

Objective Use models to act out subtraction problems.

Resources Reteach, Practice, Enrichment, Problem Solving, Homework, English Learners, Transparencies, Math Center

Materials counters, real or play coins, tagboard

Activity

Warm-Up Activity
Modeling a Story Problem

| ⚇⚇⚇⚇ Whole Group | ⏱ 5 minutes | Visual, Auditory |

Materials: *counters*

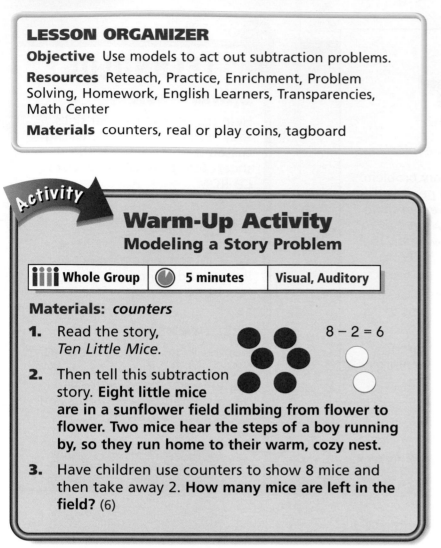

1. Read the story, *Ten Little Mice.*

   $8 - 2 = 6$

2. Then tell this subtraction story. **Eight little mice are in a sunflower field climbing from flower to flower. Two mice hear the steps of a boy running by, so they run home to their warm, cozy nest.**

3. Have children use counters to show 8 mice and then take away 2. **How many mice are left in the field?** (6)

Name_____

Act It Out With Models

Objective Use models to act out subtraction problems.

There are **6** animals playing.
2 animals leave the game.
How many animals are still playing?

UNDERSTAND

What do you know?
· **6** animals are playing.
· **2** animals leave.

PLAN

Act it out.
Circle the model you would use to act out the problem.

(counters)

cubes

SOLVE

Solve.

Show **6**.
Take away **2**.   There are __4__ animals left.

LOOK BACK

How can you check your answer?

Chapter 3 Lesson 8   seventy-seven **77**

---

1 Introduce

Activity

Discuss Act It Out With Models

| ⚇⚇⚇⚇ Whole Group | ⏱ 10–15 minutes | Visual, Tactile |

Materials: *counters*

1. *Act out a problem.* Write this problem on the board. **There are 4 boys in the kitchen. 2 boys leave to go skating. How many boys are still in the kitchen?**

2. Ask a volunteer to read the problem.

3. Ask the children what they already know. **What do you need to find out?** (How many boys are left in the kitchen.) **What can you use to act this problem out?** (counters)

4. Have children place 4 counters in a row and then take away 2. **How many boys are still in the kitchen?** (2)

2 Develop

Guided Learning

Teaching Example Have counters available for children to use. Read the objective with children. Guide them through the example problem. Ask them which model they would choose and why. (Either model should be accepted.) Have children explain how they could check their answer. Guide them to check their answer by adding 2 + 4 to arrive at the starting number.

Guided Practice

Have children complete **Exercises 1–2** as you observe. Encourage children to explain how they found their answers.

Guided Practice

Act out the problem with counters.
Write the answer.

Remember:
► Understand
► Plan
► Solve
► Look Back

Remember to
use the 4 steps.

1. Kayla has 4 jars of jam. She gives 1 away. How many jars of jam does she have left?

Draw or write to explain.

Think
I start by showing
4 counters.

___3___ jars of jam

2. Mike has 8 rabbits. 3 are brown. The other rabbits are white. How many rabbits are white?

Think
I know how many in all.
I know one part.

___5___ white rabbits

Practice

3. There are 7 birds in the yard. 2 fly away. How many birds are left?

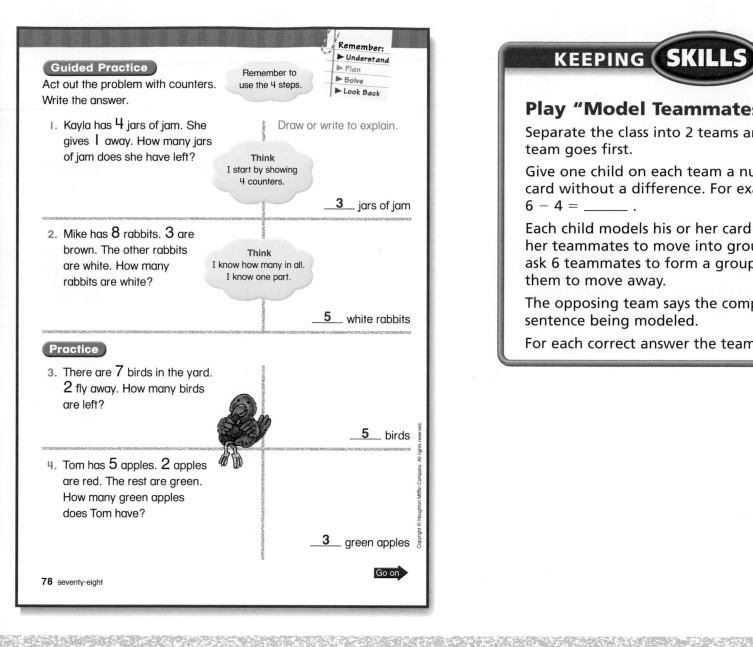

___5___ birds

4. Tom has 5 apples. 2 apples are red. The rest are green. How many green apples does Tom have?

___3___ green apples

78 seventy-eight

Go on →

Play "Model Teammates"

Separate the class into 2 teams and decide which team goes first.

Give one child on each team a number sentence card without a difference. For example,
$6 - 4 = $ _____ .

Each child models his or her card by asking his or her teammates to move into groups. For example: ask 6 teammates to form a group. Then ask 4 of them to move away.

The opposing team says the complete subtraction sentence being modeled.

For each correct answer the team receives a point.

③ Practice

Independent Practice

Children complete **Exercises 3–4** on page 78 independently.

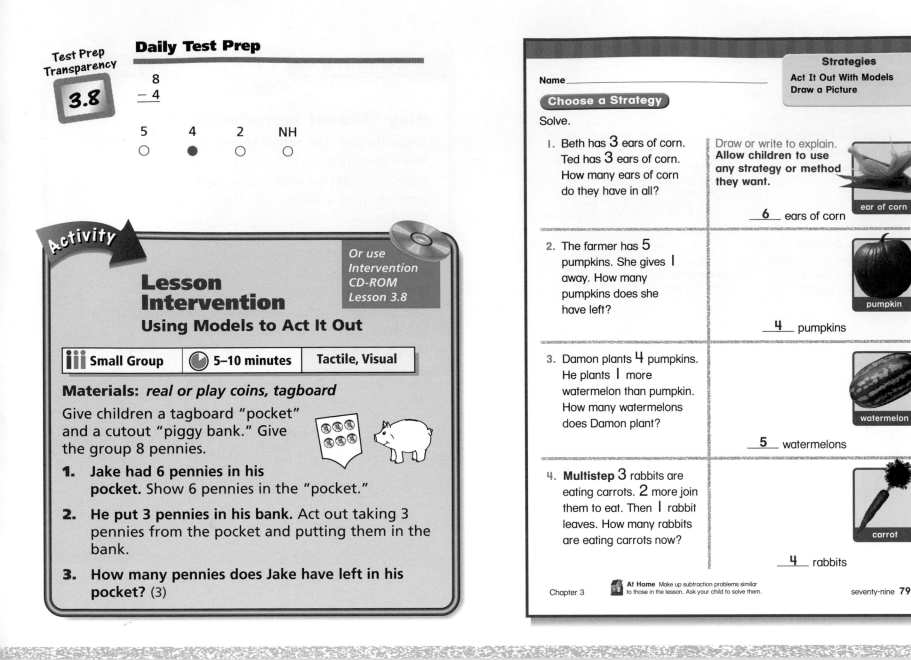

Test Prep Transparency 3.8

Daily Test Prep

$$\begin{array}{r} 8 \\ -\ 4 \\ \hline \end{array}$$

5 ○   4 ●   2 ○   NH ○

Activity

Lesson Intervention

Using Models to Act It Out

Or use Intervention CD-ROM Lesson 3.8

Small Group	5–10 minutes	Tactile, Visual

Materials: ***real or play coins, tagboard***

Give children a tagboard "pocket" and a cutout "piggy bank." Give the group 8 pennies.

1. **Jake had 6 pennies in his pocket.** Show 6 pennies in the "pocket."
2. **He put 3 pennies in his bank.** Act out taking 3 pennies from the pocket and putting them in the bank.
3. **How many pennies does Jake have left in his pocket?** (3)

Name____________________

Strategies
Act It Out With Models
Draw a Picture

Choose a Strategy

Solve.

1. Beth has 3 ears of corn. Ted has 3 ears of corn. How many ears of corn do they have in all?

Draw or write to explain. **Allow children to use any strategy or method they want.**

_6_ ears of corn

2. The farmer has 5 pumpkins. She gives 1 away. How many pumpkins does she have left?

_4_ pumpkins

3. Damon plants 4 pumpkins. He plants 1 more watermelon than pumpkin. How many watermelons does Damon plant?

_5_ watermelons

4. **Multistep** 3 rabbits are eating carrots. 2 more join them to eat. Then 1 rabbit leaves. How many rabbits are eating carrots now?

_4_ rabbits

Chapter 3 **At Home** Make up subtraction problems similar to those in the lesson. Ask your child to solve them. seventy-nine **79**

3 Practice

Mixed Strategy Practice

Read the problem-solving strategies with children. Make sure children can read and comprehend the problems in **Exercises 1–4** on page 79. If necessary, pair more proficient readers with less-proficient readers. Encourage them to discuss the problems before solving.

Common Error

Incorrect Modeling
Have children look back at each problem saying each number aloud and checking their counters.

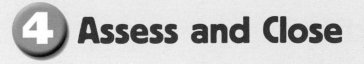

4 Assess and Close

Five children are in line. Two children sit down. How many children are still in line? (3 children) **How can you act out this problem?** (Show 5 counters and then take 2 away.)

Keeping a Journal

Seven turtles are in the pond. Two turtles climb onto the rock. How many are still in the pond? (5) Draw a picture to show how to act out the problem. Write the subtraction sentence.

Problem-Solving for Tests

Listening Skills

Listen to your teacher read the problem. Solve.

1. Lucy has 6 peppers. She puts 2 in a salad. How many peppers does she have left?

Show your work using pictures, numbers, or words.

___4___ peppers

2. There are 7 apples on a tree in the yard. 4 of the apples fall off. How many apples are still on the tree?

___3___ apples

Listen to your teacher read the problem. Choose the correct answer.

3. 2 ●   3 ○   4 ○   8 ○

4. 2 ○   3 ●   4 ○   6 ○

80 eighty

Problem-Solving for Tests

Listening Skills

This page provides children practice with the oral problem-solving format used in some standardized test items.

You may want to read each item only once to mimic the style of oral tests.

Use with Items 1 and 2

Listening Strategy: Listen for important words and numbers in the problem while the teacher reads it aloud.

- *When a problem is on the page, look at the problem while I am reading it.*
- *Wait until I finish reading the problem before you start writing.*

Use with Item 3

Listening Strategy: Listen to the problem and then look at the answer choices.

- *Look at me when I read a problem that is not on the page.*

  Five rabbits are eating carrots. Three of them hop away. How many rabbits are still eating carrots?

- *Mark your answer.*

Use with Item 4

Listening Strategy: Listen for important facts and details.

- *Listen to the words in the question so you will know if you should add or subtract to answer it.*

  The children have 6 apples. They eat 3 of the apples. How many apples do they have left?

- *Find the answer to the question. Mark your answer.*

Quick Check

Have children complete the Quick Check exercises independently to assess their understanding of concepts and skills taught in **Lessons 5–8.**

Item	Lesson	Error Analysis	Intervention
1–2	3.5	Children may confuse subtracting 0 and subtracting all.	Reteach Resource 3.5 *Ways to Success* 3.5
3–8	3.6	Children may write the wrong difference.	Reteach Resource 3.6 *Ways to Success* 3.6
9–14	3.7	Children may misinterpret vertical subtraction.	Reteach Resource 3.7 *Ways to Success* 3.7
15	3.8	Children may incorrectly model the problem.	Reteach Resource 3.8 *Ways to Success* 3.8

Name_____

Quick Check

Write the difference.

1.  $4 - 4 = \underline{0}$ 2.  $5 - 0 = \underline{5}$

Write the difference.

3. $8 - 3 = \underline{5}$ 4. $7 - 2 = \underline{5}$ 5. $7 - 3 = \underline{4}$

6. $8 - 1 = \underline{7}$ 7. $7 - 0 = \underline{7}$ 8. $8 - 6 = \underline{2}$

Write the difference.

9. $\begin{array}{r} 6 \\ -5 \\ \hline 1 \end{array}$ 10. $\begin{array}{r} 8 \\ -4 \\ \hline 4 \end{array}$ 11. $\begin{array}{r} 7 \\ -4 \\ \hline 3 \end{array}$ 12. $\begin{array}{r} 8 \\ -7 \\ \hline 1 \end{array}$ 13. $\begin{array}{r} 6 \\ -3 \\ \hline 3 \end{array}$ 14. $\begin{array}{r} 7 \\ -1 \\ \hline 6 \end{array}$

Choose a model and act out the problem.
Write the answer.

15. The baker has 7 pies. He sells 5 pies. How many pies are left?

Draw or write to explain.

$\underline{2}$ pies

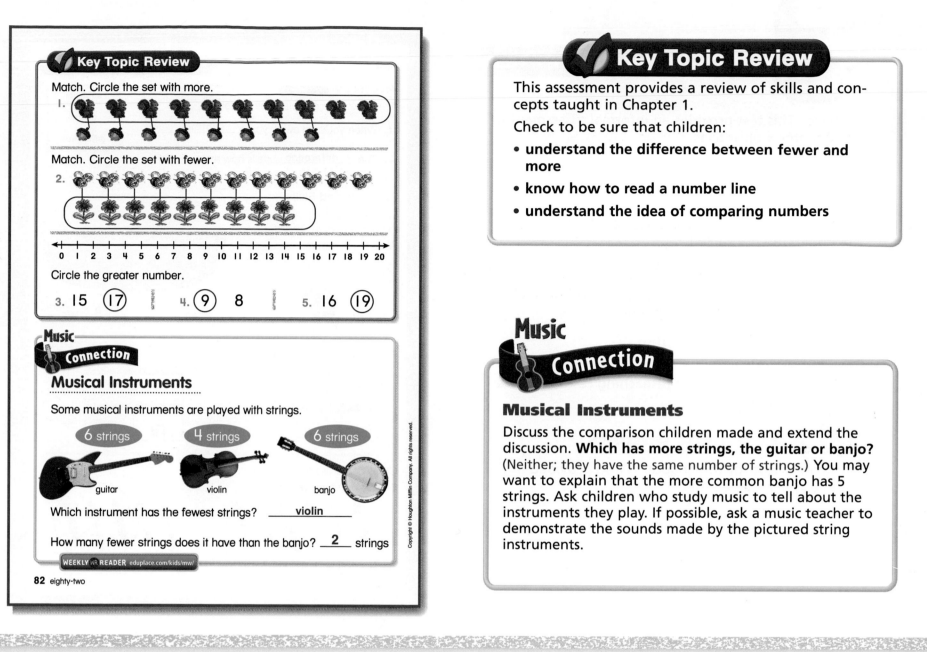

Key Topic Review

Key Topic Review

Match. Circle the set with more.

1.

Match. Circle the set with fewer.

2.

0 1 2 3 4 5 6 7 8 9 10 11 12 13 14 15 16 17 18 19 20

Circle the greater number.

3. 15 **(17)**   4. **(9)** 8   5. 16 **(19)**

Music
Connection

Musical Instruments

Some musical instruments are played with strings.

6 strings   4 strings   6 strings

guitar   violin   banjo

Which instrument has the fewest strings? ___**violin**___

How many fewer strings does it have than the banjo? __**2**__ strings

WEEKLY WR READER eduplace.com/kids/mw/

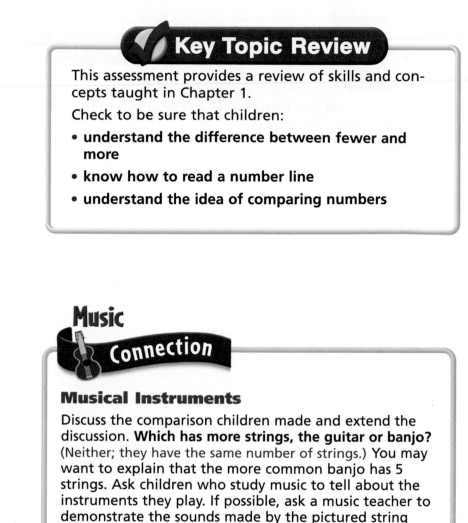

Key Topic Review

This assessment provides a review of skills and concepts taught in Chapter 1.

Check to be sure that children:

- **understand the difference between fewer and more**
- **know how to read a number line**
- **understand the idea of comparing numbers**

Music
Connection

Musical Instruments

Discuss the comparison children made and extend the discussion. **Which has more strings, the guitar or banjo?** (Neither; they have the same number of strings.) You may want to explain that the more common banjo has 5 strings. Ask children who study music to tell about the instruments they play. If possible, ask a music teacher to demonstrate the sounds made by the pictured string instruments.

Monitoring Student Progress

✓ Chapter Review/Test

Purpose: This test provides an informal assessment of the Chapter 3 objectives.

Chapter Test Items 1–25

To assign a numerical grade for this Chapter Test, use 4 points for each test item.
Item 3 story: Pat has 5 apples. He eats 1. How many apples are left? (4 apples)

Check Understanding

Use children's work on word problems to informally assess progress on chapter content.

Customizing Your Instruction

For children who have not yet mastered these objectives, you can use the reteaching resources listed in the chart below.

✓ Assessment Options

A summary test for this chapter is also provided in the Unit Resource Folder.

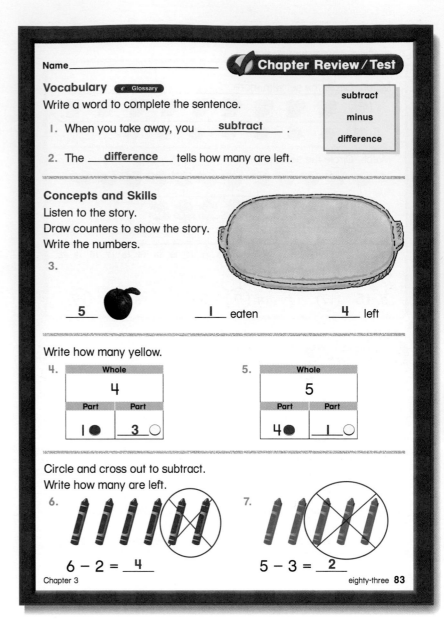

Reteaching Support

Chapter Test Items	Summary Test Items	Chapter Objectives Tested	TE Pages	Use These Reteaching Resources
1–2	1–2	**3A** Develop and use math vocabulary relating to subtraction concepts.	63A–68	Reteach Resources and *Ways to Success* CD: 3.2–3.4 Skillsheet 17
3–7	3–4	**3B** Model subtraction, with parts and wholes, in stories and write subtraction sentences.	63A–68	Reteach Resources and *Ways to Success* CD: 3.2–3.4 Skillsheet 18
8–24	5–8	**3C** Solve subtraction problems from 8 or less horizontally and vertically using − and =, including problems with 0.	71A–76	Reteach Resources and *Ways to Success* CD: 3.5–3.7 Skillsheets 19–20
25	9–10	**3D** Use models to act out subtraction problems.	77A–80	Reteach Resource and *Ways to Success* CD: 3.8 Skillsheet 21

Write the difference.

8. $5 - 2 =$ __3__   9. $6 - 5 =$ __1__   10. $4 - 1 =$ __3__

11.

$4 - 0 =$ __4__

12.

$5 - 5 =$ __0__

13. $8 - 3 =$ __5__   14. $7 - 1 =$ __6__   15. $8 - 2 =$ __6__

16. $7 - 5 =$ __2__   17. $8 - 4 =$ __4__   18. $7 - 3 =$ __4__

19. $\begin{array}{r} 6 \\ -3 \\ \hline 3 \end{array}$ 20. $\begin{array}{r} 8 \\ -5 \\ \hline 3 \end{array}$ 21. $\begin{array}{r} 7 \\ -6 \\ \hline 1 \end{array}$ 22. $\begin{array}{r} 6 \\ -1 \\ \hline 5 \end{array}$ 23. $\begin{array}{r} 8 \\ -7 \\ \hline 1 \end{array}$ 24. $\begin{array}{r} 7 \\ -2 \\ \hline 5 \end{array}$

Problem Solving

Act out the problem with counters.
Write the answer.

25. There are 8 apples on a tree.
Mai picks 1 apple and eats it.
How many apples are left?

Draw or write to explain.

__7__ apples

84 eighty-four

Adequate Yearly Progress

Use the End of Grade Test Prep Assessment Guide to help familiarize your children with the format of standardized tests.

CHAPTER SUMMARY TEST

Name _____ Date _____

Chapter 3 Test continued

Use a model to solve.

9. Maria has 6 crayons.
4 crayons are red.
The other crayons are black.
How many crayons are black?

__2__ black crayons

10. There are 5 birds.
1 bird flies away.
How many birds are left?

__4__ birds left

STOP

Subtraction Concepts   84

Lesson by Lesson Overview
Data and Graphing

Lesson 1

- This lesson introduces tally marks as a way to keep track of data and as a way to represent numbers.
- Children survey friends, record the answers with tally marks, and interpret the data.
- Pictorial data is organized on a tally chart and the data is used to solve problems.

Lesson 2

- Children are introduced to pictographs as a way to show data.
- The symbols in the graph stand for 1 item, and children count symbols to solve problems.
- Data is also compared to solve problems.
- For algebra readiness, children write a subtraction sentence to solve a problem related to the data.

Lesson 3

- Making a pictograph provides children with an opportunity to represent pictured data with symbols.
- Children analyze and compare the data in their graphs.
- The problem solving activity has children make a pictograph to represent data presented in the form of a logic problem.
- By writing their own survey question, children experience data in a real-life context. They use the data they collect to make a pictograph and then write about it.

Lesson 4

- Children are introduced to bar graphs as a way to show data.
- The spaces in the graph stand for 1 item, and children read the graph by finding the number where the bar ends.
- Data is also compared to solve problems.

Lesson 5

- Children survey friends and record the answers with tally marks.
- The tally chart is used to make a bar graph and the data is analyzed.
- Data from a picture is used to make a bar graph and the graph is used to solve problems.
- The problem solving set has children make a bar graph from a tally chart which contains data in a real-life context.

Lesson 6

- Children use bar graphs to solve problems that involve addition and subtraction.
- Subtracting to compare is presented by comparing data in a bar graph, which can be used to help find the difference.
- Previously learned strategies are chosen by children to solve additional problems.

SKILLS TRACE: DATA AND GRAPHING

Grade K	Grade 1	Grade 2
• make real/concrete graphs (ch. 3) • read and interpret pictographs (ch. 3)	• take a survey and record with tally marks • read, interpret, and make pictographs • read, interpret, and make bar graphs	• use tally marks in a survey and use and compare the data (ch. 4) • read and interpret pictographs (ch. 4) • read, interpret, and make bar graphs (ch. 4)

Chapter Planner

Lesson	Objective	Vocabulary	Materials	✔ NCTM Standards
4.1 (Hands-On) Make a Tally Chart p. 87A	Represent data with tally marks on a chart.	tally	counters, tally cards 0–10 (Learning Tool (LT) 18), cubes, paper clips, blank transparency, pencils, markers	Pose questions and gather data about themselves and their surroundings.
4.2 Read a Pictograph p. 89A	Read and use a pictograph to compare information.	pictograph	old magazines, scissors	Represent data using concrete objects, pictures, and graphs.
4.3 Make a Pictograph p. 91A	Make and use a pictograph to compare information.		container of cubes: red, green, and yellow; blank transparency	Represent data using concrete objects, pictures, and graphs.
4.4 Read a Bar Graph p. 95A	Read a bar graph and use it to compare information.	bar graph	cubes of two colors, blank transparency, ruler	Represent data using concrete objects, pictures, and graphs.
4.5 (Hands-On) Make a Bar Graph p. 97A	Use a tally chart to make a bar graph and compare information.	tally chart	blank transparency, red and blue crayons, overhead squares, graph paper (LT 21), number cards 1–20 (LT 14 and 15)	Represent data using concrete objects, pictures, and graphs.
4.6 Problem Solving: Use a Graph p. 101A	Use a bar graph to solve a problem.		number cards 0–9 (LT 14); grid paper transparency; green, blue, brown, and black cubes; two-color counters	Solve problems that arise in mathematics and other contexts.

Resources For Reaching All Learners

LESSON RESOURCES: Reteach, Practice, Enrichment, Problem Solving, Homework, English Learners, Daily Routines, Transparencies, Math Center.

ADDITIONAL RESOURCES FROM HOUGHTON MIFFLIN: Chapter Challenges, Combination Classroom Planning Guide, Every Day Counts, Math to Learn (Student Handbook)

Every Day Counts
The Graph and Birthday Data activities in Every Day Counts support the math in this chapter.

Assessing Prior Knowledge

Before beginning this chapter, you can assess student understandings in order to assist you in differentiating instruction.

Complete Chapter Pretest in Unit Resource Folder

Use this test to assess both prerequisite skills (**Are You Ready?** — one page) and chapter content (**Check What You Know** — two pages).

Chapter 4 Prerequisite Skills Pretest

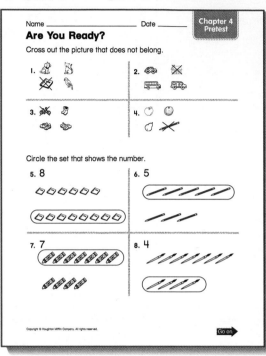

Chapter 4 New Content Pretest

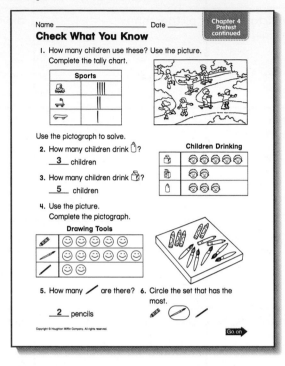

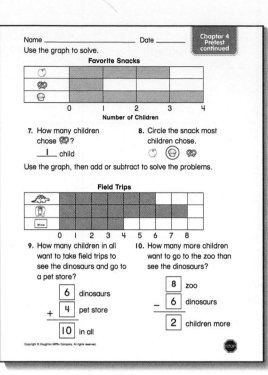

Customizing Instruction

For Students Having Difficulty

Items	Prerequisites	Ways to Success
1–4	Understands how to sort and compare objects.	Skillsheet 22
5-8	Understands how to count and identify sets.	CD: 1.2 Skillsheet 22

Ways to Success: Intervention for every concept and skill (CD-ROM or Chapter Intervention Skillsheets).

For Students Having Success

Items	Objectives	Resources
1–3	4A Develop and use math vocabulary relating to data and graphing.	Enrichment 4.1, 4.2, 4.4
4–8	4B Read, make, and use tally charts, pictographs and bar graphs to compare information.	Enrichment 4.1–4.5
9-10	4C Use graphs to solve problems.	Enrichment 4.6

Use **Chapter Challenges** with any students who have success with all new chapter content.

Other Pretest Options

Informal Pretest

The pretest assesses vocabulary and prerequisite skills needed for success in this chapter.

Ways to Success CD-ROM

The *Ways to Success* chapter pretest has automatic assignment of appropriate review lessons.

Chapter Resources

Assessing Prior Knowledge

Daily Favorites (one-to-one correspondence)

- Each day, write a choice on the board such as *Beans or Broccoli?* or *Winter or Summer?*
- Read the choices aloud, and have children write their names under the choice they like best.
- At the end of the day, record the results. Point out the one-to-one correspondence between the names and the numbers.

Targeted Ongoing Activity

Graph Items from the Class Store (make a pictograph)

- Periodically, have small groups of children count several kinds of items found in the class store, such as erasers, crayons, and paper clips.
- Have them record the data in a pictograph.

Connecting to the Unit Project

- On the board, draw the following fruits and vegetables as they might appear in a supermarket advertisement: 1 pumpkin, 3 apples, 4 bananas, 6 cherries, 8 potatoes.
- Invite children to identify each kind of fruit and vegetable.
- Ask children to count the fruits and vegetables in the drawing and use tally marks to record the number of each kind.

Professional Resources Handbook

Research, Mathematics Content, and Language Intervention

Research-Based Teaching

The study of data and graphing shows children that what they are learning is useful. Children enjoy collecting data. Ginsburg (1989) suggests that providing game-like formats helps children learn in a non-threatening environment. Games can also be used to enhance mathematical connections. See *Professional Resources Handbook, Grade 1,* Unit 1.

For more ideas relating to Unit 1, see the Teacher Support Handbook at the back of this Teacher's Edition.

Language Intervention

When new vocabulary words (for example, tally chart, pictograph, bar graph) are introduced in a lesson, have students write their own definitions. Use the students' definitions to help you identify misconceptions students have.

Technology

Time-Saving Technology Support
Ways to Assess Customized Spiral Review
   Test Generator CD
Lesson Planner CD-ROM
Ways to Success Intervention CD-ROM
MathTracks CD-ROM
Education Place: www.eduplace.com/math/mw
Houghton Mifflin Math eBook CD-ROM
eManipulatives
eGames

Starting Chapter 4
Data and Graphing

CHAPTER OBJECTIVES

4A Develop and use math vocabulary relating to data and graphing.

4B Read, make, and use tally charts, pictographs, and bar graphs to compare information.

4C Use graphs to solve problems.

Math Background

Data and Graphing

Collecting, organizing, and interpreting data are common real-life activities. It is important to present the data in a way that makes interpretation easy. There are many forms in which data can be organized and presented. Whether to use a tally chart, a bar graph, a pictograph, or another graph depends on the type of data to be displayed.

If a child is collecting data about which of three activities is the favorite of twenty children, it would be appropriate to use a tally chart, making a mark for each response as the survey is being taken.

A pictograph represents data with pictures. For example, a pictograph could be used to show how many children are at a playground. At this grade level, each picture represents one object.

A bar graph is used to display data that can be counted. Bar graphs may use horizontal or vertical bars. The length of each bar represents the number of each item. Bar graphs make comparison of data simpler.

The possibility for the discussion of mode and range may occur in some lessons. Mode is defined as the number or numbers that occur most often in a set of data. For example, in the set of data (11, 26, 35, 35, 42) 35 is the mode. In the set of data (16, 22, 16, 32, 22, 43) 16 and 22 are the modes. Range is defined as the difference between the greatest and the least number in a set of data. For example, in the set of data (4, 7, 12, 16, 20) the range is $20 - 4 = 16$ or from 4 to 20.

Data and Graphing

INVESTIGATION

Are there more children playing in the sandbox or with the ball?

Using The Investigation

- Draw a table on the board with boxes in the left column labeled *Boys* and *Girls*. Label the right column *Number*. Use a symbol to fill in the table to reflect the number of boys and girls in the class. Tell children that a *row* is horizontal, and a *column* is vertical.

- **What does this table show us?** (How many boys and girls are in the class.) Ask a volunteer to tell how many boys and how many girls.

- Read the question to children. **Look at the picture. Use the information you see there to answer the question. Are there more children playing in the sandbox or with the ball?** (There are more children playing in the sandbox.)

 For more information about projects and investigations, visit Education Place. **eduplace.com/math/mw/**